Nurturing Equity Minded Healthcare Providers

An Evidence-Based Curriculum Designed to Provide Implicit Bias Training and Address Healthcare Disparities

WORKBOOK

REV. DR. CANDACE COLE-KELLY

FOREWORD BY KENDRA L. SMITH, PH.D.

Nurturing Equity Minded Healthcare Providers

1st edition Copyright © September 2023
2nd edition Copyright © April 2025 by Cole Publishing
All rights reserved. Printed and bound in the United States of America. No reproduction of any part of this format, contents or artistic contributions can be made without written permission from the author.

Image Credits: pages 25, 31, 37, 55, 65, 75, 89, 105, 119, 127, 137, 143, 163, 169, 183, 195, 199, 205, 233, 245, 263, 255, 263, 271, 279 used with permission from Unsplash+

Library of Congress Cataloging-in-Publication Data ISBN: 979-8-9918058-2-7

Cole Publishing
Cole Publishing
4067 Hardwick Street #282
Lakewood, CA 90712

Email: ccpprod@aol.com
Book Cover Design by CCP Productions
For Book Orders:
Contact us at Cole Publishing Company

DEDICATION

To All Healthcare Professions, Researchers,
Mental Health Professions: Psychologists,
Social Workers, Chaplains, EMT's, Firefighters,
Law Enforcement, Community Advocates,
Educators, and to all in the service of human life.

CONTENT

Acknowledgements	VII
Purpose and Structure	IX
How To Use This Workbook as a Cohort or Individual	XI
A Look Inside	XII
Foreword by Kendra L. Smith, Ph.D., MPH	XIII
Preface by Shawya Mogharabi	XV
Introduction by Rev. Dr. Candace Cole-Kelly	XVII

Section I Reflection on Personal Development	**21**
Ch. 1 - Exploring Your Compassionate-Heart	25
Ch. 2 - The Gift of Surrender	31
Ch. 3 - Important Foundations of Self Actualization	37
Ch. 4 - Self-Awareness That Supports Equitable Care	49
Ch. 5 - Building Your Own Resilience Toolkit	55
Ch. 6 - Workplace Boundaries	65
Ch. 7 - Identifying Personal Loss and Grief	75
Section Resources	83

Section II Structural Racism in Obstetric Care	**89**
Ch. 8 - The History of Obstetric Trauma	93
Ch. 9 - The Origins of Midwifery	99
Ch. 10 - Doulas	105
Ch. 11 - Wet Nursing & Breastfeeding Disparities	111
Ch. 12 - Weathering & Epigenetics: Social Determinants	119
Ch. 13 - Leading Causes of Death in Black Maternal Mortality and Infant Mortalitys	127

Section II Health Inequalities in the NICU   **133**

Ch. 14 - Health and Racial Inequity in the NICU   137

Ch. 15 - Belonging in the NICU   143

Ch. 16 - Family-Centered Care in the NICU   155

Ch. 17 - Trauma-Informed Care in the NICU   163

Ch. 18 - Infant Mental Health   169

Ch. 19 - Language and Communication   173

Ch. 20 - Caring Beyond Beliefs: The Complexity of Supporting Same-Gender Loving Couples in Healthcare   183

Section IV Providing Care with Heart   **191**

Ch. 21 - Empathy, Part 1: A Tool to Mitigate Implicit Bias   195

Ch. 22 - Empathy at the Bedside, Part 2: A Healthcare Provider's Sacred Presence   199

Ch. 23 - Cultural Humility   205

Ch. 24 - Commit to S.E.A.L   213

Ch. 25 - Fitted for Equity Lens   217

Ch. 26 - Delivering Bad News with R.E.S.P.E.C.T   221

Ch. 27 - Supporting Partners in Traumatic Deliveries   227

Ch. 28 - Perinatal and Neonatal Loss   233

Ch. 29 - Medical and Emotional Debriefings: Processing Traumatic Events and Self-Care   245

Section V Where Do We Go From Here?   **251**

Ch. 30 - Modern Laws   255

Ch. 31 - Team Building for Birth Equity Groups: A Response to SBA 464   263

Ch. 32 - Racism Amid Nursing Staff   271

Ch. 33 - Ethnic Diversity in the Nursing Workforce   275

Ch. 34 - Anti-Racism: Leaders, Step It Up!   279

Ch. 35 - The Heart of Justice   285

Ch. 36 – Closing Letter to All Healthcare Providers: A Plea from the Author's Heart   289

Post Workbook Birth Equity Survey   **293**

Tools for Healthcare Providers: Quick Reference Guide   **299**

References   311

About the Author   317

ACKNOWLEDGEMENTS

There are countless voices that have supported me in writing this two-volume book for the greater good of those without advocacy, voice, autonomy and consent. I acknowledge those of you who I have conversed with, cried with, prayed with and entertained hours of deliberation on these important topics. Your support has meant the world to me, and you have truly been the wind beneath my wings.

Then there are those of you who helped to shape and validate my voice amid many conflicted thoughts throughout my life. You have helped me process the emotional impacts after experiencing unjust interactions and racism. You know them, the impact of discrimination, intimidation, microaggressions and blatant words that caused me to second guess myself, my value and my worth. I want to thank my gentle giant CPE (Clinical Pastoral Education) Supervisor, Teleso Satele, my eternal sister and friend, Pastor Joyce Kitchen, and my Spiritual Mom, Carstella Cook, who sings the promises of God over me when life gets a little too rough - thank you all!

In addition, I am grateful for colleagues and co-laborers in this field, advocating for justice and equity, and scholars who give voice speaking truth to power. These extraordinary individuals are: Dr. Robert Stevenson, Dr. Mark Whitlock, Mr. Sydney Butler, Chief Alvin Brewer, Nedra Gayles, Dr. Kendra L. Smith, Dr. Danisha McCall, Dr. Lauren Yu, Rev. BJ Jenkins, Dr. Sharilyn Kelly, Sheryl Faulk, Dr. Jennifer McNulty, Brenda Darby, Carole Pierce and Deb Mars. I am especially thankful for the staff at Cornell University, and the USC Passing the Mantle Program for their robust curriculum and programs in diversity, equity and inclusion, as well as civic engagement and public policy. I am so much better equipped to be a voice in this work because of these programs.

The influences of a large number of people (clinicians, researchers, and authors) have contributed to the evolution of the ideas in this book. In putting it together, I have collaborated closely on every topic with trusted medical providers, Fire Chiefs, EMTs, clinicians, psycho-social professionals, grief counselors, midwives, doulas, lactations, chaplains, birth equity advocates, and first responders whose skills in serving patients gave Nurturing Equity Minded Healthcare Providers its welcoming praise!

To my literary team: proofreaders, cover designer, copy editors, accountants, formatting experts, coaches and editors who spent tireless hours, days, weeks and months in collaboration who helped me in reading, re-reading, writing and re-writing until we all were simply satisfied with bringing this two-part volume book to a timely finish. I will forever be deeply indebted to: Shawya Mogharabi, Janet Sasser, Chantae Taylor, Atilla Morgan, DesignAnneli.com, and Carolyn Habersham. Your wisdom, expertise, objectivity and expertism has truly been so valuable and more than a blessing to me.

And finally to the unsung heroes - those silenced partners and fathers that for too long have been the sole advocates for Black mothers. I commend Mr. Ariel Robinson, Mr. Robert Smith, Mr. Michael Mayeda, and countless additional partners like them. I honor your heroic voices in the face of resistance and lack of compassionate care shown toward you. No one should be made to feel invisible, or ignored, during such traumatic experiences, and your persistent advocacy for your partners through it all must be acknowledged.

PURPOSE AND STRUCTURE

The purpose of *Nurturing Equity-Minded Healthcare Providers* is to provide evidence-based learning exercises and case studies that relate to each book chapter and will help deepen the learner's understanding of providing equitable care.

In **Nurturing Equity-Minded Healthcare Providers Workbook,** you'll learn the values of:

- Exploring one's own **personal development** in becoming a well-balanced healthcare provider
- Processing **historical data** in order to understand and reform present day structural racism in obstetric care
- Understanding the impact of **weathering** in health disparities
- Understanding how **epigenetics** inform marginalized communities and their trust in the medical field
- Learning about **Trauma-Informed Care**
- Challenging your own **implicit biases** with openness and humility
- Integrating **cultural empathy**
- Integrating **team (multidisciplinary) based care** to optimize better outcomes and resources for your patients
- Integrating **active listening** in your care so that you can advocate for your patient with clarity
- Caring with **H.E.A.R.T**. (**H**ear her, **E**mpathize with her, **A**dvocate for her, **R**espect her, and **T**rust her voice) in order to provide best practices for all patients and partners/support systems
- **Increasing diversity** in your workforce
- Maintaining ongoing DEI training and education to **eradicate workplace racism** amid clinical staff.

In recent years, healthcare providers have been tasked to integrate DEI training for their hospitals, clinics and agencies to advocate for evidenced based care with an equity lens in order to mitigate vast disparities in Black maternal mortality and infant mortality. Our hope is that this learning workbook will help prepare you for this role by facilitating your own personal development as an equity healthcare provider. This workbook is designed to equip you with the educational tools and skills to disrupt systemic racism by transforming healthcare institutions with a new understanding of equitable care.

HOW TO USE THIS WORKBOOK AS A COHORT OR INDIVIDUAL

For Facilitator(s):

1. At the beginning of each chapter, you will find an excerpt from the textbook. Each cohort exercise section has 3 parts: 1) Didactic 2) Case Study/or Nurturing Equity Exercise 3) Group or individual processing

2. As a Facilitator, read through the entire lesson and reflection questions.

3. Make sure you begin with check ins. Everyone reads through the lesson during the same time. Then begin to teach the lesson prescribed for the session.

4. Create small groups after the lesson for peer to peer processing and learning. Ask one person to speak on behalf of the group sharing once processing is complete.

5. Approximately 2 minutes before the end of each session, provide a "gentle" nudge to the group(s). For example, say "we have about 2 minutes remaining before we begin sharing." If you want, add, "after sharing we will begin a short journaling session."

6. Provide time for journaling after each activity (if appropriate) 5-10 minutes of what impacts them the most from the lesson or small group sharing.

7. Thank each clinician for their presence and participation and ask for one takeaway from each participant.

For Learner(s):

1. Each chapter has 3 parts: 1) Didactic 2) Case Study/or Nurturing Equity Exercise 3) Group or individual processing.

2. Take a moment to prepare mentally by doing a brief breathing exercise or centering. Bring your full self to this learning experience.

3. As a learner, read through the entire lesson and reflection questions.

4. Sit with any difficult emotions or new understandings that the material may evoke. Remember not to judge any thoughts as they come, just notice them and let them pass you by before deeper reflection.

5. As you break into small groups, be authentic and open in your sharing. Reflect for a moment and share one thing that you take away from this learning experience.

A LOOK INSIDE:

Nurturing Equity Minded Healthcare Providers consists of two books, each containing 36 Chapters organized into 4 Parts: 1) It is an interactive workbook designed for new or specialty nurses and new physicians to engage with as groups or cohorts, and 2) A companion Textbook meant for facilitators of these groups, as well as for individual learning and development. This book endeavors to evaluate current research on health- care disparities, and maternal health in particular.

Part 1 encourages one's personal development as a healthcare provider, and includes the following subjects: one's capacity for compassion, the gift of surrender, important foundations, self-awareness, self-actualization, wholeness and wellness, self-compassion, resilience, personal loss and grief, boundaries, and cultural integration. It is designed to nurture providers to be their best selves while sensitizing oneself to broader cultures.

Part 2 is comprised of the history of structural racism in Obstetric Care, and is meant to provide history and context for the experience of Black patients in American healthcare. It includes a history of obstetric trauma (focusing on the traumatic procedures done by Dr. Marion Sims in the 1800s), midwifery, wet nursing, breastfeeding, weathering, the segregation of birth clinics, epigenetics, maternal mortality and preventable deaths in Black mothers, and inequities in the NICU.

Halfway through this body of work, you will find a powerful equity survey that will encourage you to reflect on your current perceptions of equity in healthcare, before continuing with the learning and training offered in Parts 3 and 4.

Part 3 integrates both what a healthcare provider has hopefully learned about themselves, and about their Black patients, by considering the heart and compassion needed when caring for marginalized communities and addressing disparities. Offered in this section are chapters on equitable care, cultural humility, cultural empathy for Black families, committing to patients using equity, promoting maternal and infant health in Black patients, and supporting partners. Also included in this section are chapters on how to deliver bad news, and how to build an equity clinic with diversity in mind.

Part 4 is a comprehensive look at where we are headed moving forward. It delves into modern legislation, such as Law SBA 464, team-building strategies for groups committed to birth equity, racism in nursing staffs, creating a diverse workforce, and how leaders can improve in these areas, followed by a post-workbook equity survey. Finally, a rousing and passionate speech directed to new physicians, titled "The Heart of Justice," and a closing plea from the author concludes this comprehensive work.

FOREWORD
KENDRA SMITH, PH.D., MPH

Nurturing Equity-Minded Healthcare Providers is designed to take healthcare professionals on a personal journey of self-reflection and development to understand and address the structural racism often found in obstetric care. The workbook compels the user to have a 'stop and think' moment about themselves and their own experiences. It then pushes the user to 'stop and address' their understanding of structural racism in obstetric care and how they can dismantle it from where they are.

While not the first tool to address racism in healthcare, this workbook is unique because it is totally focused on the individual user and aiding them in their own journey. The workbook also creates an opportunity for the user to reconnect with themselves through thoughtful reflection and reconnect to the ideals with which they started the profession.

The desire to help has driven most healthcare professionals into their profession and chosen specialty. Like most students who are pursuing credentials to work in a helping profession like healthcare, the drive to care for and help heal others is likely rooted in their own lived experiences with a loved one, a love of science, and an understanding that every human deserves good health.

Along their journey, healthcare providers have likely experienced the highest of highs in helping to save someone's life and the lowest of lows in experiencing the loss of a patient. This is the ebb and flow that colors many healthcare professionals' lives. It is direct, present, fast-paced, and constantly changing.

Additionally, healthcare professionals' work exists in a big ball of systems that shape how people seek care and how care is delivered. One of the systems that is most damaging in healthcare is discrimination that comes in the form of racism. By now, we have heard and seen the statistics about the disparities in care and birthing outcomes for birthing people of color that are stark and devastating. Black and American Indian birthing people have higher rates of pregnancy-related death compared to White[1] women. Maternal death rates increased during the COVID-19 pandemic, further widening racial disparities for Black birthing people. There are few physiological explanations for these outcomes, but plenty of social, structural, and healthcare related reasons rooted in racism that explain this stark reality.

Racialized populations like Black, Indigenous, Latinx, and others have suffered from health inequities in the United States. Oftentimes, racism is tied to the actions of an individual perpetrator; however, this ignores a sobering reality about the structural way the healthcare system perpetuates racism.

Much of the inequities experienced by these populations can be found in the way in which health policy has been developed in the United States and the slow efforts to dismantle it. Structural racism in healthcare operates through policies that allocate resources that serve

---

1 There is much debate on the correct use of capitalization where race is concerned. While the capitalization of "Black" grew from the need to acknowledge the shared histories, culture, and experience of being discriminated against because of skin color, the argument can be made that "White" should not be capitalized as it does not share those same criteria. This author, however, chooses to capitalize "White" as well, in order to address the role that White people and systems have played in racial inequities, and to avoid any suggestion of "White" as a default by not capitalizing it. Furthermore, the author will capitalize both "White" and "Black" so as not to discriminate in either direction, and for grammatical consistency.

as a mechanism to disempower and devalue members of racialized groups which results in inequitable access, quality, financing, and insurance coverage for care.

Over the years, imperfect mechanisms such as the Affordable Care Act, Medicaid expansion across states, and the Momnibus Act have been put in place to address the inequities found in the very structure of the health system. However, these changes are not enough. Changes at every level of the healthcare system must happen to address the racism found within the system.

This workbook is working at the individual level to help healthcare professionals realize the role racism is playing in their work and how to address it by providing useful information and thoughtful exercises.

Through her years of experience, Rev. Dr. Candace Cole-Kelly has shaped this workbook to meet any healthcare professional where they are and help them get started or continue their work in understanding themselves and structural racism. Her thoughtfulness is reflected in each page and exercise throughout the workbook. This workbook is something to be experienced and enjoyed privately but could also be a discussion starter for nursing cohorts and a small group. This workbook is not only for nurses, but physicians, first responders, psycho-social professionals and anyone in the helping profession. Either way, prepare yourself for a journey that can only make you a better personal and healthcare professional.

PREFACE
SHAWYA MOGHARABI

Our world is a messy one. We turn on the news and are immediately assailed with the worrisome complications that surround us - from senseless deaths, gun violence, political divide, war, disease/COVID-19, police brutality, oppression, sexism, racism, injustice, mental health disorders, economic disadvantages….the list could go on and on - and those are just the problems we face as a society, not to mention the many issues we must all deal with privately, in our individual lives. It's enough to make anyone feel down, discouraged, and hopeless. When I get weighed down by all this, I turn to the good, as many of us often do. I look to the people around me who are doing the good work, taking the actions we need, making the changes for the betterment of us all. I look to people like Reverend Dr. Candace Cole-Kelly.

When Dr. Kelly first approached me about being part of her upcoming work, I was unsure if I could be of much assistance. The ever-present doubt and lack of confidence that always seem to plague me were as strong as ever in my mind. I had never worked on a nonfiction publication before, I was unfamiliar with much of the content, and I was far removed from the medical field profession. In a word - I felt unqualified. And yet, as Dr. Kelly explained her work and the vision for this publication, I knew it was something so much bigger than me, and something I had to be a part of if I could. So, with some hesitancy, but determined clarity, I embarked on this journey with her - thinking that we would be spending a few months working together, at most. My, oh my, was that naive thinking! Multiple simultaneous working google docs, countless emails, hundreds of zoom calls, many versions, and a full 9 months later - this truly was a birthing labor of love! Every time we thought we were finished, Dr. Kelly would come to a call with new research, new findings, new webinars, new information - and we always agreed that it was too important, too meaningful not to include. So, we worked away, on what sometimes felt like a never-ending, and daunting mission, keeping the end goal in sight. This work could feel like too much at times - too hard to take in, too much to tackle, too large of a problem to solve - but it was also too important to just walk away from. And I am so grateful I had the honor and privilege to do so.

As an educator and nurturer by profession, and a Bahai by faith, I believe education must be valued as a top priority. And my goodness, does this book educate! This is a body of work that not only teaches one how to be more compassionate and understanding of ourselves, but of others who are far from similar to us, as well. Dr. Kelly uses shocking, but true historical facts and medical statistics to illustrate the ways in which our healthcare systems have often failed our most vulnerable communities - namely, the disadvantaged, minorities, the underprivileged - and ultimately, Black birthing persons and their babies. She then teaches us how to begin to remedy these shortcomings. She enlightens us on how in order to change the systems around us, we must begin with compassion - first to ourselves, and then to everyone around us - and then set out to do the hard work with integrity, and intention. I have learned so much from my time working on this book, and from Dr. Kelly herself, and I will be forever indebted to her for trusting me to be a part of this project.

The work, and the knowledge gained from being a part of it, was not always easy to bear. It was often heartbreaking, traumatic, and painful to learn some of the realities presented. But the information discovered, and shared here, is of vital importance for anyone who hopes to better our world in any way. One particularly heart wrenching moment for me was watching the documentary film Aftershock as part of the research for this book. Learning the stories of Amber and Shamony, and their fully preventable deaths, was unfathomably devastating. But once again, I tried to look to the good - learning their stories meant that they could be heard and shared. And their stories must be heard, must be shared. Because ultimately it is the stories like those in Aftershock that will serve as a warning on what happens when women, particularly Black women, are not listened to, or believed. And they are only two of the countless other Black women whose deaths could have been prevented, had they been treated with dignity and compassion.

As you will learn in this work, 60% of maternal mortality in Black mothers is believed to have been preventable - 60%! That is more than half. And that is truly unacceptable. You will also learn the ways in which Black bodies have been experimented on, exploited for profits, practiced on without consent, and unknowingly used in inhumane ways by healthcare systems. It is enough to leave you speechless. And I was left, once again feeling weighed down by these injustices. How long must Black bodies continue to suffer? How long must it take before we as a society learn what equality truly means, and how to advocate for it? How long until the ugly roots of systemic racism that have continued to take hold of this country, are finally severed, once and for all? How long before being Black in America does not equate to having a decreased chance at long life?

When I would begin to feel discouraged, I had to remind myself to look to the good. Look to the reason I was learning some of these horrifying truths. Look to the work I was taking part in. Look to the good of Dr. Kelly and the work she is doing to save these lives. Because when some healthcare providers who work in hospitals can learn to stop putting profits over patient care, to stop treating Black bodies as commodities and guinea pigs, to listen to and believe Black women, to give the power back to Black voices, and to put patient care and communication at the forefront of their healthcare practice with all patients, they will literally be saving countless lives. That is the work Dr. Kelly is trying to encourage and advocate for in this book. And isn't that what healthcare systems are meant to do – what we expect of them, what it commits to provide? We are judging systems. Our healthcare systems must advocate for all lives as worth saving, and uphold all voices, not just the ones with private insurance, and White skin.

In Aftershock, Dr. Neel Shah, physician, and professor at Harvard University, says "affirming a person's dignity is the way you make them safe. It is not a luxury." Believing Black women, dignifying them with proper care, sharing their stories - this is how we keep them safe, this is how we save their lives, and this is not a luxury. This is what Dr. Kelly is doing in this book, and why I knew I must be a part of it in any way I could - to try and be a part of all the good she is bravely doing.

What Dr. Kelly has done, in not just nurturing staff, but advocating for patients, is of deep empathy, compassion, and humanity, for all fellow beings walking our great Earth. She skillfully navigates between the heart-wrenching, but fact-based, research of our past, the staggering conclusions that must therefore be drawn about the statistics of our present, and the empathetic solutions that we must walk toward for securing equity in our future. My hope is that you will take that journey with her, and walk this path towards justice hand-in-hand with us. It is this hope that helps guide me, that I continue to turn toward, when everything else in the world can seem so heavy and bleak. It is this hope that keeps me believing that our future is a bright one, if only we can continue to work for it. It is this hope that brought me on to this project in the first place, and has me believing in it more than ever. And I hope you believe in it, too. For it is work like this, and those who believe in it, that help us to become the good that we are all looking for in our messy, but beautiful, world.

INTRODUCTION

I am a hospital Chaplain and am deeply passionate about the work I do serving in maternal health. I want to share my journey with you, leading up to this very moment, which I hope will provide some necessary insight into how a staff Chaplain came about writing a book to Healthcare Providers.

While completing my Master of Divinity Degree (M.Div.), my academic advisor recommended I do a field internship at Hoag Presbyterian Memorial Hospital to see if I would be interested in a career in Chaplaincy. With full trust, and urgency to complete my masters, I took her up on it, even though I was unsure of what Chaplaincy work was all about. I was interviewed, and accepted, and seriously considered a career in Chaplaincy after completing my year at Hoag. So I applied for a Clinical Pastoral Education ("CPE") residency program, but was not accepted at first. I then applied for a doctoral program in Dayton, Ohio and was accepted after a three month application process. Ironically, within that time, the Chaplaincy residency reconsidered my application and also accepted me into their program. Now, I was part of two major programs: A 1 year Hospital Chaplain Residency and a 4 year Doctoral Program. Instead of choosing between one or the other, I accepted the challenge of doing both concurrently. I would not advise in hindsight. Just saying…

While reflecting on my time as a resident at Little Company of Mary Hospital, I realized it was more than I could have ever imagined. Having just completed my M.Div. Degree, I rested for 6 months before entering the United Theological Seminary for my Doctoral studies, while simultaneously continuing my Clinical Pastoral Education (CPE). In this residency, I was introduced to many disciplines. I remember secretly wondering - what do these various disciplines have to do with becoming a hospital Chaplain where you only see and visit with patients? I was not prepared for the psychological, sociological, spiritual, theological, philosophical, and physical learnings that I would receive in this program.

We started with working on self-development through discovering our personality type with the enneagram test, doing a historical background on ourselves, and processing our profiles together as a cohort. Many of our profiles included, as you can imagine, intimate experiences of joys, celebrations, achievements, pain, suffering and lived experiences. While this was an often grueling experience, it was one I am most thankful for, and something I would recommend to anyone wishing to pursue a career in healthcare.

My internship cohort consisted of 7 people of diverse backgrounds. We were women and men of multiple ethnicities, including those of Native American, Black, Korean, Chinese, Jewish, and Caucasian descents. What a well-varied group to journey with during your entire residency! Part of our time together included group processing, group reflections, and group accountability as it related to patient care. This meant reading one another's verbatims (a word by word accounting of the clinical visit between Chaplain and a patient that is typed up in a very methodical way). We would choose two of the hardest cases and present them for group review and feedback.

Sometimes it proved very helpful, and other times, certain members of the group really tested and taunted your reasons for why you did this or avoided doing that. It began to feel very uncomfortable at times. We were vulnerable and had all signed an agreement to participate in group practice with authenticity and transparency. Often times, members of the group were able to see angles that the Chaplain on "trial" could not see - i.e., their discomforts, their biases, their prejudice, their fears and insecurities. It was not uncommon for some of the sharing to get heated as defenses rose and offenses were made bare. It made us think deeply and critically about our actions and the ethics of our actions, in particular. This type of scrutiny also provided additional learnings and perspectives if we could remain open to collegiate insights and recommendations.

Toward the end of residency, it all began finally making sense to us. After months of feeling picked on, singled out, interrogated or made to feel incompetent through observations and feedback, we discovered as a group how much we needed one another, and the ship began to turn toward the tide of unity, mutual respect, and honor.

Eventually, instead of begrudging group reflection, we began going to each other before group reflections to run clinical visits by others and get their feedback or recommendations. It felt like we were no longer in a silo, afraid of being vulnerable or judged for not knowing all the answers. It felt like a team of comrades - each one respecting the person, culture, ethnicity, language, and lived experiences that every individual brought to the team. We learned about other cultures by listening to each other in the group. We saw how different we were, but more importantly, we knew that different didn't mean deficient. It just meant, different.

We worked our quarterly character growth opportunities with openness and excitement to see how other peers noticed change and transformation in areas where we needed strengthening. What was once a source of shame, was now a source of celebration and opportunity for growth. We didn't have to be perfect, but we needed one another to begin to perfect our personal journey and clinical vocation. Still, somewhere in the back of my mind, I would from time to time ask - how does all of this connect with the patient care at the bedside?

Now, many years later, and after working in 3 different hospitals, I realize that these internal experiences are the very things that encouraged me to pursue respectful compassionate care for all patients. I am indebted to this intense, in-depth residency that shaped my awareness and compassion for humanity. I see why every healthcare provider, multidisciplinary team member and clergy, should have this training. My supervisor highly recommends every discipline in healthcare would benefit from a program like this, or one similar, which helps shape the clinician from the inside out to become that compassionate, healing presence in every situation. Nurturing personal development is critical. As I have continued my work in a hospital setting, I realize how these disciplines became the jewels in my toolkit that would allow me to optimize best practices for every patient, every time, no matter race, ethnicity, gender, sexuality or creed. Every life is sacred and valuable.

A significant part of our learning included webinars and workshops. The webinar hosted by NBC that left the most impact on my life had to do with healthcare disparities in Black America. The context included caring for maternal mortality and infant mortality, oncology patients, and diabetic, hypertension disease in Black patients. What was striking was the stark contrast of care provided to Black patients and their non-Black counter parts. There was a lack of referrals to appropriate resources and interventions for the patients who were Black. I cried quietly for a third of the webinar. It was the first time I saw a documentary demonstrating how Black people are the most underserved and marginalized group in every area of the United States - from education, housing (redlining), employment, and criminal justice, to healthcare and major diseases (i.e. diabetes, cancer, kidney failure, hypertension, maternal mortality, infant death, etc). These statistics brought silent tears that saturated my face as I watched frozen - the statistics alone were criminal. I found myself questioning over, and over "how could this be happening?" as the narrator continued to spew forth, without hesitation, atrocious data.

When the lights came on, I felt many things as the only Black in the room - powerless, outraged, vulnerable, shamed - I wanted to hide but there was nowhere to run. My life heretofore had not afforded me this type of exposure - or maybe it did, but I would pick and choose what I wanted to hear. Maybe it was so overwhelming, that I decided (like so many Blacks do) to turn a deaf ear to it - to just continue taking care of my business, trying to stay as safe and far away from the danger zones of this White America as possible. But whether I wanted to face it or not, I had to recognize the truth that I was part of those statistics. And when I stopped to really think about it more, I realized it was not just me, but my mother with hypertension, my sister with kidney failure, and my younger siblings born severely premature at birth.

Someone read the room and threw out a general and vague question. Something simple, like "Is everyone okay?" But I didn't say a word - I couldn't. Being an introvert, I had not even processed my thoughts yet, nor had I allowed everything to fully download and resonate for myself.

I came across this same feeling when I was first assigned to sit on the ethics board as an observer. At first, I thought it was quite impressive to be at the same table with doctors, with men and women of this calibur and prominence. I felt proud, and honored - until I had my first experience of a look I had come to learn well - a look that clearly said "what is she doing here?"

It may have been unspoken, but the meaning was loud and clear. Refusal to even speak to me. I withstood and remained. I didn't understand, at the time, how these providers could be in the healthcare field, serving on an ethics team, and still have these issues written all over their faces. I had a lot to learn, indeed.

During my residency, I learned a lot, saw a lot and heard a lot - some of which were the launching pads for my future focus on structural racism, though I did not know it at the time.

I was doing a dual track - completing my Doctoral Degree and residency at the same time. Between the two, my passion was being stretched. I am a lover of learning. If I could be in school all my life, I probably would. I began with an emphasis in social justice, but switched to spiritual formation right at the deadline to lock in your focus.

The powerlessness, shame, and embarrassment I felt secretly as an introverted minority began to erode after the case of Trayvon Martin. His story set a fire in me to be alert, to be aware, and to be an advocate for civil rights. I was inspired to be an educator, a voice for the underrepresented, and a presence that could not be ignored.

I began to take part in the conversations about race relations that I used to shy away from. Instead, I was drawn to lean in to the cause. I began to learn more about my history, to study the truth about Black history in America - the real and full truth of my people - not just the erroneous, often White-washed, version presented in schools.

I was already beginning to do the work, when the murder of George Floyd happened. This is what fully opened up the disparity dam in front of me, flooding me with truths that were hard to acknowledge, but impossible to continue to ignore. I could not stay away from the glaring research I was uncovering brick by brick - from the unequal criminal justice system, to the stolen cells of a nonconsenting Henrietta Lacks, to learning about the "White Bill of Rights" in the south and how the reconstruction era was a farce. I was uncovering the histories buried away in cellars; locked away in the catacombs of libraries; hidden, for fear that the real truths would be revealed. I devoured the painful histories of my people - from the devastation of Black Wall Street in Tulsa, Oklahoma, to the innocent Black boy who was given the very first lethal injection at 14 years old, only to be declared innocent 70 years later, when the accuser was on his deathbed, to the shocking numbers of preventable deaths in Black mothers even today. I uncovered countless examples of innocent lives being lost, just because they were born with a different skin color. And it begged the question - if there are this many recorded stories hidden away, how many more have been buried and lost to the sands of time? How many more undeserving Black people died, without anyone remembering their story?

Coinciding with the murder of George Floyd, was the worldwide pandemic of Covid-19. With the stay at home orders in place, and the atrocity laid bare for all to see, people could no longer dismiss this police brutality as "just another bad Black man." Instead, they had to witness the cruelty of a 9+ minute execution filmed for the world to see. They had to come face to face with the arrogance of a White man as he held his knee on the neck of a Black man, suffocating him to death in broad daylight.

The story filled every channel as each "breaking news" banner broke through to the hearts of every home. To those who viewed the devastating crime laid bare in front of them, there could be no more denial, no more sweeping under the rug with the label of "just another Black criminal." Simmering cries filled the streets of our nation as our souls were touched and countless individuals stood up to protest one way or another! From the daily news, to nightly talk shows, to neighbors talking in the street - there was mass outrage at such an injustice! The Black Lives Matter movement spread worldwide - from the US, to Germany, England, Paris, and countless other countries - the calls for equality could no longer be ignored. At the same time as these newly invigorated calls for justice, a transformative law (SBA 464) was also passed that aimed to combat the disparities in maternal mortality.

The culmination of these events inspired me to write Nurturing Equity Minded Healthcare Providers. Too long has healthcare in America mirrored the bullying system of structural-malpractice. Too long have Black families suffered less care at the hands of presumptuous authority and White privilege. Too long have these inequities gone unaddressed. This work aims to not only address many of these inequities, but to offer suggestions and ways to mitigate these long-standing disparities.

Though the task of creating this work has been a daunting one, I am grateful for the many ways in which writing this book has driven me to engage with thousands of pages of research, studies, statistics and data. These findings are the realities of research as the prima facie raw data reveals the torturous and traumatic care of Black people in America - from slavery until today.

I have uncovered countless instances of the appalling ways Black people have been treated in the medical community - whether they are dismissed as patients, ignored in their pain, or experimented on as non-consenting research subjects, Black Americans have consistently been at a disadvantage when it comes to healthcare.

One such resource that my research led me to was Dr. Harriet A. Washington's book Medical Apartheid: The Dark History of Medical Experimentation on Black Americans from Colonial Times to the Present.[1] In this book, Washington spends hundreds of pages laying out the many atrocities committed upon Black people in America "in the name of research." She provides countless instances of Black people being experimented on, and argues that "Research is an utterly essential and desirable component of treatment, but its subjects must be aware that they are participating, must be informed, must consent, and must be allowed to weigh the possible risk and benefits." Unfortunately, as she makes clear in her book, these conditions are only haphazardly met, or often not met at all, when the subjects are Black.

---

1   Washington, Harriet A. "Introduction: The American Janus of Medicine and Race." *Medical Apartheid: The Dark History of Medical Experimentation on Black Americans from Colonial Times to the Present,* Anchor Books (Random House), New York, NY, 2008, pp. 1–25.

Washington's work is a masterful presentation of the many ways in which our so called "healthcare" in America has failed to actually care for the health of its Black citizens. She unfolds the long history of experimentation, exploitation, and dismissal of Black people in healthcare, from pre-colonial times, to today. And she describes how these truths have often been hidden away in medical journals as "The slave appropriated by physicians for experimental surgeries, the impoverished clinic patient operated upon to devise or demonstrate a surgical technique, the sharecropper whose body is spirited from the morgue for dissection, the young girl whose fertility is stolen via an untested contraceptive technique or a "Mississippi appendectomy" (involuntary sterilization), the soldiers, prisoners, and children who find themselves without options when government physicians foist novel medications and techniques upon those with little legal protection - all these Blacks, and many more, have found themselves voiceless as medical lions have chosen to present this research in bowdlerized manner."

What's more, Washington goes on to share how the divide between White physicians and their Black patients continued to widen over time, due to these very mistreatments.

She reveals how through her own research, she found that "The stories physicians told mixed stereotyped comedy with exasperation as they dismissed Blacks as disease-ridden, unintelligent, fearful, distrustful, and above all, 'noncompliant' patients…such negative presumptions hampered physicians' ability to care for Black patients or even to see them as worthy of the same excellent care rendered to others. For their part, the Black patients…shared their own medical lore, which warned against trusting Western medical practices and physicians, a matrix they characterized as racist, rapacious, and eager to exploit Black bodies for medical gain at the cost of health. Thus, the disparate narratives Blacks and physicians tell unveil a state of undeclared war or, at best, an uneasy truce between physicians and their Black patients."

These truths, and the many others, that Washington lays bare in her book continued to leave me speechless, time and time again, and I encourage all others serious about this work, to read her words in full. It is truths like these, of "an undeclared war…between physicians and their Black patients" that reminds me why I continue to do this work, and why I believe it is so important to nurture both sides of the coin when it comes to healthcare. To encourage personal development and growth in healthcare providers, as well as to share the stories, histories, and truths of Black patients in healthcare. I truly believe that it is through this encouragement, and education, that we can begin to bridge the divide of this "uneasy truce" and transform healthcare from an "undeclared war," to a thriving partnership. That is the goal I aim to work toward with Nurturing Equity Minded Healthcare Providers, and I hope you join me in this journey.

REV. DR. CANDACE COLE-KELLY

Section I

REFLECTION ON PERSONAL DEVELOPMENT

OVERVIEW OF SECTION I

WHAT YOU WILL LEARN (AND DO) IN THIS SECTION:

Part 1 encourages one's personal development as a healthcare provider, and includes the following subjects:

Chapter 1: Personal Development: Wholeness and Wellness for Healthcare Providers: What does wholeness and wellness mean for you? What do you bring to the bedside? How well do you care for yourself after caring for others?

Chapter 2: The Gift of Surrender: How do you process regrets, errors or mistakes? What is your process of release? What does surrender have to do with equity?

Chapter 3: Important Foundations Towards Self-Actualization: Identify the building blocks of your personal and work life, and how awareness of our own foundations leads to cultural integration and humility. Discover your basic needs and goals, explore what you still need to achieve, and consider what this means while caring for your patients as you assess their actualization.

Chapter 4: Benefits of Self-awareness: How well do you know yourself and your behavior? What are helpful and hurtful attributes? How can self-awareness help you work toward equitable empathy and dignity for all patients, especially traditionally marginalized patients? How do you engage your compassion towards justice without experiencing compassion fatigue?

Chapter 5: Building Your Own Resilience Toolkit: Learn how to recover from trauma and crises using healthy coping tools. Master the "art of the restart" and avoid compassion fatigue by activating self-compassion.

Chapter 6: Workplace boundaries: Do you know how to enforce your boundaries? How do boundaries keep us from knee-jerk reactions and bias? Are there any toxic boundaries that need to be released?

Chapter 7: Identifying Personal Loss and Grief: Assess any areas in your life journey that may need to be grieved to make room for new life, love, and self. How does loss and grief work impact your presence with those in your care?

INTRODUCTION: EMBARKING ON PERSONAL DEVELOPMENT, THE JOURNEY TOWARD EQUITY AND COMPASSIONATE CARE

As healthcare providers, nurses, and clinicians, your role goes beyond treating illnesses—it encompasses fostering trust, delivering equitable care, and ensuring dignity for all patients. In a diverse and interconnected world, achieving this level of care requires introspection, self-awareness, and a commitment to personal and professional development.

Structural racism and implicit biases often operate invisibly, influencing healthcare delivery and perpetuating disparities, particularly within marginalized communities. Addressing these issues requires not only clinical expertise but also a deep understanding of the social determinants of health and a sensitivity to how historical and systemic inequities affect patient outcomes.

This initiative invites you to embark on a transformative journey of internal work and personal development. Through this process, you will:

- Assess Your Current Knowledge: Reflect on your understanding of structural racism and its impact on healthcare.
- Cultivate Self-Awareness: Identify implicit biases and explore how they influence your clinical interactions.
- Enhance Empathy and Sensitivity: Develop tools to engage patients with compassion and respect, ensuring their voices are heard and valued.
- Commit to Equitable Care: Equip yourself to provide care that embodies dignity, respect, and empathy, especially for those from marginalized and underserved communities.

This journey is not about perfection; it is about progress. By confronting uncomfortable truths and embracing a mindset of growth, you will strengthen your ability to deliver care that is as inclusive as it is effective. Together, we can create a healthcare system that not only treats diseases but also uplifts humanity.

Let us begin this essential work—because every patient deserves not just care, but compassionate care.

When it comes to equity work, the saying is true: you cannot impact who you insult. For this reason, Section One encourages one's personal development as a healthcare provider. By focusing first on themes such as wholeness, surrender, self awareness, compassion, boundaries, grief, and resilience, we set an important foundation for future interactions with patients and coworkers and our own interactions with ourselves.

CHAPTER ONE
Personal Development: Wholeness and Wellness for Healthcare Providers

"PEOPLE MAY NOT REMEMBER YOUR NAME,
BUT THEY WILL ALWAYS REMEMBER HOW YOU MADE THEM FEEL."
-- MAYA ANGELOU

"IF YOU WANT OTHERS TO BE HAPPY, PRACTICE COMPASSION.
IF YOU WANT TO BE HAPPY, PRACTICE COMPASSION."
-- DALAI LAMA

"I DISCOVERED THAT COMPASSION FATIGUE IS A REAL THING.
EMOTIONS, SO STRONG AT FIRST, CAN EASILY SHIFT INTO APATHY."
-- CHRIS MARLOW

What is personal development, and why is it critical in this sensitive work?

Personal development is a comprehensive approach to becoming your whole self for the benefit of others and the work that you do. Personal development includes examining your heart, passions, convictions, values, and beliefs. These tenets inform how you impact the world around you, including your family, friends, community, and workspace. Lastly, healthy personal development benefits the individual in the broader scope of life, empowering one to be their best self while embracing all cultures, no matter socio-economic status, race/ethnicity, gender, or religion. It is critical in the field of healthcare that each healthcare provider is a well-balanced clinician who sees each patient in their unique intersectionality. Hence, the healthcare provider will then offer care without bias and stereotypes, but rather give respectful maternal care to all birthing persons. This should be every healthcare provider's true north. Only then can we disrupt the disparities of maternal morbidity and mortality that exist in Black mothers and mothers in traditionally marginalized communities, closing the disparity gaps in Black maternal health by using an equity lens in all of our care.

In this chapter, we will explore personal development through wholeness and wellness, focusing not only on the *what* of the work we do, but the *why*.

The old adage is true - we cannot give what we do not have. The more self-aware we are, the more we can react in daily situations with wisdom, compassion, and equity. The more actualized we have become, the more we can recognize the systemic barriers that keep others from the fullness of life. The more whole and healthier we become, the more we can use our compassionate hearts and platforms to advocate for the needs of those in our care.

DEVELOPING YOUR COMPASSIONATE-HEART

True self-awareness will not only lead us to compassion for ourselves, but compassion for our fellow human beings who suffer just as we do. For those of us working in the field of healthcare, it is important for us to be self-aware in the way that our compassion motivates us to action, while remaining a healthy force for good.

WHAT IS COMPASSION?

Compassion comes from the Latin roots that mean "to suffer with."[1] Many of us entered the healthcare field out of compassion for those who were suffering, and a desire to help.

Compassion in healthcare is the practice of recognizing and empathizing with a patient's feelings, accompanied by a genuine willingness to help, and taking rational actions to find solutions to their problems. It requires healthcare professionals to not only understand and share the emotional state of their patients but also to be motivated to alleviate their suffering. This compassionate approach aims to improve patient outcomes by fostering a supportive and empathetic environment.

However, the demanding nature of healthcare can challenge the ability of professionals to consistently act with compassion. Factors such as burnout and hierarchical power dynamics can impede their capacity to empathize and respond effectively to patient needs. Because of this, the concept of compassion in healthcare has sparked significant discussion within the healthcare community. These ongoing discussions are shedding light on the tangible medical value that compassion can bring to both patients and healthcare providers. Proponents argue that compassionate care not only enhances the patient experience but also contributes to better health outcomes by fostering trust, improving communication, and encouraging patient adherence to treatment plans. Additionally, compassion can benefit healthcare providers by increasing job satisfaction and reducing burnout, leading to a more positive work

---

[1] Oxford English Dictionary, https://www.oed.com/dictionary/compassion_n?tl=true

environment. As the conversation continues, there is a growing recognition of the importance of integrating compassion into healthcare practices and policies.

Research and application of the concepts of caring and compassion are vital in addressing these challenges. By exploring these concepts, healthcare systems can implement strategies that support healthcare professionals, enhance their ability to act compassionately, and ultimately improve the quality of patient care.

COMPASSIONATE CARE VS. TECHNOLOGY

In his book, Called to Care,[2] Larry Benz describes his first role as a physical therapist in treating soldiers in the US Army. His story is both heroic and insightful.

Important to his practice, he notes, "patients depend wholly on their healthcare providers."[3] As a result of attentive quality healthcare services, Benz experienced that his patients put their full trust in his hands so they could diligently and quickly recover and return to the field to fulfill their mission. This is a very common, and human, experience as patients often have no choice but to trust their healthcare professionals. And more often than not, providers rise to this occasion, providing incredible efforts to care for their patients. Unfortunately, however, this does not always remain the case - as providers experience burnout, fatigue, malpractice and emotional wearing, especially when it comes to dealing with the administrative side of healthcare as well.

Benz further addresses the healthcare system threat to the quality of care, stating, "over the past several years in an attempt to make healthcare more efficient, various 'process improvements' (excessive documentation, regulations, and a variety of other hoops and ladders) have replaced time spent with patients."[3] This is most unfortunate and negatively impacts the provider-patient relationship. While it is important to acknowledge the heroic work our providers do, when they lose sight of their intrinsic motivators, not only do they suffer emotionally but their patients often also pay the price in how they are cared for.

In the research article, Patients' Trust in Physicians,[4] published by the National Library of Medicine, authors Pearson and Raeke assert that, "Trust is a defining element in any interpersonal relationship, but is particularly central to the patient-physician relationship. Although evidence shows that the majority of patients continue to trust physicians to act in their best interest, concern is growing that the rapid and far-reaching changes in the healthcare system have placed great pressure on that trust and may be undermining it."[4] These patient concerns are valid and vital, as we witness the widespread disparities in healthcare. And it is these very concerns that clinicians in every field must work to address.

As we have seen through Benz's research,[2] easy to lose track of the heart behind our work as healthcare providers, especially when we must incorporate certain system-wide requirements into our care. And as we try to stay mindful of these two goals, often at odds with each other, it is easy to get over-worked, over-tired, and just plain "over all of it." We stop allowing for emotions entirely, and become a "robot" just going through our daily motions. We stop feeling, stop caring, and ultimately stop trying. And while it can be overwhelming at times to sit with the painful emotions sometimes involved in our profession, it is worthwhile to reflect back on who we wish to be, and how we hope to care as healthcare providers, to keep us motivated through our patient care responsibilities.

---

2   Benz, Laurence N. *Called to Care: A Medical Provider's Guide for Humanizing Healthcare*. Lioncrest Publishing, 2020. (Whole Book)

3   Benz, Larry. "Compassionate Care Is Being Replaced by Institutional Care." *Medium*, Renee Kemper, 17 Sept. 2020, (Excerpt from Book in Note 2). https://medium.com/book-bites/compassionate-care-is-being-replaced-by-institutional-care-ab5328472cd.

4   Pearson SD, Raeke LH. "Patients' trust in physicians: many theories, few measures, and little data." *J Gen Intern Med*. 2000 Jul;15(7):509-13. doi: 10.1046/j.1525-1497.2000.11002.x. PMID: 10940139; PMCID: PMC1495476. https://www.ncbi.nlm.nih.gov/pmc/articles/PMC1495476.

It is important to remember to provide care with H.E.A.R.T. by following these steps:

1. Hearing and validating our patient's concerns through active listening.
2. Empathizing with their lived experiences.
3. Advocating for our patients' needs and exploring appropriate resources.
4. Respecting our patients with dignity and honor no matter race and ethnicity.
5. Transformational care is care that builds trust, changing both patient and provider. You know you are doing a good work with others when you begin to change yourself.

Healthcare institutions that respect each member of the multidisciplinary team model ensure best practices when providing patient-family centered care. Finally, we must always remember the Hippocratic Oath we took to do no harm as physicians and clinicians.[5]

Nurturing Equity Minded Healthcare Providers is written to empower healthcare professionals in reconnecting with the heart of their practice. In so doing, five principles are recommended:

1. Promote and encourage family-centered care that nurtures the needs of the patient and respectfully supports their family.
2. Respect each sub-specialist (Multidisciplinary teams), i.e., Provider, Nurses, Psychologists, Chaplaincy (Pastoral Care), Social Work, Music Therapy, Case Manager, Child Life Specialist, CNA's, etc.
3. Allow compassionate caring to be a mainstay in presenting the plan of care.
4. Establish in your institution equitable healthcare professionals working together in a worldwide movement to transform healthcare to be void of structural racism. (This author shares the values and convictions supported by the team at *Hearts in Healthcare*[6] for the purposes of humanizing healthcare.)
5. Support the well-being and resilience of all staff.

As we continue this chapter on personal development, let's consider what role wholeness and wellness play in enhancing your personal development. It is important to remember effective advocacy begins in ourselves first, which is a healthy sign of our wholeness. Only then are we in a position to advocate for others.

WHOLENESS AND WELLNESS

The journal article Nurse, Heal Yourself: Wholeness for Nurses, reminds us that, "Nursing, at its wholeness best, involves the head, the hand, and the heart, that is, knowledge, direct patient care, and compassion, respectively. Nurses should bring this same dynamic balance into their personal lives, caring for themselves as whole persons."[7]

---

[5] Though it has been contested that the exact phrase "do no harm" is not actually a part of the Hippocratic Oath, this author uses the phrase to represent the ideals physicians take to do good for their patient and to "abstain from whatever is deleterious and mischievous," as *is* written in the Hippocratic Oath, according to the Encyclopedia Britannica: Britannica, The Editors of Encyclopaedia. "Hippocratic oath". *Encyclopedia Britannica,* 29 Apr. 2023, https://www.britannica.com/topic/Hippocratic-oath.

[6] "Hearts in Healthcare." *Charter for Compassion,* 2022, https://charterforcompassion.org/healthcare-partners/hearts-in-healthcare.
"HEARTS in HEALTHCARE is an inspirational community of health professionals, students, patient advocates, health leaders, and many others who are champions for compassionate care. We believe bringing like-minded people together is the first step to re-humanizing healthcare around the world."

[7] Ojewole, Foluso Oladayo, and Afolarin Olutunde Ojewole. "Nurse, Heal Yourself: Wholeness for Nurses." *Journal of Natural Sciences Research,* IISTE - International Knowledge Sharing Platform, 2017; ISSN 2224-3186 (Paper) ISSN 2225-0921 (Online) Vol.7, No.18, 2017 https://www.iiste.org/Journals/index.php/JNSR/article/view/38723/39824.

Physician Heal Thyself

This section in our chapter is a call for wholeness in multiple facets of life, including mental, emotional, psychological, spiritual, relational, physical, and financial. All those in the medical profession are constantly helping to heal others, but it is imperative for them to be sure to take care of themselves as well.

A Vision of Wholeness

In recent years, the idea of caring for oneself is quickly gaining ascendance and becoming a priority in nursing. Healthcare providers are acutely aware of the power in caring for others, and are therefore joining together to strengthen each other in the commitment to care for themselves.

LeAnn Thieman in her book, Self Care for Healthcare asserts, "Yet it is evident that caregivers who are strong in mind, body and spirit give better patient care, which results in better outcomes and patient satisfaction."[8]

If we are truly going to succeed in bringing equity to all, we need to have practiced the kind of self-awareness that leads us into awareness of others that is unobstructed.

We invite you to explore your wholeness and wellness by viewing the wheel below. Take some moments to reflect on each domain asking yourself, "How am I doing in this area?"

---

[8] Thieman, LeAnn. *Selfcare for Healthcare: Your Guide to Physical, Spiritual, and Mental Health*. Priority Pub., 2012.

NURTURING EQUITY MINDED GROUP EXERCISES

Considering the Wellness Wheel, list your strongest areas in descending order:

1. _____

2. _____

3. _____

4. _____

5. _____

6. _____

7. _____

8. _____

Discuss with your small group what you have discovered and share: which areas need improving upon to achieve more wholeness?

CHAPTER TWO
The Gift of Surrender

> "THE MOMENT OF SURRENDER IS NOT WHEN LIFE IS OVER, IT'S WHEN IT BEGINS."
> -- MARIANNE WILLIAMSON

> "SOMETIMES, IT'S NOT THE TIMES YOU DECIDE TO FIGHT, BUT THE TIMES YOU DECIDE TO SURRENDER, THAT MAKES ALL THE DIFFERENCE."
> -- SISSY GAVRILAKI

> "THE GREATNESS OF THE MAN'S POWER IS THE MEASURE OF HIS SURRENDER."
> --WILLIAM BOOTH

What comes to your mind when you think of the word, *surrender*?

Surrender is the act of giving up or yielding to the power, control, or possession of another, often after a struggle or conflict. It can occur in various contexts, such as:

Military: When a force ceases fighting and submits to the authority of the opposing side, often marked by a formal ceremony or document.

Personal: When an individual gives up resistance or the attempt to continue a certain behavior, often in the context of addiction or personal struggle.

Negotiations: When one party concedes or gives in to the demands or conditions of another party.

Domestic Affairs: When a person surrenders in divorce, they demonstrate the ability to let go of what cannot be controlled, focus on what can be positively influenced, and move forward with grace and resilience. This approach can lead to a more amicable separation, healthier emotional state, and a brighter future.

In all cases, surrender implies a relinquishment of control or power.

Surrendering in challenging situations is often about recognizing and accepting the limits of our control. It involves understanding that despite our best efforts, some outcomes or situations are beyond our ability to influence. This truth can be particularly hard to accept because it goes against our natural desires as healthcare providers to fix, help, heal, or make things better. But there are some things, including many diagnoses and prognoses, we will have to surrender to a greater reality. Our challenge is discerning when to surrender after we have spent our wheels and energy.

As we continue in this theme, try to keep in mind that surrender is not necessarily defeat, negative or bad. Surrender can in fact be the most respectful, compassionate, honorable, and respectful act one human can yield to another.

Below are some key steps to consider for when to surrender: Let's make it personal by using "I" statements.

Recognizing the Signs: I usually notice it is time to surrender when I start feeling consistently stressed, anxious, or frustrated about a situation. If I am putting in a lot of effort without seeing any positive change, it is a clear sign that I need to step back.

Reflection and Acceptance: I take time to reflect on what is happening and accept that there are aspects I cannot control. This acceptance does not mean giving up entirely, but rather acknowledging the reality of the situation.

Seeking Perspective: Talking with trusted friends, mentors, or my small group helps me gain perspective. They can offer insights and support that make it easier to see the situation more clearly and decide what I need to let go of.

Setting Boundaries: Part of surrendering is setting boundaries to protect my well-being. This might mean limiting my involvement or emotional investment in a situation that I can't change.

Letting Go: This is the most challenging part. Letting go means releasing my attachment to a specific outcome and trusting that things will work out as they are meant to. It often involves a lot of internal work, such as mindfulness practices, prayer, or meditation, to help me find peace.

> **THE SERENITY MANTRA[1]**
>
> GRANT ME THE SERENITY TO ACCEPT THE THINGS I CANNOT CHANGE. THE COURAGE TO CHANGE THE THINGS I CAN. AND THE WISDOM TO KNOW THE DIFFERENCE.

---

1. The Serenity Mantra (or Prayer) is originally attributed to Reinhold Niebuhr from 1943, as described in the article Who Wrote the Serenity Prayer, cited below:
Shapiro, Fred R. "Who Wrote the Serenity Prayer." *Yale Alumni Magazine*, Yale Alumni Publications, July 2008, http://archives.yalealumnimagazine.com/issues/2008_07/serenity.html

Knowing when it's time to surrender often comes down to a combination of self-awareness, external feedback, and an honest assessment of the situation. When the emotional and physical toll becomes too great and the impact of our efforts remains unchanged, it's usually a strong indicator that surrendering is the healthiest and most compassionate choice for ourselves and others involved.

In your small group setting, discuss an experience where you had to surrender and share how valuable it was. Share any struggle, insights, and the process you entered in order to surrender.

It is liberating to come to terms with being okay with not having all the answers or solutions. Now, in light of the equity work we are embarking upon, let's consider how surrender fits in patient family- centered care.

SURRENDERING OUR BIASES

We have heard of the scenario with a white woman passing a Black man and immediately clutching her purse. She does this because of the implicit bias or stereotype of how all Black men are, embedded deep in her cognitive reality. Likewise, there is an inherent mistrust in the healthcare system in marginalized communities due to a lack of trauma-informed care. How do we work around these glaring realities?

Surrendering biases and stereotypes in the context of Diversity, Equity, and Inclusion (DEI) in healthcare is a critical step toward creating a more trusting, equitable and effective environment for both patients and healthcare professionals. This process requires ongoing self-reflection, education, and commitment. Here are some strategies to help with this process:

Self-Reflection and Awareness

- **Acknowledge Biases:** The first step is to recognize that everyone has biases and stereotypes, often unconsciously. Acknowledging their existence is crucial for change.
- **Reflect on Personal Experiences:** Consider how your experiences and background may have shaped your biases. Reflect on situations where these biases may have influenced your actions or decisions.

Education and Training

- **Engage in Continuous Learning:** Participate in DEI training programs that address implicit bias, cultural competence, and the impact of stereotypes in healthcare.
- **Read and Listen:** Educate yourself through books, articles, podcasts, and other resources that provide diverse perspectives, especially those from marginalized communities.

Seek Diverse Perspectives

- **Listen to Others:** Engage in conversations with colleagues, patients, and community members from diverse backgrounds. Listening to their experiences can provide valuable insights and challenge preconceived notions.
- **Encourage Diverse Voices:** Support and promote diversity in decision-making processes and leadership positions within healthcare settings.

Practice Empathy and Compassion

- **Empathy Exercises:** Put yourself in others' shoes by imagining their experiences and challenges. This can help reduce biases and increase understanding.
- **Patient-Centered Care:** Focus on providing care that respects and responds to the individual patient's preferences, needs, and values.

Implement Structural Changes
- **Policy Reforms:** Advocate for and implement policies that promote equity and inclusivity within healthcare institutions. This includes recruitment, hiring practices, and patient care protocols.
- **Inclusive Practices:** Develop and enforce practices that ensure all patients receive equitable care, regardless of their background.

Accountability and Feedback
- **Self-Assessment:** Regularly assess your own behaviors and attitudes. Use tools such as the Implicit Association Test (IAT) to uncover hidden biases.
- **Peer Feedback:** Encourage a culture where colleagues can provide and receive constructive feedback on behaviors that may reflect biases or stereotypes.

Mindfulness and Reflection
- **Mindfulness Practices:** Engage in mindfulness and meditation to become more aware of your thoughts and reactions. This can help you catch and address biases as they arise.
- **Journaling:** Keep a journal to reflect on your interactions and experiences, noting any biases that emerge and how you can address them.

Commitment to Change
- **Set Goals:** Establish clear, achievable goals for reducing biases and promoting inclusivity in your professional and personal life.
- **Stay Committed:** Understand that overcoming biases is an ongoing process that requires persistent effort and dedication.

Incorporating these strategies into your daily patient care practice can help you surrender old biases and stereotypes, fostering a more inclusive and equitable healthcare environment. This not only improves patient care but also enhances the working conditions and relationships among healthcare professionals.

EQUITY ROLE PLAY

Choose three people from your group to role play, then switch places. Each time take several minutes to role play the following scenario:

A nurse has an unconscious racial bias toward Hispanic people. While caring for a young Hispanic woman who is non-English-speaking, the nurse is very impatient and does want to arrange or coordinate interpretive services. You are a colleague and observe this happening. What do you do as a respectful maternal care nurse?

A. Ignore the situation.

B. Advocate for this patient who is terrified.

C. Gently or compassionately speak to your peer to see if she needs assistance.

CASE STUDY

You are a white nurse caring for a Black postpartum patient. Your patient tells you she is in pain. You believe her. So, you approach the doctor about increasing her pain medication. To your surprise, the doctor responds, "She's just drug seeking. That's what those people do."

You try to explain to the doctor that in patient advocacy we must believe the patient when they say they are in pain, and it is not our job to judge them.

The doctor looks at you in disgust. You want the doctor to respect and support you, but you feel you have lost a colleague. The doctor says, "No, take her vitals." You remain committed to advocating for this patient's needs. What do you do?

Discuss the following scenarios:

A. Do you escalate the situation to your director/manager/AUM? How would you advocate for this patient?

B. Imagine that your efforts, while difficult, are successful.

C. What part of the encounter with the doctor do you need to surrender?

D. Imagine that after escalating the situation and advocating for your patient, your efforts remain unsuccessful. Discuss how you feel.

- What does surrender look like in this scenario, knowing that you did everything you could to be their advocate but to no avail?

- How do you think your patient feels about her care and care team?

NURTURING EQUITY MINDED GROUP EXERCISE

Reflection Time

Take a moment to reflect on the physical benefits of surrender:

1. In your personal life: Describe your process of letting go of any regrets, mistakes, and actions you wish you could change.
2. Discuss the advantage in surrendering situations in patient care that you cannot change.

Take time to list 5 areas you need to surrender:

An area you need to surrender:	List the benefits you will receive:
1. Ex. Surrender my belief that I can always control a patient's outcome	1. Ex. Less anxiety, self-judgment, and shame
2.	2.
3.	3.
4.	4.
5.	5.

CHAPTER THREE
Important Foundations for Self Actualization

"YOU CAN'T BUILD A GREAT BUILDING ON A WEAK FOUNDATION. YOU MUST HAVE A SOLID FOUNDATION IF YOU'RE GOING TO HAVE A STRONG SUPERSTRUCTURE."
-- GORDON B. HINCKLEY

"THE IMPORTANT THING IS THAT YOU'VE GOT A STRONG FOUNDATION BEFORE YOU START TO TRY TO SAVE THE WORLD OR HELP OTHER PEOPLE."
-- RICHARD BRANSON

"GREAT PERSONS ARE GREAT BECAUSE OF GOOD, STRONG FOUNDATIONS ON WHICH THEY WERE ABLE TO BUILD A CHARACTER."
-- ALFRED ARMAND MONTAPERT

Foundations consist of the many influences that have contributed to our lives. Ask yourself: what systems have made you what you are and who you are as a healthcare provider?

As the Dean of Harvard's 2018 Commencement Speech, found at the end of this book, admits, "health disparities, income inequality, bigotry, racism, discrimination…you will encounter these on your hospital rounds, in the operating room, in your labs and in your community. These are maladies that ail modern society and modern medicine."

Not everyone walks in the room with the same foundations. It is critical that we examine our own foundational systems to understand how sound we are as an individual and how culturally competent, sensitive and integrated we are with the greater world around us. To do this, let's first examine our personal foundations:

Personal Foundations

In the nursery rhyme The Three Little Pigs,[1] the big, bad wolf says, "I'll huff and I'll puff and I'll blow your house down." He knows that a weaker foundation leaves everyone vulnerable. The inherent lesson is that the strength of your foundation will ensure your sustainability and success for both healthcare provider and patient.

Did you know that every great work and every successful person begins with a strong foundation? These include:

- **Family of Origin:** Parents, grandparents, and community are designed to provide a solid and healthy psycho-social foundation of belonging. One's family of origin is critical in a child's personal development and introduction to love. This unit establishes norms, values, a healthy sense of belonging, and provides empowerment and validation.

- **Immediate Family:** Spouse, children, parents/in-laws. This unit represents core connecting, building trust, and being responsible for others.

- **Cultural Integration: Diversity of races and ethnicities**, schoolmates, neighbors, friends, and co-workers. This represents connecting socially, and building external relationships with different races and ethnicities. Having ongoing positive personal relationships with people of color as a norm in your upbringing creates a solid and balanced foundation.

- **Education:** Education is a major foundation to prepare oneself for life. From pre-school to higher learning, you are taught the skills and lay the groundwork needed for a successful life and desired career.

- **Spiritual:** This provides individuals with a strong sense of transcendence, identity, value, inner strength, guidance, hope, respect, and love. A spiritual foundation ensures vision to see the opportunities that are ahead that provide purpose as opposed to fear-based perceptions which can leave you with uncertainty and bias. One's spirituality undergirds one in the midst of crises, traumas, losses and heartbreaks. It provides answers for those existential matters.

- **Moral:** Having a respectful moral compass as a foundation provides support for one's values, convictions, and beliefs. A healthcare provider who grew up with a foundation of good morals carries the values instilled in them from an early age into their professional life. Raised to respect others, show kindness, and act with integrity, they naturally extend these principles to their patients and colleagues. Their upbringing taught them the importance of honesty, empathy, and fairness, which now guide their decision-making and patient care. This moral grounding creates a sense of trustworthiness and compassion that resonates in their interactions, making them not only skilled in their profession but also deeply committed to the well-being and dignity of those they serve.

---

[1] The classic children's tale, The Three Little Pigs is well-known and has been re-told many times over. A citation is listed below where the full story can be accessed, for reference:
Steel, Flora Annie. "The Three Little Pigs." Short Stories & Classic Literature for Readers & Teachers, American Literature, 2014, https://americanliterature.com/childrens-stories/the-three-little-pigs.

- **Physical/Mental:** A strong physical and mental foundation is instrumental in facilitating all other foundations. This provides a healthy perspective in one's care for self: mental health, compassionate care, healthy relationships, good sleep patterns, and balanced activities. Physical foundations include exercise, healthy food choices, routine doctor's appointments, and spending time with Mother Earth.

- **Financial:** Being a good steward over one's resources is essential for developing a strong financial foundation. This includes being conscientious in our spending, savings, budget, and investments.

- **A Spiritual World View:** A spiritual worldview for any healthcare provider integrates the recognition of patients as holistic beings—body, mind, and spirit—while acknowledging that healing extends beyond physical care. This perspective embraces kindness, a sense of belonging, empathy, compassion, and respect for diverse beliefs, fostering an environment where patients feel valued and understood. It encourages providers to approach care with humility, offering support not only for physical ailments but also for emotional and spiritual needs. Such a worldview motivates healthcare providers to see their work as a vocation, promoting dignity, hope, and healing as part of a greater purpose.

- **Resilience:** Learning resilience as a foundation comes as a result of significant trauma-informed experiences. Through support, reflection, and healing, one can transform their pain into resilience, learning to navigate life with grace despite their hardships. These experiences deepen a person's empathy and compassion, as they intimately understand the weight of struggle and the power of kindness. As one matures, this resilience becomes a foundation for connecting with others, offering a listening ear, heartfelt encouragement, and unwavering support to those in need. The trauma-informed person can move from trauma to healing being shaped into a beacon of hope, embodying the belief that hardship can forge strength, kindness and compassion.

NURTURING EQUITY MINDED GROUP EXERCISE #1

For each of the following foundations listed, write the person or thing that comes immediately to your mind when you think of a strong foundation:

- Family of Origin:
- Immediate Family:
- Cultural Integration:
- Education:
- Moral:
- Spiritual:
- Physical/Mental:
- Financial:
- Spiritual World View:
- Resilience:

Assessing Your Foundations:

Let's go deeper into our foundations. On a scale of 1-5, with 5 being highest, rate how strong you feel your foundations are in each of the following categories:

1. Family of Origin   _____
2. Immediate Family   _____
3. Cultural Integration   _____
4. Education   _____
5. Spiritual   _____
6. Moral   _____
7. Physical/Mental   _____
8. Financial   _____
9. Spiritual World View   _____
10. Resilience   _____

Which foundation contributes most to you being an equitable healthcare provider? Which have impacted you the most?

Where did you see these foundations present in your neighborhood? How diverse was the community you grew up in?

If you find that you have been influenced greatly in 5 out of 6 of these foundations, you are, in the philosophy of Maslov's hierarchy, well-actualized and advanced in achieving your life's purpose and goals.

On the other hand, there are many communities of color that lack resources, opportunities, representation, and inalienable basic rights. How do you see them? How do they impact your heart? What do you wish for them? And now, how can you help?

As we consider these factors, it is important to take into account the influence of culture in each of our foundations and consider what cultural integration looks like in the workplace. Does it mirror the place where you live?

CULTURAL INTEGRATION

> "LET'S STOP BELIEVING THAT OUR DIFFERENCES MAKE US SUPERIOR OR INFERIOR TO ONE ANOTHER."
> -- CON MIGUEL RUIZ

> "IN MULTICULTURAL SOCIETY LIKE OURS, THE ISSUE OF BELONGING IS ESPECIALLY IMPORTANT. ONE OF THE FIRST ISSUES FOR AN ADOLESCENT WALKING THROUGH THE DOOR OR EVEN THINKING ABOUT TRYING A COMMUNITY PROGRAM IS WHETHER HE OR SHE CAN BELONG TO THIS GROUP OF PEOPLE."
> -- ECCLES & GOOTMAN

> "EACH CULTURE IS A SYSTEM OF VALUES WHICH MAY WELL COMPLEMENT THE VALUES IN ANOTHER."
> -- RUTH BENEDICT

Does the work we've just done cause us to have compassion on the foundational systems of others? Does it cause us to assess where our patient is coming from? Do we blame them, or does empathy bubble up inside us? Can we open our eyes wide to see structural racism at hand? A healthy awareness of cultural awareness can strengthen us in our work towards equity.

As we prepare to serve humanity in all of their beautiful colors, hues, and cultural diversities, it is critical that we focus on cultural integration so that every patient feels seen, heard, and has a sense of belonging.

The more culturally sensitive you are as a healthcare provider, the more effective your care will be for your patients. Cultural integration is vital as it exposes one to various cultures, customs and perspectives, which will all add to your lived experiences. All cultural integration starts in our primal stages - our foundations. Parents are the first to provide their children the opportunities for exposure to this beautiful world of diverse humanity. It is awesome to witness children enjoying one another despite their various differences. It is also unfortunate that over time, and as we grow, we focus on our differences to the exclusion of celebrating our similarities.

Before we take a deep dive into cultural integration, let's spend some time understanding and defining what culture is. There are many definitions for culture. Germany Daily[2] defines culture as follows: "Culture is a word that is derived from a French term that means to tend to the Earth. Culture can include things such as creed, social habits, language, music, arts, and religion."

Definitions of Culture

The Oxford Dictionary[3] defines culture as:

> "The arts, customs, social institutions, other social group or nation, and other manifestations of human intellectual achievement regarded collectively."

The Cambridge Dictionary[4] defines culture as:

> "The way of life, the general customs and beliefs, of a particular group of people at a particular time."

Cultural Integration involves:

1. **Cultural Humility:** When healthcare providers approach their care by honoring their patient's uniqueness and voice, they acknowledge that they may not have all the answers but are open and curious about learning from the patient's experiences and perspectives. Further, educating oneself on the cultural norms and expectations of your patients will help you avoid unintentional disrespect or boundary violation.
2. **Respecting each other's uniqueness:** Being aware of those nano-second biased judgments, mindful of cultural stereotypes, and avoiding assumptions about colleagues and patients based on their cultural backgrounds.
3. **Integrating other cultures into the fabric of the workplace:** Diversity speaks to uniqueness, and inclusion speaks to a sense of belonging. This means cultural integration invites all voices to be heard and respected.
4. **Cultural Communication:** Mindful to practice active listening when patients discuss their cultural perspectives and communicate their needs.

---

2   Müller, Sanan. "Cultural Integration: Definition, Examples, and Benefits." *Germany Daily*, 14 Dec. 2021, https://germanydaily.de/culture/cultural-integration/.

3   Simpson, John A. "Culture." *The Oxford English Dictionary*, Clarendon Press, 1991.

4   Cambridge University. "Culture." *Definition in the Cambridge English Dictionary*, Cambridge Dictionary, 2023, https://dictionary.cambridge.org/us/dictionary/english/culture.

Cultural Humility

Healthcare providers who embrace, respect, and honor working with diverse communities are more likely to develop cultural humility. This means they have an understanding of and respect for the cultural backgrounds, beliefs, values, and practices of their patients. They can navigate cultural differences effectively and provide more patient-centered care.

Healthcare providers who have explored and deliberated on their own cultural connections are often more empathetic and understanding toward patients from diverse backgrounds. They can better relate to the experiences and perspectives of patients with different cultural norms and beliefs.

Cultural humility can also help you adapt your communication strategies to better connect with patients from similar or different cultural backgrounds. This includes being able to navigate language barriers, understand non-verbal cues, and adapt communication styles to meet the needs of patients from diverse cultural backgrounds.

To summarize, Cultural Humility spaces are where diverse cultural identities are not just acknowledged but are actively integrated into the fabric of our communities and workplaces. This process requires conscious effort and commitment to inclusivity, ensuring that all individuals feel valued and empowered to contribute their unique perspectives and talents.

Building Cultural Awareness

Healthcare providers should strive to develop cultural awareness by learning about different cultures, cultural traumas, traditions, beliefs, and values that may impact how patients perceive health and healthcare. This awareness helps providers avoid making assumptions based on their own cultural norms and enables them to provide more patient-centered care.

When language barriers exist, healthcare providers should collaborate with professional interpreters and cultural liaisons to ensure effective communication with patients. They serve to provide trust, respect and dignity.

Healthcare providers can also promote inclusive practices by creating a welcoming and inclusive healthcare environment, which may include displaying diversity in materials and imagery and offering culturally relevant resources.

Discuss with your group: Have you ever been a part of a space like this? What do you think it takes to make this possible in your workplace?

Cultural Integration in Hospital Settings

When we reflect on the different definitions of culture provided earlier, it is important to notice that both define culture in the context of a particular (social) group. Therefore, it is not just families/ethnicities that share a unique culture, but groups that spend a large amount of time together can develop their own cultural values and dynamics as well - such as colleagues. This is especially true for hospital settings, as hospital culture is a large part of what can make a hospital run smoothly and effectively.

"Culture provides a context through which meaning is gained from information, and provides the purpose by which people come to understand their health status and comprehend options for diagnoses and treatments."[5]

Oftentimes, this includes a shared understanding between employees on how the dynamics of the hospital work. It can, importantly, also mean being mindful not to impose your own ethics, spiritual beliefs, or opinions on your fellow employees, or your work and care as a clinician.

Cultural norms in hospital settings place great value, understandably so, on medical authority. Yet though we sit in seats of authority, our patients are the best experts in how they want their care. Hearing their voices is important. Unfortunately, however, it is easy for healthcare providers to see themselves as an "authority" or as the experts in the room when it comes to caring for their patients - and for good reason, as they have had years of education and experience. But when a provider fails to humble themselves while talking to their patients, they fail to take lived experiences into account. This can be detrimental to patient care, as well as to provider-patient relations. A foundation of mutual understanding, trust, and respect must be established in order for the patient to receive the best care possible.

When clinicians can enter a room seeking to understand and accept another's culture/beliefs/lived experiences (rather than to force their own culture and beliefs onto their patients as the only "right" way), best practices can thrive. This is the importance of cultural integration.

---

[5] Institute of Medicine (US) Committee on Health Literacy; Nielsen-Bohlman L, Panzer AM, Kindig DA, editors. *Health Literacy: A Prescription to End Confusion*. Washington (DC): National Academies Press (US); 2004. 4, Culture and Society. Available from: https://www.ncbi.nlm.nih.gov/books/NBK216037/

POEM – COLORS, COLORS, COLORS
CANDACE KELLY

Colors, Colors, Colors,
The shades of Grace
Embodying the human race
Producing majestic hues
to reflect God's sacred views
Casting the beauty of the Son
Never meant to shun anyone
The beauty of colors, colors, colors,

Made in His image and glorious likeness
Hard to comprehend in our human finiteness
And with one blood He made all nations
Hung on a cross to give salvation
Catch the selfless revelation
The beauty of colors, colors, colors

The mystery of our history
Causes great misjudgment
due to our pigmentation
Provoking great lamentation
Don't we know we're all God's Creation?
Black, Red, Yellow and White
We are all precious, valuable and worthwhile in His sight The beauty of colors, colors, colors

Society and culture has birthed years of torture
Let's turn it all around by
Standing for equal grounds
Proclaiming diverse sounds
Extending unconditional love as a resolution
It's the response to the Cross that gives us the racial solution
The beauty of colors, colors, colors

NURTURING EQUITY MINDED GROUP EXERCISE #2

Remember: our discussion on cultural integration is part of a larger framework of foundations - both ourselves and others. Only when we recognize our own foundations, and their process in our development, can we have empathy and respect for those whose foundations may have been different than ours.

How did your parents or your own culture encourage you to embrace other cultures? What did diversity look like for you?

Reflect on the first time you remember interacting with someone of another culture.
1. How old were you?
2. How did you feel?
3. Did you have any stereotypical impulse?
4. What did you learn valuable about the other person/group?
5. Did you have a positive experience or a negative one?

Check the boxes of close friends you have from the following races: (Friends, not acquaintances)

[ ] Black

[ ] Hispanic/Latinx

[ ] White

[ ] Asian

[ ] Pacific Islander

[ ] Middle Eastern

[ ] Native American

[ ] Other _____

NURTURING EQUITY MINDED GROUP EXERCISE #3

Our foundations continue to impact the relationships and social networks we have today. In groups of 2, reflect on your relationships with people of color friends or colleagues and answer the following questions:
1. How often do you go to social events together?
2. Reflect on areas that you feel you are both united in.
3. Are you comfortable with people of color?

Now that we have a better understanding of our own foundations and the foundations of others, it is time to move into a discussion on self-actualization.

Self-Actualization

What is Self-Actualization?

Self-actualization is the process by which an individual reaches his or her full potential (Brittanica.com). One of the most broadly accepted definitions comes from Abraham Maslow, a psychologist who described self-actualization as the process of becoming "everything you are capable of becoming."[6] Maslow defined self-actualization as the goal of human life, and the need to which all our other needs drive us. Only when one's basic needs have been met, he reasoned, can work begin on psychological and self-fulfillment needs.

Maslow's five-stage model presents two main areas:

1. The deficiency needs (the bottom four levels)
2. The growth needs (the very top level)

As you study this hierarchy,[1] reflect on how you are meeting your goals and where you may find areas for growth in your work to achieve self-actualization.

Consider also the patients you care for. Using an equity lens, assess where they may be on the hierarchy of needs. Where is your compassion activated? Might there be some who are labeled "noncompliant," who sadly haven't achieved the deficiency needs needed for further progression?

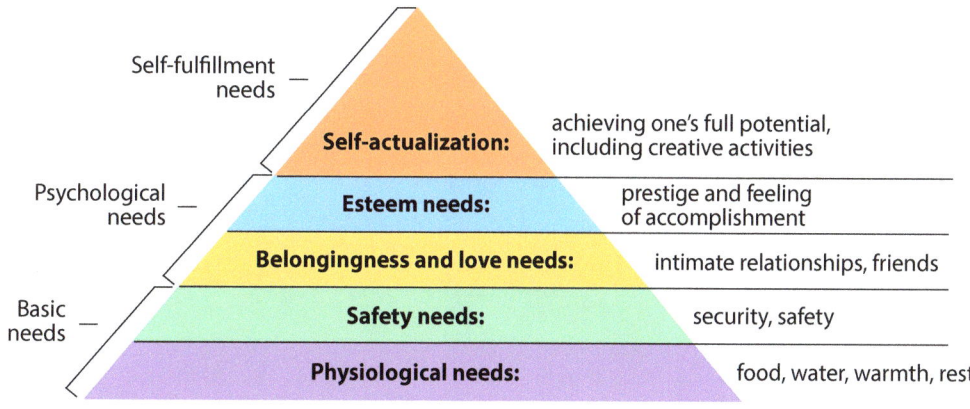

---

6   https://www.healthline.com/health/self-actualization#what-it-isnt

Understanding Our Patient's Self-Actualization

Understanding the hierarchy of needs can help us understand some patients whom we might be tempted to label "uncooperative" or "lazy." It could be that there are systemic barriers in place that have hindered or contributed to their food or housing insecurity, and basic living conditions.

Moreover, as healthcare providers, patients come to us and are usually facing some kind of physiological need. It is important to realize that, as they stand in front of us, we are only seeing one piece of the story. What kind of other needs might be impacting the reason they are here in front of us? How can we provide them not only with physical healing, but a sense of safety and esteem? The greater our own self awareness, cultural integration, and self-actualization, the more we will be able to care for our patients with equity, empathy, and compassion.

When providing compassionate care, it is critical that we as providers do not make quick judgements or stereotype those who come from these urban areas. Instead, our goal should be to understand where the patient sits on the hierarchy of needs, and how we can best support them on their journey to wholeness.

TOOL: S.H.O.W.

When thinking about self-awareness in the context of patient care, you can use the S.H.O.W. tool to show them you are listening and aware:

1. Sensitivity
2. Honoring
3. Offering
4. Weakness

NURTURING EQUITY-MINDED GROUP EXERCISE

Discuss with your group: How does self-actualization fit into all that we have discussed so far (wholeness and wellness, compassion, surrender, foundations, cultural integration, and self-awareness)? How can you better serve your diverse range of patients with this knowledge?

RESOURCE

For more tools towards self-awareness and self-actualization, consider exploring the personality theory resources at the end of this section.

CHAPTER FOUR
Self-Awareness That Supports Equitable Care

"SELF-AWARENESS GIVES YOU THE CAPACITY TO LEARN FROM YOUR MISTAKES AS WELL AS YOUR SUCCESSES. IT ENABLES YOU TO KEEP GROWING."
-- LAWRENCE BOSSIDY

"WHENEVER YOU ARE ABOUT TO FIND FAULT WITH SOMEONE, ASK YOURSELF...WHAT FAULT OF MINE MOST NEARLY RESEMBLES THE ONE I AM ABOUT TO CRITICIZE?"
— MARCUS AURELIUS

"IF YOU DON'T HAVE SELF-AWARENESS...IF YOU CAN'T HAVE EMPATHY AND HAVE EFFECTIVE RELATIONSHIPS, THEN NO MATTER HOW SMART YOU ARE, YOU ARE NOT GOING TO GET VERY FAR."
-- DANIEL GOLEMAN

As you will see in the following pages, self-awareness is a critical tool in our work towards providing equitable healthcare. This awareness is what will enable us to utilize resources rather than weaponize them, advocate for patients rather than be intimidated by or stereotype them, and maintain our own boundaries while referring to the appropriate resources. But what is self-awareness, and how do we cultivate it? First, we must explore its role in our personal lives.

Self-awareness in the Clinician's Personal Life

When we learn to become more introspective, and understand ourselves better, we also become more well-rounded and confident people. In her article, What Self-Awareness Really Is,[1] researcher Tasha Eurich suggests that when we are more self-aware, "we are more confident and more creative. We make sounder decisions, build stronger relationships, and communicate more effectively. We're less likely to lie, cheat, and steal. We are better workers who get more promotions. And we're more-effective leaders with more-satisfied employees and more-profitable outcomes."[1]

Eurich has had the unique ability to see self-awareness at work for more than fifteen years with her role as an organizational psychologist and executive coach. She states, "I've also seen how attainable this skill is. Yet, when I first began to delve into the research on self-awareness, I was surprised by the striking gap between the science and the practice of self-awareness... Four years ago, my team of researchers and I embarked on a large-scale scientific study of self-awareness. In ten separate investigations with nearly 5,000 participants, we examined what self-awareness really is, why we need it, and how we can increase it."[1]

As a result of these studies, Eurich and her research team found many surprising revelations about what self-awareness really means. Through their research, they discovered that while many of their participants thought themselves to be self-aware already, "only 10%–15% of the people [they] studied actually fit the criteria,"[1] further confirming what a unique quality it is to have.

NURTURING EQUITY MINDED GROUP EXERCISE:

Discuss among your group: What are your beliefs about self-awareness? How might it impact your work, both with patients and with your team, to advance optimum health outcomes?

---

1 Eurich, Tasha. "What Self-Awareness Really Is (and How to Cultivate It)." *Harvard Business Review*, 18 Jan. 2023, https://hbr.org/2018/01/what-self-awareness-really-is-and-how-to-cultivate-it.

Internal and External Self-Awareness

One contributing factor to this disconnect between believing oneself to be self-aware, and actually meeting the criteria for self-awareness, may be because of unclear definitions on what self-awareness really means. Varying interpretations have included introspection and reflection, learning to be aware of our inner thoughts, a state of self-consciousness, or the ability to differentiate between how we see ourselves and how we are seen by others.

In her article, Eurich suggests breaking self-awareness up into two distinct categories, internal self-awareness and external self-awareness, in order to better understand what self-awareness really is. She says, "**internal self-awareness**, represents how clearly we see our own values, passions, aspirations that fit with our environment, reactions (including thoughts, feelings, behaviors, strengths, and weaknesses), and impact on others…it is associated with higher job and relationship satisfaction, personal and social control, and happiness. The second category, external self-awareness, means understanding how other people view us in terms of those same factors listed above. [Their] research shows that people who know how others see them are more skilled at showing empathy and taking others' perspectives."[1]

For our purposes, clinicians who can see themselves how their peers or patients see them can improve overall relationships within their workplace. This can also increase overall patient satisfaction and experience by seeing their providers as more effective caregivers.

Assessing Self-Awareness Exercise

Discuss amongst your cohort your understanding of the two definitions. Next, review the four self-awareness archetypes in the graphic below,1 and identify yourself by writing it down on paper. Then ask your colleague to write their perception and awareness of you and compare. Finally, write down what it would take for you to achieve the self-awareness archetype you want for yourself.

MAPPING INTERNAL VERSUS EXTERNAL SELF-AWARENESS

	Low external self-awareness	**High external self-awareness**
High internal self-awareness	**INTROSPECTORS:** They're clear on who they are but don't challenge their own view or search for blind spots by getting feedback from others. This can harm their relationships and limit their success.	**AWARE:** They know who they are, what they want to accomplish, and seek out and value others' opinions. This is where leaders begin to fully realize the true benefits of self-awareness.
Low internal self-awareness	**SEEKERS:** They don't yet know who they are, what they stand for or how their teams see them. As a result, they might feel stuck or frustrated with their performance and relationships.	**PLEASERS:** They can be so focused on appearing a certain way to others that they could be overlooking what matters to them. Over time, they tend to make choices that aren't in service of their own success and fulfillment.

Based on the previous chart, I identify as:_____

My colleague identifies me as:_____

What self-awareness archetype do I want for myself, and what would it take to get there?

_____

_____

_____

_____

When it comes to internal and external self-awareness, it's tempting to prefer one over the other. But clinicians must actively work on both seeing themselves clearly and getting feedback to understand how others see them. The highly self-aware clinician finds wisdom in embracing both.

Self-awareness of One's Own Lived Experiences: The Temptation for Transference

"Transference" refers to the redirection of emotions that we originally felt in childhood to someone in the present. For example, a nurse might walk into a room when a patient and their partner are arguing, and immediately transfer her experience of growing up in a home full of domestic violence. Transference can affect us with overwhelming emotions of fear, anger, defensiveness, shame, or other strong feelings.

It is important to realize in these moments of transference that your reaction is more about you than the patient or situation. Self-awareness is key to preventing our past experiences from continuing to control our present, and to understand when we are tempted to transference. Only when we are self-aware enough to recognize this process in the present moment and make different choices will we be able to effectively and disinterestedly advocate for a patient's true needs.

Awareness of Our Biases: Self-Awareness in Weaponizing Resources

Bias is any thought or action that discriminates or disproportionately favors one person or group of people over another, based on superficial or inaccurate perceptions of the person or group.[2] Bias can be explicit or implicit, and most of it is unconscious - and it affects the millions of decisions we make every day. This is why self-awareness is critical when working from an equity lens.

For example, how do you decide when to refer a patient to resources, or what resources to refer them to? What about decisions about who to call first in a crisis? If we are not self-aware, resources can become weaponized and used in ways that we may not have intended - with potentially disastrous outcomes for patients and their families.

If you'd like to examine your unconscious bias, now might be a good time to take the survey found between Sections 2 and 3. If you have coworkers whom you trust to be fair and honest with you, consider asking them if they have noticed any unconscious bias you might have. Remember, it's important to build both internal and external self-awareness in order to care for patients in the most holistic and equitable way possible.

Self-awareness in De-escalating Patient Domestic Matters

During conflict, how can we de-escalate a situation in a dignified way, so both patient and staff feel safe? As mentioned above, who do we call first, and why? Self-awareness is key to understanding the situation from both perspectives and uncovering what exactly caused the rupture in communication or understanding. When we have true self-awareness, we can

---

2   https://www.knowyourrightsandresponsibilities.psu.edu/pages/bias/bias-the-basics

remain outside the emotions of the conflict and see it from an unbiased perspective, thus assessing the next steps in a way that honors the dignity and boundaries of all involved.

Self-awareness in Patient Care Boundaries

Lastly, self-awareness can help us understand when we might be about to cross boundaries of familiarity or language in patient interactions. Are we self-aware of our professionalism and maintaining language centered on equity and cultural humility? For example, questions such as "Where is your baby's daddy?" instead of "Where is the child's father?" reflect certain assumptions that we would do well to uproot. With proper self-awareness, we can identify these assumptions internally, deal with them, and maintain clear patient care boundaries that consider all the cultural humility and integration discussed in the previous chapter. Only then will we be able to give truly equitable care that advocates for a patient's deepest needs.

Awareness: Performative versus Transformative

"Performative" refers to any action that is done based on its appearance in a social group, rather than rising up authentically from within (Dictionary.com). Sometimes, you may see people or organizations using the language of self-awareness simply to align themselves with a public image rather than for personal transformation.

Discuss among your group: What do you think is the best way to approach performative efforts amid your staff or your workforce? How can we ensure that our equity work for our patients is the result of nurses and providers who have been transformed, and are not merely checking boxes but are coming from a place of authenticity and truth? In other words, when the DEI meetings are over, do we continue to be those allies, advocates, and ambassadors for equity?

CHAPTER FIVE
Building Your Own Resilience Toolkit

> "THE MOST POWERFUL RELATIONSHIP YOU WILL EVER HAVE
> IS THE RELATIONSHIP WITH YOURSELF."
> -- STEVE MARABOLI

> "SELF-COMPASSION IS SIMPLY GIVING THE SAME KINDNESS TO OURSELVES
> THAT WE WOULD GIVE TO OTHERS."
> -- CHRISTOPHER GERMER

> "LOVE YOURSELF AND LOVE THOSE AROUND YOU. TAKE CARE OF YOURSELF AND TAKE CARE
> OF THOSE AROUND YOU. LEAD BY EXAMPLE. GIVE LOVE."
> -- JEFFREY I. MOORE

The Crisis of Compassion Fatigue

Compassion Fatigue among helping professions is real and affects thousands of professionals every year. A 2019 study of factors associated with Compassion Fatigue in healthcare providers found that approximately 86% of nurses had moderate to high levels of Compassion Fatigue. Among emergency nurses specifically, levels of Burnout were found to be as high as 82%.[1]

When examining these kinds of statistics, it is important to remember that compassion is not the enemy. Your compassionate and caring heart is a gift to the world - and it, more than anything else, is what will make an Equity-Minded Healthcare Provider possible.

How do we suffer with others in a way that leads to healing, rather than burnout? How do we embrace the compassionate hearts that brought us here, rather than become emotionless robots simply doing our jobs? These are questions we will continue to explore in this and the following chapters. It is critical that we care for our compassionate hearts in order to preserve a certain sense of tenderness and concern for others, but also so that we can continue to care for ourselves.

Most individuals enter the medical field for the honorable and heroic purposes of saving lives, curing disease, and birthing new life into the world. What an awesome feeling to do any of these noble deeds. But over time, case by case, it takes a toll on you. Unfortunately, all outcomes do not render the same results. A delivery can very well turn into a fetal demise and maternal mortality. Depending on the set of conditions, outcomes can change before we know it, and that causes deep and lasting impressions upon us each time. In addition to these professional wear-and-tears, the current world state of affairs and systemic injustices can also take a toll: people are worn down by health, economic, and political systems that disenfranchise individuals, families, and cultural systems, and that perpetuate violence and isolation.

In light of these realities, healthcare providers experiencing burnout and fatigue are real and prevalent (see statistics below). In an effort to cope with these truths, the question of resilience arises: How do we address and recover from traumas, crises, and losses?

STATISTICS OF PHYSICIAN BURNOUT[2]

The Physician Burnout Crisis:	Clinical Documentation Burden is Causing Burnout:
58% of physicians often have feelings of burnout.	60% of physicians say bureaucratic task contribute to burnout
68% of clinicians say burn out has negatively affected their relationships	Physicians report spending nearly 50% of their work day E H R (Electronic Health Record) and desk work while spending only 27% to their total time on direct clinical face time with patients.
54% of burnout say it severely impacts their lives	More than one-third of physicians reported moderately high or excessive time spent on the E H R at home

1 Halzden Betty Ford Foundation, https://www.hazeldenbettyford.org/research-studies/addiction-research/healthcare-professionals-compassion-fatigue#:~:text=A%202019%20study%20of%20factors,high%20levels%20of%20Compassion%20Fatigue.&text=Among%20emergency%20nurses%20specifically%2C%20levels,be%20as%20high%20as%2082%25.

2 3M. "Soothe the Burn Infographic." *3M In the United States*, M*Modal - Health Information Systems, 2022, https://www.3m.com/3M/en_US/health-information-systems-us/resources/library/soothe-the-burn-infographic.

Surviving Compassion Fatigue

There are no cookie-cutter formulas for resilience. For example, using mindful interventions to de-escalate a stressed person when they are stuck in cycles of traumatic circumstances may work in the moment; but it will not acknowledge the source of distress or empower the person to create appropriate change. To truly reduce stress and trauma in society, we must travel upstream to the source of people's suffering. We must process their trauma and get to the origin in order to appropriate the correct intervention.

This is of vital importance, especially for our caregivers. The unfortunate reality is that when proper tools are not accessed, and burnout is not addressed, clinicians might turn to the unthinkable, and, devastatingly, die by suicide as a result.

The research presented in A Call for Action: Cultivating Resilience in Healthcare Providers,[3] provides tragic insight into the statistics on suicide. "While the exact nature of the association between burnout and suicide is unknown, we know the ratio for male physicians, compared with the general population, was 1.41…while female physicians took their lives at a rate 2.27 times that of the general population. Approximately one physician dies by suicide every day, and suicidal ideation increases approximately 4-fold during the first 3 months of residency training."

This is overwhelming to think about. Many suffer in silence without reaching out for support and resources. Before moving on to the following reflection questions, take a moment to process the above statistics with your group. How have you seen them reflected in your experience as a healthcare provider?

---

[3] Rakesh, Gopalkumar, et al. "A Call for Action: Cultivating Resilience in Healthcare Providers." *Psychiatry Online*, The American Journal of Psychiatry, 3 Apr. 2017; Vol. 12, Issue #4 https://ajp.psychiatryonline.org/doi/10.1176/appi.ajp-rj.2017.120402.

Thinking about Resilience:

Opening Questions:

1. What comes to mind when you hear the word resilience?

2. Define resilience and share where resilience shows up in your life, practice and/or experience.

3. Define burnout in your own words. Have you ever experienced burnout? Explain.

4. What resources and support do you believe are necessary to solve the problem of burnout in healthcare workers?

Defining Resilience:

The word "resilience" has become a vital sign for healthcare providers in all fields. In the article A Call for Action,[3] the authors define resilience as **"the ability to adapt successfully in the face of trauma, adversity, tragedy or significant threat."** Healthcare providers who engage in resilience building can benefit from less severe PTSD symptoms.

When you consider the many years, months and hours medical students spend in studying how to heal others, there should be just as much effort in learning how to sustain one's emotional, physical and psychological health. If healthcare providers only master healing others, and do not learn the art of self-care, then the feelings of burnout and compassion fatigue are sure to happen.

The article, Resilience in nursing,[4] describes resilience as "the ability to recover and recuperate quickly from a difficult or challenging situation." This should not be mistaken for diminishing the very real impacts that stressors have, but rather taken as a call to understand how to properly process such traumas, in order to manage their outcomes more effectively. In other words, it is not about simply covering wounds with a band-aid in order to quickly return to "business, as usual," but rather, about finding ways to use appropriate, individualized tools that will help properly heal these deep wounds. The overall goal in doing this is to combat trainee and physician burnout.

---

[4] HealthTimes. "Resilience in Nursing." *Health Times*, 2 Sept. 2022, https://healthtimes.com.au/hub/nursing-careers/6/practice/healthinsights/resilience-in-nursing/2353/.

RECOVERY: THE ART OF THE RESTART

I am delighted that I had the privilege to attend a transformative webinar by Jenay Hicks at the Equity Empowerment Experience Program at Miller Children's Hospital on April 24, 2024. Her talk, titled "Mastering the Restart," was full of wisdom from someone who knows first-hand the specific traumas faced by healthcare providers. Here are some of my takeaways:

TAKEAWAY #1:

Grief and Loss

Jenay Hicks chose to specialize in trauma, grief and loss because it was very clear that being a healthcare provider was often a thankless job. She invites us as healthcare providers to consider what it means to prioritize both our professional ambition and our care. If our baseline has always been to push through the pain, then that is what we have trained our brains to do. As we learn to care for ourselves, we will need to create new neural pathways to consider a different perspective.

She asks: "How often do you ignore the screams of your body? How often do you come to work when you are sick? Do you know the somatic presentation of your stress when stress shows up in your body? Are you willing to give the body that has worked so hard for you the care and the nurturing that it deserves?" We often learn to work sick, to push our own needs aside, and just keep going. But Hicks is suggesting a radical approach: that we consider ourselves first, and then we consider the system that "needs" us.

Jenay Hicks provided evidence-based research that allowed us to see how prevalent and critical self-care is for each of us as leaders. She shares, "The World Health Organization consistently reminds us that over 700,000 people die by suicide every year. And within that space, there are an estimated 20 suicide attempts for every death. Physicians specifically are two times more likely than the general population to die by suicide."

I am convinced that we have to care for ourselves, because the feeling of hopelessness leads us to think that we don't have any other options. But there are options, and there is healing.

Reflection Question: How often do you ignore the screams of your body? What does that look like? Are you willing to care for yourself?

TAKEAWAY #2

Complex Trauma

We learned in this webinar that trauma by definition is anything unbearable - anything that the body perceives as too much, too fast, too soon. When we talk about trauma specifically as it relates to our work as healthcare providers, we're considering complex traumatic stress, which means that the care that we offer this stress must consider the intersection between work stress and grief. There are major transitions at work, high turnover, and spaces we feel we have to erase parts of our identity and abandon who we are.

It was helpful to learn the variations of grief and loss. Jenay suggested that we must know and understand the many phases of grief, because when we walk through the door at work, we're not walking into the door as just the provider - we're walking in with our full human experience.

Crucial Self-Care Message:

As we talk about equity, it's also important to recognize that there are many factors influencing how we can advocate for our own well-being. It doesn't matter how many vacations we take or how many spa treatments we have; if we are going back into the same dehumanizing social system, then we will feel the same way eventually. Instead, we must change how we interact within the system. For example, female positions are still just 74% for every dollar earned by males, women only represent a small percentage of C-suite jobs, and women of color are just one in sixteen. Black promotion rates have fallen since 2018, and Black women are two times more likely to feel pressure to change their appearance to be perceived as more professional. When we talk about the barriers to peace in the workplace, we are battling organizational structures, systems, and policies that perpetuate exclusion and inequality. We can't be a part of a different conversation if we don't acknowledge that these things are happening.

As we discussed in Chapter Four, every person grew up in a family system. We may have learned to manage group emotions by withholding or neglecting our own. If we find ourselves in dynamics where we are withholding or hiding, where we're pretending or are uncertain if we can use our voice, Hicks wants us to remember that this is learned behavior. The good news is that what is learned can also be unlearned.

Reflection Question: How are you advocating for your well-being? What is a barrier to your peace? How do you manage your emotions?

TAKEAWAY #3

Transformational Change

Research supports that we only spend 5% of the day in the present moment. Most of the time we are either stuck in the past trying to figure out what happened, or we are in the future trying to protect ourselves from a future threat. Most healthcare providers work a high-stakes job where the requirements and expectations of excellence are high, and we must repeat them over and over and over again. Yet, as Hicks reminds us, it is in those moments before things feel unbearable that we have the greatest power to make a difference.

When we are inside our window of tolerance, we are able to name our feelings. We stay curious, know our strengths, and are okay with asking for support when needed. We're able to let go, knowing that people are human and make mistakes; able to embrace change, to be flexible; to be assertive, not aggressive. But when we're outside our window of tolerance, everything stresses us out. We make assumptions quickly and then defend those assumptions. We let our minds create a story about the current situation and then begin to create evidence to support that narrative. We often feel misunderstood. We're not aware of our triggers and often blame others for how they make us feel versus taking responsibility for the interaction.

Trauma also makes us impulsive. Trauma says that you must do something "right now", because there's a threat in front of you. We often do things without thinking and then we end up regretting them. Sometimes, depression and grief can look like anger - everybody's getting on our nerves, and everything is aggravating to us. This is when we must take a step back, reassess, and master the restart.

Reflection Question: How do you know when you are outside your window of tolerance? What are the emotional triggers? How do you regain your window of tolerance?

TAKEAWAY #4

Mastering the Restart

Hicks continues: if you find yourself in that space, take a deep breath and ask yourself: what do I need? Where am I over-nurturing, overextending, and overcompensating? Can I advocate for my time differently? To master the restart, we need to get clear on what we need. In order for us to change how we're showing up, which is our adaptive response, we're going to have to put different inputs into our schedule.

My biggest takeaway taught me that our healing journey begins with a commitment to ourselves. Change doesn't begin at the macro level: change begins at the micro level with small steps intentionally repeated over time. Mental health is about balancing, integrating and finding our personal power and agency, because the opposite of trauma is choice. When we are not in a threat response, we're able to clearly identify what our choice is in any situation. We can choose to put as much energy and intention into caring for ourselves as we do our professional work and ambitions, so we can continue to work at our highest level.

For healthcare workers, Hicks recommends we take a restart every six weeks. A restart looks like this: Take time to ask yourself: Is what I'm doing right now working? Where am I outside my window of tolerance? If I don't change anything that I'm doing right now to care for myself, is it sustainable?

We are always modeling what it means to care for others in ourselves. Oftentimes, caring for ourselves means that we have to say no to someone else. But saying no to someone else means saying yes to us. It means having just a little bit more in our battery to be able to show up in our work towards equity for all.

Reflection Questions: Do you know what you need? Where are you over-nurturing, overextending, and overcompensating? Can you advocate for my time differently? Where does your healing journey begin?

EXAMPLES OF TRAUMA EVENTS & RESILIENCE TOOLS

Understanding Your Needs

How does one truly recover from lived experiences of tragedies, traumas and loss?

As Jenay Hicks showed us, the answer is not simple, but very much individualized for each person. Careful reflection and personal assessment has to be invested in knowing the interventions you need and when you need them in order to recover well and walk in resilience.

Below is a list of a few examples for the kinds of traumas, tragedies, and losses a person can experience, as well as possible tools for coping effectively with each example. Consider the list, and then add your own example to the last line.

EXAMPLES OF NAMED TRAUMAS:	EXAMPLES OF RESILIENCE TOOLS:
• Loss of Job • Adultery • Sexual Assault • Bankruptcy • Pregnancy ending in stillbirth	• Therapy • Counseling • Trusted Community/Validation • Financial Planner • Support Group

Resilience Toolkit:

When we build a resilience toolkit, we find options best suited to us for building up our resilience and combating compassion fatigue and burnout. Having a toolkit readily available to draw from can also help us be better prepared in moments of trauma. Here are some examples of tools we can use:

- Healthy Boundaries
- Spiritual Therapy/Mental Therapy/PsychoTherapy
- Meditation/Centering
- Prayer/Reading Sacred Texts
- Journaling
- Lighting Candles/Aromatherapy
- Purging Toxic Relationships
- Art/Painting/Dancing/Tai Chi

Not all tragedies can be avoided, but it is important to recognize and combat long-term, ongoing stressors as much as possible. Use the following chart as an ongoing check-in for yourself as you experience new, or on-going, stressors:

List sources of stress in your life/work that need to be reduced	List stress reduction tool(s) that prove helpful to reduce your stress
Ex. Working long hours without enough sleep	Ex. Adjusting work hours and balancing sleep by setting healthy boundaries
1	1
2	2
3	3
4	4
5	5
6	6
7	7

CASE STUDY:

Dr. Carrie Sanders is the head obstetrician, leading a team of labor and delivery doctors at a birth care center. Over the last four years, she has experienced more infant loss and maternal death than she ever anticipated in her 35 years of practice. Time and again, she has empathized with her patients' caregivers, often longing to express how intimately she understands their pain. For fear of being seen as out of control, she avoids sharing her feelings not only with patients and their families, but also with her colleagues and even herself.

Dr. Sanders attends her annual wellness visit with employee health. She acknowledges feeling continuously fatigued and says that engaging as she typically would with patients has become too difficult. She denies feeling hopeless, depressed, or suicidal but does disclose feeling dread each time she enters the hospital, concerned that things will inevitably go wrong under her care. With her family residing across country and no current partner, she has no one to confide in. She shared her sleep is often disrupted, and she often finds herself relying on sleep medication. Dr. Sanders is given a referral to speak to a mental health provider, but struggles with authenticity and is hesitant to disclose her true feelings for fear of how she is perceived. She is a perfectionist and often self-critical, making the thought of revealing how vulnerable she has become all but impossible and unbearable.

Together with your group:
1. Identify the stressors in this doctor's life/practice.
2. What are the barriers to her caring for herself?
3. Does Dr. Sanders really know what she needs?
4. If you were consulting with her, what would you recommend? What might her "restart" look like?
5. Have you seen people like this in your workplace?

NURTURING EQUITY MINDED GROUP EXERCISES

In teams of two, discuss the following:
1. Recall a stressful, traumatic, or troubling incident that occurred recently at your workplace.
2. What were the emotions you experienced?
3. Did you overcome the emotions? If yes, share how?
4. Do you have someone in your workplace that you trust to discuss your emotions with?
5. What tools might you utilize to help de-stress?
6. After a trauma, what do you need to help you cope?

A POEM OF RESILIENCE - "I'M BACK!"

BY DR. CANDACE COLE-KELLY

Imagine the Pacific Ocean - the waters receding deep into the recesses of its depths and then suddenly reappearing with buoyancy as if to say "surprise, I'm back."

Likewise, our lives can resemble the compulsions of the water swelling and receding indicative of times that cause us to recede from traumas faced, names erased, pains experienced, death befriended, compassion fatigue, moral distresses ignored, disappointments endured and tragedies one after another…that cause us to recoil, but because of what resides deep inside of us, before long, the buoyancy of life compels us also forward saying, "surprise, I'm back."

I'M BACK!

I'm back after the crisis situation
I'm back after caring for multiple RTS patients
I'm back after end of life conversations
I'm back after the cancer treatments
after the car crash and bills
after recovering from the pandemic ills
after anxiety and panic attacks
I'm back, I'm back, I'm back!
after a trauma changed me forever
after my near death experience
after the economic melt-down
Because my house burned to the ground
Causing me a nervous breakdown
after my addiction that led to my eviction
I'm back, I'm back, I'm back!

After losing faith in God
losing my parents and siblings, Oh Lawd
forgiving the infidelity
and infant mortality
the trauma of maternal morbidity
after fighting police brutality
the sexual assault - no it was not my fault
the domestic violence for years kept in silence
my husband's sudden death that took away my breath
and America's continual racist theft
after losing confidence in myself
I'm back for what I was born to do,
to provide compassionate care and save lives too.
How? You might ask
Ahhhh, it's transcendence!!
What is it that propels you to emerge?
What is it that causes you to hope again?
How does the audacity to survive and thrive the adversity expand your capacity?
What is it that causes you to rise? It's Resilience!
It summons you after awhile
to sit in a silent, sacred space
that calms the hearts that race
to hear beyond the vain orations
to gaze upon the beauty of creation
to flow in a new rhythm of life
restoring the broken plight
giving renewal of sight
to find that which was lost
to mend at all cost
to rebuild that which was torn down
to be strengthened by a new sound
to acknowledge your vulnerability made weak
the wholeness of person is what we seek

Did you know that…
trauma and resilience can co-habitat?
for authentically they relate!
And it's this resilience that summons you still
to mend your mind and
to heal your heart
to forge your future and live your part
to strive stress-free and build new boundaries
care for your cause and not defy your laws
to awake and not sleep
to hear deep calling to deep
to bend and not break, to do whatever it takes
to stand and not fall, to reach for it all.
Your inner resilience summons you because it's your divine call…!

CHAPTER SIX
Workplace Boundaries

"DARING TO SET BOUNDARIES IS ABOUT HAVING THE COURAGE TO LOVE OURSELVES, EVEN WHEN WE RISK DISAPPOINTING OTHERS."
-- BRENÉ BROWN

"BEING ABLE TO SAY "NO" IS A NECESSARY INGREDIENT IN A HEALTHY LIFESTYLE."
-- DAVID W. EARLE

"BOUNDARIES ARE BASICALLY ABOUT PROVIDING STRUCTURE, AND STRUCTURE IS ESSENTIAL IN BUILDING ANYTHING THAT THRIVES."
-- HENRY CLOUD

"BOUNDARIES ARE A PART OF SELF-CARE. THEY ARE HEALTHY, NORMAL, AND NECESSARY."
-- DOREEN VIRTUE

WHAT ARE BOUNDARIES AND WHY DO WE NEED THEM?

Boundaries are essential to our health, happiness, and success. However, setting boundaries is a challenge for many of us, especially when we are grieving. We are not used to standing up for ourselves and asking for what we need. We are afraid to say no because we don't want to disappoint or offend people. We lose track of who we are and what is important to us because we are so focused on what other people want or need. Consequently, we end up frustrated, exhausted, unappreciated, and mistreated. But we can learn to set boundaries with kindness, by assertively asking for what we need, and thereby create more satisfying and respectful relationships.

Maintaining Boundaries in Workplace Relationships

In David Richo's deeply transformative work, How to Be An Adult (A Handbook on Psychological and Spiritual Integration),[1] he offers powerful insights to the importance of boundaries that empower us to live our best selves. According to Richo, "Our journeys began at birth with no sense of boundaries. We did not know where mother ended and we began. What we did know was our continuous need for fulfillment of our intimate desires through our maternal sources."

Richo further provides his readers instructions on how to walk through the matriculation process from dependence to independence. He proposes that each person must be aware of how their age and stage in life plays a part in their level of responsibility for themselves. Richo answers this dilemma stating, "Growth spurt was obtained with the realization of separateness from that source. Our first task was letting go, i.e., acknowledge a personal boundary: I am separate and so are those who care about me. This was a departure and a struggle."

I find this to be true in my own journey from childhood. Preschool was the first for me, letting go of my mom's hands to reach for a stranger's hand (my teacher) was devastating until I adjusted. Yes, it did feel like abandonment at first, until I realized that this was just different, not deficient. When one is stretched to adjust to new surroundings or authorities, this can often feel like a loss of security. Richo suggests, in fact, "it is the adult inside of us letting go of inordinate affections and clinging obsessions (attachments) that hinder our full potential of becoming."

BOUNDARY BUILDING BLOCKS

A boundary is a diving line that defines who you are as an individual and how you'll interact with others. Boundaries define what's me (my body, my feelings, my property, my responsibilities, and so forth) and what's not me. Boundaries also communicate how we want to be treated by others, what's okay and not okay with us, and how close we want to get (physically and emotionally) to others.

SO, WHAT DO BOUNDARIES DO?

- They provide emotional and physical safety.
- They ensure you focus on what's most important to you.
  They improve relationships.
- They improve our health.
- They improve self-esteem.

---

1   Richo, David. *How to Be an Adult: A Handbook on Psychological and Spiritual Integration*, Paulist, Mahwah, NJ, 2018, pp. 57–63.

The following are some examples of important boundary building blocks:

Personal Boundaries are boundaries we set for ourselves to ensure awareness of our needs and that we will respect them in a healthy manner.

Physical Boundaries are boundaries we establish to guarantee our physical safety and proximity, including boundaries surrounding intimacy and what is comfortable for us physically.

Relational Boundaries are boundaries that we decide and agree upon with our partners, families, coworkers, and close friends.

Conversational Boundaries include establishing limits about topics we are comfortable discussing and being authentic about topics we do not care to talk about. This can range from violence, sexuality, politics, death, age, weight, and more.

Time Boundaries are those we create that allow us to maintain a healthy and comfortable schedule to accomplish our goals. Time boundaries include managing time spent on certain activities, with someone in a personal setting, and time budgeted for work/school and home life.

It is important to note here that boundaries are not demands or ultimatums. Boundaries are simply a request – a way to communicate our needs or expectations – not a demand or an attempt to force someone to do what we want. And although it is normal to want to feel in control, especially when we are in unpredictable or uncontrollable situations, demands rarely work.

Assessing My Boundaries

When you set boundaries, you assert your individuality. We all have our own thoughts, feelings, values, goals, and interests. But sometimes others are threatened or confused by our differences and want us to think, feel, and act as they do. And we, too, may be afraid of being different – assuming it will lead to criticism or rejection – so we hide our true selves, allowing others to tell us who we are. Psychologists use the term "enmeshment" to describe this type of undifferentiation. In enmeshed relationships, there aren't boundaries. Everyone is expected to toe the line, meaning everyone should think, feel, and behave the same.

Excerpt from David Richo's How to Be An Adult:[1]

Codependency is unconditional love for someone else that has turned against oneself. I know I have lost my boundaries and become co-dependent when 'I don't let go of what doesn't work' and it feels like 'I can't let go of what could work.'

The left column of the checklist [on the following pages] provides a working definition of 'codependency.'"

BOUNDARIES: COMPROMISED AND HONORED

When you compromise your boundaries in your relationship, you are "codependent." This means you:	When you honor your boundaries in a relationship, you are "self-parenting." This means you:
1. Are ambivalent about your choices	1. Possess, and act on, solid preferences
2. Do not notice discontentment, since prevailing is primary	2. Notice when you are content/discontent
3. Adjust your ways, schedules, or opinions to adapt to the present attitudes or situations (you're reactive, not proactive)	3. Are aware of moods and situations present within you while remaining grounded (you're proactive)
4. The last opinion you've heard is the one you value most	4. Value your own wisdom most while welcoming the thoughts of others
5. Hope for change, but passively wait for it to happen	5. Actively work on the changes you hope to see
6. Uphold excuses for this person for things you would not allow in anyone else and would advocate against	6. Honor personal boundaries without apology, and expect accountability from all relationships
7. Allow compliments to cloud your judgment	7. Welcome input without letting it affect your authenticity
8. Let someone else influence you to the point of losing yourself	8. Let someone's actions influence you as welcomed knowledge
9. Depend on your partner for your happiness	9. Appreciate the added happiness your partner provides, without depending it
10. Play the victim while suppressing your true emotions	10. Acknowledge and be true to your emotions, while actively working on shifting relationships, as necessary
11. Avoid confrontation, even at the expense of your values	11. Lead with strength, and your own convictions, to find mutual agreement
12. Never say no, even when it goes against your better judgment or desires	12. Lead with authenticity, maintaining the ability to say no without guilt
13. Stand idly by while your loved ones are abused by this person	13. Secure safe boundaries for all loved ones in your care
14. Act from a place of fear and uncertainty	14. Act from a place of courage and confidence
15. Feel powerless in your own life. You live for others, and feel you cannot change it.	15. Live your life with agency, as a fully actualized individual

NURTURING EQUITY MINDED GROUP EXERCISES:

Let's explore what type of boundaries are needed in each context.

1. Which of the following best describes a reason why you might want to set workplace boundaries concerning romantic or intimate relationships at work? Choose the best answer.

    a. Romantic or intimate relationships at work can make you a focus of a rumor or sexual harassment.

    b. Romantic or intimate relationships at work can lead to inequitable ways of receiving promotions.

    c. Romantic or intimate relationships at work can be a safety hazard.

    d. All of the above.

2. You are having lunch with your co-workers. Your waitress is Hispanic. After she takes the orders and leave, one of your co-workers tells a mildly racist joke about her physicality and poor English and where she needs to go back to. They get a big laugh out of it from the rest of your co-workers, but it makes you uncomfortable. Do you:

    a. Slightly smile and excuse yourself to the restroom

    b. Say, "that's not very nice"

    c. Challenge your co-workers directly about their implicit bias

    d. Speak up and say the joke is offensive

    e. Laugh (but not as loud as the group) to be accepted

3. Circle the following that best describes how you might set **ethical, equitable boundaries at work** in the following exercise.

    You are the manager facilitating safety rounds and hand offs. In your reporting you include the race of each of your patients. You noticed that it's been an entire year that one of your White nurses continues to decline accepting Black patients when she is asked. As her manager, do you:

    a. Inquire if there are any racial concerns about Black patients.

    b. Ignore and assign her to an Black patient but monitor her closely.

    c. Insist, without consent, she begins to care for Black populations.

    d. Seek to understand why she feels this way and educate her on explicit biases while continuing to observe her.

4. You are answering a code for an emergent C-Section and you and other attendants are responsible for rolling the patient to the OR. You overhear the nurses talking about the fun they had at Disneyland this past weekend while the patient is visibly in distress and pain. The husband has total panic written in his eyes. You are irritated at their insensitivity and wish they would quiet themselves. Do you:

   a. Motion to them to be considerate of the patient and husband going into emergency surgery.

   b. Look annoyed hoping they will catch on.

   c. Ask more questions about the events of their weekend.

   d. Speak to them alone about appropriate communications in the presence of a patient.

   e. Remind them about best practices and respectful care.

5. You are shadowing your preceptor who is caring for an Asian patient. After the clinical visit, as you both are walking out the room, your preceptor says, "I wish they didn't smell like that. All Asians have this fish smell about themselves, have you noticed?" Do you:

   a. Become overwhelmed at her statement.

   b. Say nothing.

   c. Share what you learned from your DEI education on implicit bias: negative attitudes or stereotypes towards people.

   d. Speak up and tell her how inappropriate her comments are.

Discuss your answers with your group.

COMMUNICATING BOUNDARIES

Communicating your boundaries can be challenging and scary, especially if it hasn't gone well in the past. As a result, many of us avoid asking for what we want and need, or we make demands and lash out in anger.

There are three types of communication: passive, aggressive, and assertive. It's important to remember when setting boundaries to be appropriately assertive.

1. When we're passive, we don't demonstrate self-respect because we aren't speaking up about what we need or being honest about how we feel; we minimize our needs and feelings to please or appease others.

2. When we're aggressive, we don't respect other people's needs and feelings; we're harsh, hurtful, and demanding, believing that our needs and feelings supersede others'.

3. But when we're assertive, we convey our needs and feelings clearly and directly, in a way that respects ourselves and others.

An "I-statement" uses a set formula to communicate how you feel and what you want. I-statements work well because when you focus on how you feel, not on how egregious the other person's behavior is, you're likely to build empathy rather than defensiveness.

Sometimes, people aren't aware of how their behavior negatively affects others, but when we let them know they're hurting us, they're more willing to change or compromise. I-statements are a tool that can help others understand your experiences and needs, and, as a result, be open to finding a solution.

NURTURING EQUITY GROUP EXERCISE: FINDING AN "I" STATEMENT

Think about a boundary you'd like to set and who you need to communicate this with. Use the formula below to craft an "I-statement" to communicate how you feel and what you want.

I feel _____ when/that _____

and I'd like _____

_____

Is that something you are willing to do?

"IT WOULD MEAN A LOT"

Not all requests are equally important, so when your request is important, you should communicate this. The Assertiveness model suggests using the phrase "it would mean a lot to me if _____."

This phrase is effective because it starts with owning that this request is meaningful to you. This makes it more likely that the other person will remain open to hearing your request and won't shut down or become defensive. This phrase also helps the recipient differentiate it from less important issues or requests – and hopefully take it more seriously.

Variations of this phrase include:

- This is really important to me.
- I would appreciate it if…
- I have a request that means a lot to me.
- I'm very concerned about this

    Share your statement with a partner and role-play using it in the scenario you envisioned.

Our Nursing and Physician Oath: Advocacy for our Patients

I hope you know by now that in discussing our wholeness and resilience as healthcare providers, boundaries for ourselves within the workplace are a critical piece of compassionate care we should give to each of our patients every time.

However, it is also important to use our equity lens and consider what healthy boundaries also mean for those we serve. As we will discuss in Section Two, many patients of color have a complicated history with healthcare professionals and know first-hand the pain of boundaries crossed or ignored. Our commitment to "first do no harm" brings up several ethical questions around the question of patients and boundaries within the healthcare setting. This is where all of the skills we have discussed so far - self-awareness, self-actualization, personal development, and surrender, to name a few - are critical to setting healthy boundaries while not weaponizing resources.

Boundaries in the workplace mean not just being reactive, but proactive - leading with our convictions and upholding the needs and boundaries of our patients as well as ourselves.

CASE STUDY

Conflict Management: Responding to Crisis versus Reacting from Fear

A San Francisco Community hospital noticed an increase in their Code Greys in both their postpartum and NICU units. Specifically, Black parents were receiving an extremely high number of Code Greys (VIOLENCE) called on them, which not only brought security but involved the local police and DCF.

On December 5th, 2019, Deborah Jenkins (African American) delivered a severely pre-term 28 week baby girl. She had a very complex delivery IVF. The baby went directly to the NICU without Deborah being able to bond or even see her baby who was in great distress. Deborah had two previous fetal demise which caused her great distress throughout her pregnancy and then when her water broke at 28 weeks. Deborah's sister was present to support her during her delivery.

Psycho-socially, she and her wife (Danny) are currently separated. She has tattoos on her arms leading up to her neck. The nurses talked about how "mean" she looked. To make matters worse, Deborah learned from her sister that her wife brought her girlfriend to the hospital while she was delivering their baby. The nurses chatted about the domestic separation near Deborah's room. The sister also was venting with the nurses about how inappropriate the wife had been.

Later that same day the bedside nurse went in to provide care and check on mom. Deborah responded "I've had better days." The nurse said, "I just can't believe your wife brought her girlfriend to the hospital after all you two have been through with losing 2 IVF's, and now with a premature baby." The patient thanked the nurse for her support and siding with her and commented she needed sleep.

Later, the wife came to the room to visit and a big fight ensued. The nurse rushed in and told them to lower their voices, saying, "the other patients are getting scared along with the staff." Hearing this, the patient lost it and told the nurse "where to go." The nurses were afraid and called a social worker and the local police on the patient and wife. In response, the patient was angry with the nurse and began to tell her to stay out of her business. The nurse was offended, saying, "I was only trying to advocate for you!" When the social worker arrived, they threatened that they may have to put the baby on a DCF hold. By then, the mother had escalated to threats from the fear of her baby being taken away from her.

Break into your group and discuss the following questions:

1. What was the primary nurse's responsibility to her patient?
2. Did she cross any boundaries? If yes, please list them.
3. How would you assess the patient (mom) in this scenario?
4. Were any boundaries crossed from her?
5. What about the office chatter amongst nursing staff?
6. Should social work have been called?
7. How did social work help or hurt the situation?
8. How should this dispute have been handled from the beginning?
9. Does the patient (mom) have the right to feel safe and advocated for? Did that happen?
10. How does postpartum psychosis play in this scenario, and was it considered?
11. This is the third Code Grey in two months. How does that impact your view of the situation?
12. Using the PAUSE Tool on the following page, let's enact how this could have gone differently.

In response to excessive Code Greys within a two-year span involving Black and brown families, this community hospital developed and trained a multi-disciplinary team to be the first-line interim responder to domestic encounters for the purposes of response protocol. Before involving social work or police, their aim was to use de-escalation tools to manage the situation and realign the response towards equitable empathy and compassionate care.

With working with the DEI de-escalation team, they noted that within 6 months, there were significantly fewer behavioral contracts, Code Greys, and DCF placements, because they were able to get patients the psychological help they needed and reinforce appropriate interactions between family members and boundaries with staff members and their patients.

DEI P.A.U.S.E. TOOL

P: Patient safety first.

A: Assess your patient's need for advocacy

U: Unit protocol (call Equity Team)

S: Seek to understand the scenario

E: Empathy approach in your responses

CHAPTER SEVEN
Identifying Personal Loss and Grief

"GIVE SORROW WORDS; THE GRIEF THAT DOES NOT SPEAK WHISPERS THE O'ER-FRAUGHT HEART AND BIDS IT BREAK."
-- WILLIAM SHAKESPEARE

"THERE ARE THREE NEEDS OF THE GRIEVER: TO FIND THE WORDS FOR THE LOSS, TO SAY THE WORDS ALOUD, AND TO KNOW THAT THE WORDS HAVE BEEN HEARD."
-- VICTORIA ALEXANDER

"LIFE IS NOT THE WAY IT IS SUPPOSED TO BE. IT IS THE WAY IT IS. THE WAY YOU COPE WITH IT IS WHAT MAKES THE DIFFERENCE."
-- VIRGINIA SATIR

GRIEF AS TABOO

A Lived Experience: *The Death Divide* by Kelley Pierce

One thing no one tells you when someone close to you dies, is that you don't get to grieve, not really, not at first. No, you, the most adjacent to death, are required, no forced, to comfort the people who did not know him all that well, who met him that one time, who heard about him through you, who saw him exclusively on holidays and birthdays. You're forced to listen to the inane thoughts they come up with to make sense of tragedy, to find a moral in this fucked-up story. You must smile and nod (don't you dare disagree) when they tell you what a good person he was, how much he loved you, how much he will be missed. When they ask you how you're "holding up" with that wrinkled brow and condescending, I mean encouraging nod, you can answer one of two things: "I'm hanging in there" or "It's tough, but we're managing." You might get fed up, tired of keeping the not-too-happy-but-not-too-sad-smile glued to your face. You might try to answer honestly, let out a huge groan and say "I'm miserable and I'm angry and I'm tired and I thought feeling this kind of emotion would make me stop caring about stupid little things but I still want to have yummy snacks and why does that make me feel like a monster. I thought this death would make me soft and loving and gentle with my siblings and mother but all I feel is brittle and sharp, like one too-tight hug and I'll snap in to pieces and cut them as I do." But before those words come out, let me tell you, it won't matter. It won't make them understand anymore, it'll just make everything uncomfortable and maybe you'll like that because they can feel one ounce of the heaving weight behind your eyes, but it won't last. They'll resent you because they're just trying.

They're trying to fix you. And one thing people can't stand is a person in stasis, suffering and feeling and floating in grief, even if it's the only choice they have. They'll do anything to get you to move forward, move on, move past. They'll tell you exactly what to do (even though they've never had their father or husband die). They'll tell (not suggest, but tell) you, "You all need to take turns sleeping with your mom. You can't leave her alone." And even though you know your mom would hate that as much as you would, you have to smile and nod, even as they repeat themselves, gripping your forearm like it'll help you hear them better. They'll tell you, "You just need to go out, be around people," "you just need to have a good cry, let it all out," "you need to share all your happiest memories of him," "you need to forgive him," "you can't be angry anymore, you have to let it go." Don't disagree; they know what's best for you.

You absolutely cannot tell people you hated your dead dad. Without a doubt, it will not go well. Sometimes it's fun, for the shock value of course. But that wears off quickly, and you're left with the uncrossable chasm between what you know to be true and what the other person is able to comprehend. In the same way we clean a corpse, people must wash away the ambiguities of the dead. Everything becomes an absolute: "He was such a wonderful man; I know he loved you so much," "he was so proud of you," "he was always so nice to me." Great, I'm glad he was nice to one of us. Whoever said "don't speak ill of the dead" was an asshole who didn't want his dirty laundry aired after he wasn't around to hide it.

People will ask you questions that even your therapist wouldn't, and for some reason no one finds it insane but you. "So what do you think actually killed him?" they'll ask, not even blushing at their own audacity. "Do you feel guilty for how you felt about him when he was alive?" "Don't you wish you had forgiven him, told him you loved him, before he died?" It doesn't matter that you stutter and stumble through a haphazard response, they won't apologize, they'll just wait for you to give more of yourself than there is left to give.

But eventually it'll be your turn. After a few weeks, the novelty wears off. People stop stopping by, sending food and flowers, they get tired of using their meaningful "how are you?" and start reverting back to the I-expect-the-answer-to-be-'good and you'" how are you?" They'll leave you alone, because they already blessed you with all of their best advice, sage knowledge, loaded shoulder-squeezes, so you must be finished being sad, right? Then you're allowed to feel things however you want to, in private of course.

You still have to go to work and stuff, but at least when you come home, you can put on comfy clothes and have a glass of wine and some yummy snacks and think all of the following, equally-valid, equally-painful thoughts. Thoughts like: "I thought grief would be feeling sad all the time, but it goes from making a mean joke about your dead dad to ugly-crying, not because he's dead but because you're bitter, you deserved better and you never got it." Like: "Do those EMTs who were walking past my brother and I standing in the middle of the sidewalk at 11pm, clutching each other, clutching our phones, waiting for an update, remember us? Do they think about us?" Like: "Dad would hate how we rearranged the living room." Like: "What does it mean to be fatherless?" Like: "Will my mom be okay?" Like: "Why can't death be more graceful, more moving, more intentional? Why is it messy and too fast and ordinary and logistical?" Like: "How awful to not know you're about to die, to not get a chance to say something beautiful and poignant as your last words." You can cry or laugh or watch TV, or all three at once. But you can't ever tell those people what they did, how much they hurt you even when they were trying to heal you. You can't say that those weeks were the worst weeks of your life, not for the reason they think, but because of how they treated you, like they were stripping you down, taking something sacred from you when you were too weak to stop them. You can't because it's the most ungrateful thing you can say to the people who were only trying to help. But that doesn't make it untrue.

Identifying Personal Grief and Loss:

After reading Kelley Pierce's story, we learn of the myriad of well-intended, yet insensitive, external responses she encountered after her personal loss. Those that have not properly processed their own grief may not be well prepared to offer comfort to others and can often perpetuate the internal hardships others face as they mourn.

Sooner or later, everyone will grieve the loss of a close relative or friend - whether the cause is a sudden heart attack, car accident, lengthy illness, COVID-19, old age, infant death or other. In the work you do, caring for medically fragile infants through adults, you have undoubtedly experienced loss in your workplace as well. And yet, not everyone is taught how to honor and process these losses.

As physicians and professionals, we are often at the forefront of human experiences, witnessing the spectrum of emotions that accompany life's most significant moments. Among these experiences, grief is one of the most profound, complex, and challenging emotions we encounter, both in our patients and at times within ourselves.

Grief can manifest in a myriad of ways, impacting physical health, mental wellbeing, and overall quality of life. It does not follow a linear path, and is uniquely personal to each individual. As healthcare providers, our role extends beyond medical treatment. It encompasses understanding, empathy, and support during some of the most difficult times our patients face. In this chapter, we will explore the intricacies of grief, gaining insights into psychological and physiological impacts. We will discuss effective communication strategies, supportive interventions, and self care practices essential to those who provide care. By deepening our understanding of grief, we aim to enhance our ability to support our patients compassionately and effectively.

Coping with Loss:

Our culture teaches us how to gain and accumulate. It does not prepare people on how to lose or grieve properly in either physical or symbolic loss. Meaning making and rituals after traumatic events and losses help heal and begin the resilience recovery.

It is important to remember that loss does not always mean the death of a person. There are symbolic losses as well. Sometimes loss can mean the death of a hope or a dream. These types of deaths must be grieved as well. Here is a list of examples for the kinds of losses a person can experience. Check the ones you have experienced:

- Child
- Autonomy
- Career
- Family member
- Parent
- Spouse
- Pet
- Health
- Dreams
- Divorce
- Other: _____

Take a moment of reflection and list all losses in the last 5-years. Refer back to the list of examples of different types of loss:

Description	Years	Intervention/Support Received

NURTURING EQUITY MINDED GROUP EXERCISES

PART I: IDENTIFYING YOUR GRIEF-WRITING ASSIGNMENT

From the losses you listed, choose one and answer the following questions:
1. Name your loss.
2. Where were you and what were you doing when you found out about your loss?
3. How did you find out about it? (i.e. text, email, phone, or in person)
4. What was your immediate response to the news?
5. What did you appreciate about how you were informed?
6. What did you least appreciate about how you were informed?
7. In retrospect, do you wish you had received the information differently? And if so, how?
8. What do you regret the most?

Write your answers on the lines below. After the writing assignment, share your story of loss with your partner or co-hort.

1. _____

2. _____

3. _____

4. _____

5. _____

6. _____

7. _____

8. _____

PART 2: PROCESSING YOUR GRIEF

1. Who was the safe person that listened to your grief?
2. How did you process this painful loss? Did you join a grief support group or receive individual grief counseling for your loss?
3. Did you place any blame upon yourself or anyone else?
4. Are you still suffering from this loss?
5. How difficult is it to give yourself permission to grieve on a scale of 1-10 (10 being extremely hard)?
6. How did you receive love through this loss?
7. What did you need most?
8. Did you receive the support you hoped for?
9. Who do you need to forgive to make more room in your heart to love and trust again?

Write your answers below:

1. _____

2. _____

3. _____

4. _____

5. _____

6. _____

7. _____

8. _____

9. _____

Honoring Your Loss Through Mindful Rituals

Saying Goodbye In A Meaningful Way:

Rituals are ways to honor our grief and loss through shared story or action. It can take many forms; sometimes our religion or cultural background offers powerful rituals for loss and grief, but sometimes we must choose to conduct them on our own.

Discuss as a group: Do you have any rituals you have used to honor grief and loss? Where did they come from? How have you seen them modeled by others around you?

You can conduct your grief rituals alone or with others. Your ritual could be an ideal time to share your grief with friends and family members grieving the same loss. If you invite others to join your ritual, you may wish to ask each person to share something about your lost loved one—a memory, story, or thought. Here are a few examples of common grief rituals:

- Sharing memories and releasing a memento such as a piece of paper or balloon
- Reading a letter aloud, and then perhaps burning it
- Celebrating anniversaries with a moment of silence, a memory, or a trip to a meaningful location
- Cooking specific foods, dancing to or singing specific music, or creating a piece of art

After your discussion and reading through the list above, consider choosing one ritual to practice this week. If you feel comfortable, share your plan with your partner.

SECTION RESOURCES
Assessing Your Personality Type

"PEOPLE OFTEN ONLY SEE ONE SIDE TO SOMEONE'S PERSONALITY, BUT THERE ARE LEVELS."
-- ROSS LYNCH

"THE SHOE THAT FITS ONE PERSON PINCHES ANOTHER; THERE IS NO RECIPE FOR LIVING THAT SUITS ALL CASES."
-- CARL JUNG

"NO PERSONALITY TYPE IS "BETTER" THAN ANY OTHER—JUST DIFFERENT. AND EACH PERSPECTIVE BRINGS SOMETHING NEW AND INTERESTING TO THE TABLE."
-- KENDRA CHERRY

Personality types are interesting to observe and very instrumental in our life journey. The better you know yourself, the better equipped you are to navigate through life with a perceptive awareness. Psychologist Kendra Cherry provides compelling revelation to the benefits of exploring one's personality. She suggests, "most personality quizzes are just for fun, but they sometimes reveal nuggets of truth and wisdom that help shed light on different aspects of personality, behavior, and preferences."[1]

Getting to know yourself is a loving act that leads to better appreciating yourself, as well as those around you. These personality tests help your self-awareness as it relates to getting to know your unique personality - whether you are assessing your many personality traits or discovering which *Lord of the Rings* character you are closest to.

Cherry adds, that "the [Myers-Briggs Type Indicator (MBTI)](), for example, is one of the most popular psychological assessments in the world today, and many people swear that knowing their 'type' has helped them gain a better understanding of themselves and others."[1]

The objective of this exercise is to explore your personality type and explore how this impacts your patient care. How does it change when your patient's type is the same or opposite from your own? How can this tool help you care for yourself and then see how to better care for others?

- Various psychological and philosophical assessment tools reveal information about our personalities, which inform our responses to life's situations.
- There are tools such as: Abraham Maslow's Self-Actualization (Ch. 5), Johari Window, Myers-Briggs, and many more.
- The following pages describe the Johari Window and Myers-Briggs Personality types. Examine them closely and try to identify which personality type best represents you.
- Analyze how understanding the differences in each personality type might better inform you in your patient care when interacting with those who might be different from you.

---

1 Cherry, Kendra. "Reasons to Learn More About Your Personality Type." *Verywell Mind*, Personality Psychology, 4 May 2020, www.verywellmind.com/reasons-to-learn-more-about-your-personality-type-4099388.

MYERS-BRIGGS TYPE INDICATOR (MTBI)

According to The Best Jobs for Every Personality Type, (Business Insider), "The Myers-Briggs Type Indicator personality test, which measures preferences like introversion and extroversion, has been part of business culture for decades… According to this system, every person falls into one of two options in four categories."[2] The four categories are: how you focus your attention (E/I), the way you process information (S/N), how you approach decision making (T/F), and the way you organize your thoughts (J/P). When a person uses the chart to determine their type, a four letter outcome is produced to represent your final personality result, i.e. "ENTP" or "ISTJ." Access a free MBTI-based test4 at https://www.16personalities.com/free-personality-test"[3]

PERSONALITY TYPES KEY

E — Extroverts are energized by people, enjoy a variety of task, at quick pace and are good at multi-tasking.

I — Introverts often like working alone or in small groups, prefer a more deliberate pace and like to focus on task at a time.

T — Thinkers – tend to make decisions using logical analysis, objectively weighs pros and cons, and value honesty, consistency, and fairness.

F — Feelers – tend to be sensitive and cooperative, and decide based on their own personal values and how others will be affected by their actions.

S — Sensors - are real people who like to focus on the facts and details and apply common sense and past experience to come up with practical solutions to problems.

N — Intuitives - prefer to focus on possibilities and the big picture, easily see patterns, value innovation, and seek creative solutions to problems.

J — Judgers- tend to be organized and prepared, like to make and stick to plans, and are comfortable following most rules.

P — Perceivers – prefer to keep their options open, like to be able to act spontaneously and like to be flexible with making plans.

---

2 Feloni, Richard, and Skye Gould. "The Best Jobs for Every Personality Type." Business Insider, Insider Inc., 28 Aug. 2015, https://www.businessinsider.com/the-best-jobs-for-every-personality-type-2015-8.

3 Though most Myers-Briggs assessments require payment, the free test referenced here is the NERIS Type Test. NERIS is a free personality assessment tool primarily based on the theories of Myers and Briggs and can be accessed at the website 16personalities.com.
NERIS Analytics. "Free Personality Test." *16Personalities*, NERIS Analytics Limited, https://www.16personalities.com/free-personality-test.

SECTION I RESOURCES   85

JOHARI WINDOW[4]

	KNOWN TO SELF	UNKNOWN TO SELF
KNOWN TO OTHERS	**OPEN SELF** Information about you that both you and others know.	**BLIND SELF** Information about you that you don't know but others do know.
UNKNOWN TO OTHERS	**HIDDEN SELF** Information about you that you know but others don't know.	**UNKNOWN SELF** Information about you that neither you know nor others know.

ENNEAGRAM TYPES[5]

Review the following Enneagram definitions:[6]

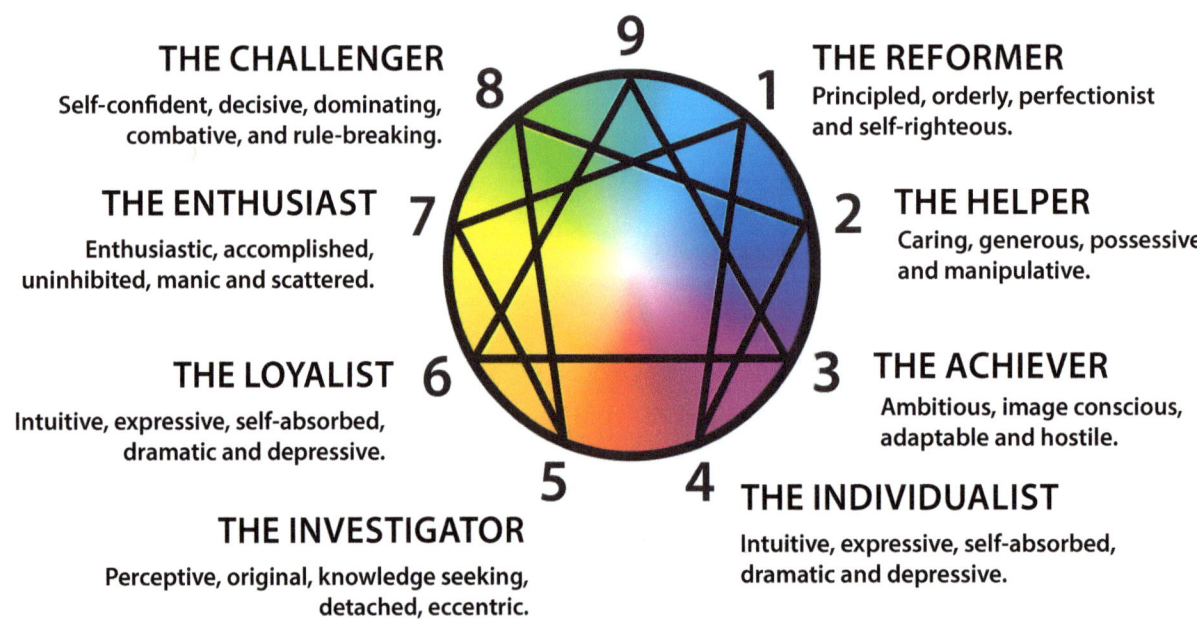

THE PEACEMAKER (9)
Peaceful, reassuring, empathetic, complacent, neglectful, avoidant.

THE REFORMER (1)
Principled, orderly, perfectionist and self-righteous.

THE HELPER (2)
Caring, generous, possessive and manipulative.

THE ACHIEVER (3)
Ambitious, image conscious, adaptable and hostile.

THE INDIVIDUALIST (4)
Intuitive, expressive, self-absorbed, dramatic and depressive.

THE INVESTIGATOR (5)
Perceptive, original, knowledge seeking, detached, eccentric.

THE LOYALIST (6)
Intuitive, expressive, self-absorbed, dramatic and depressive.

THE ENTHUSIAST (7)
Enthusiastic, accomplished, uninhibited, manic and scattered.

THE CHALLENGER (8)
Self-confident, decisive, dominating, combative, and rule-breaking.

---

4 Hampson, Sue. "The Johari Window Model: How To Improve Communication, Self-Awareness And Productivity At Work." *TSW Training*, 7 Oct. 2021, https://www.tsw.co.uk/blog/leadership-and-management/the-johari-window/.

5 Drenth, A. J. "Myers-Briggs / MBTI & Enneagram Correlations." *Personality Junkie*, 2009, https://personalityjunkie.com/07/myers-briggs-enneagram-mbti-types-correlations-relationship/.

6 The Enneagram Institute. "The Nine Enneagram Type Descriptions." *Enneagram Institute*, 2021, https://www.enneagraminstitute.com/type-descriptions.

NURTURING EQUITY MINDED GROUP EXERCISES

After analyzing the charts above, do you know any of your personality types? If yes, please list it:

[ ] Maslow's Hierarchy (which need level) _____

[ ] Johari Window _____

[ ] Myers-Briggs (MBTI) _____

[ ] Enneagram _____

- How can these instruments inform you about your patient care? I.e. If you are an MBTI characterized "thinking" decision maker, how can knowing this impact how your care for patients may need to be adjusted?
- How might you communicate with your patient more effectively, based on what you know about their perceived personality type?

Section II

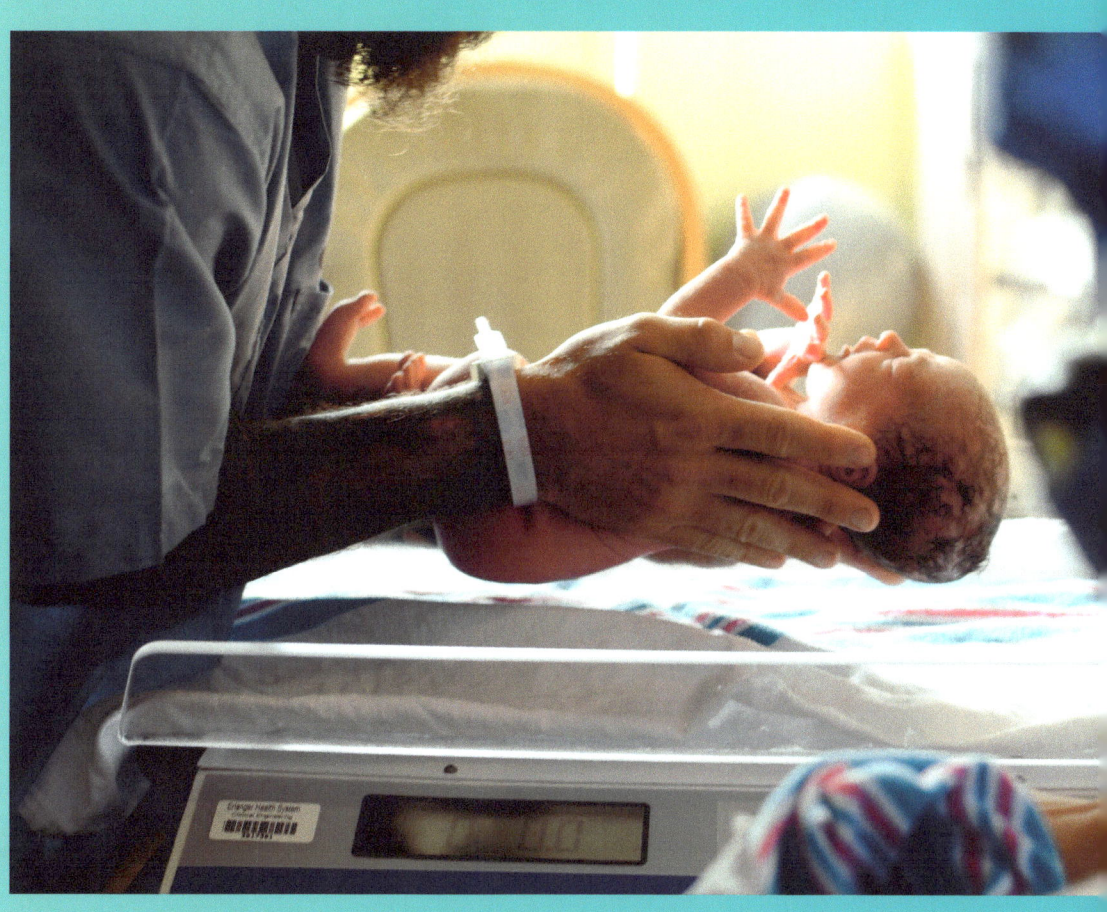

STRUCTURAL RACISM
IN OBSTETRIC CARE

OVERVIEW OF SECTION II

WHAT YOU WILL LEARN (AND DO) IN THIS SECTION:

After working through the foundations of Section 1, in Section 2 we will be asking the question, "Why?" How did we arrive with a healthcare system with such wide disparities of outcome? Section 2 educates healthcare providers on the devastating history of racism in obstetric care and includes the following subjects:

Chapter 8: History of Obstetric Trauma: Understand the history of structural racism and traumatic experiences for Black patients in obstetric care. You will process and assess those systems, determine how far we have come as a healthcare system, and contemplate where we need to go from here.

Chapter 9: The Origin of Midwifery: Learn how, historically, midwives were the first to deliver babies. You will discuss all implications to their return as part of a multidisciplinary team, or through team-based care, and will reflect on the benefits of their inclusion.

Chapter 10: Doulas: Learn about the role of a doula and their ability to further enhance patient care. Several case studies will examine specific ways they can partner with other healthcare providers for empowering birth support.

Chapter 11: Wet Nursing and Breastfeeding Disparities: This chapter discloses yet another system of privilege and oppression - the history and implications of Black mothers as wet nurses. Thoughtful conversation is invited to process these norms. You will engage in a case study and role play. Explore the reasons why we continue to see gaps in breastfeeding, and discuss how we can close them.

Chapter 12: Weathering and Epigenetics: Discover the root causes of social determinants in Black communities and their physiological eroding effects. Understand how distrust has been embedded in a people who have been used as experiments and research subjects for far too long. You will reflect and explore how epigenetics is at work in your own historical makeup.

Chapter 13: Leading Causes of Death in Black Maternal Mortality and Infant Mortality: Examine the leading causes of death in Black birthing persons and their infants. Understand the influence of bias and racism in mortality outcomes. Discover the devastating reality of maternal mortality and infant deaths in Black families. Understand how most could have, and should have, been prevented if respectful maternal care was considered and applied.

HEARTS OPEN WIDE

Our nation's history carries profound implications for the healthcare available to Black and Brown families today. The structural racism embedded within our medical systems has long shaped the experiences and outcomes of marginalized communities, particularly in obstetric care. In this section, we will explore the history of trauma faced by Black patients in the realm of obstetrics, from the origins of systemic oppression in medical practices to the painful legacy of mistreatment and neglect in maternal health.

We will delve into the roots of midwifery, doulas, and the practice of wet nursing, examining how these practices, once integral to the care of Black mothers and infants, became distorted and marginalized in the face of white supremacy and colonialism. You will learn about the concept of weathering—the accelerated health decline due to chronic stress—and epigenetics, which explains how trauma and adversity across generations can alter genetic expression and affect future health outcomes.

This section will also cover the leading causes of mortality for Black and Brown mothers, including how racial discrimination and inequities in access to quality care continue to contribute to alarmingly high maternal mortality rates within these communities.

More importantly, we will explore solutions. As healthcare providers, it is not only essential to understand the root causes of these racial disparities but also to actively engage in efforts to close the historical gaps. Together, we can rewrite the narrative of maternal healthcare, building a future grounded in equity, justice, and the hope that every mother—regardless of race—will receive the care and respect she deserves.

CHAPTER EIGHT
The History of Obstetric Trauma

HIS INVENTIONS FROM THEIR TRAUMAS

Dr. James Marion Sims was born in 1813. He attended medical school in Philadelphia before settling in Alabama to practice medicine in 1835. As he performed many successful surgeries and went on to invent the tool every gynecologist uses today in their exams (the speculum), he became hailed as the "father of modern gynecology." But the methods by which he arrived at this fame were born through unspeakable and monstrous acts.[1]

All evil acts have a day of reckoning and exposure. Two hundred years later, as wider society learned of the inhumane practices he used on innocent Black slave women for his "research," he would be stripped of many of the honors and accolades he was previously awarded.

---

1 Holland, Brynn. "The 'Father of Modern Gynecology' Performed Shocking Experiments on Enslaved Women." *History.com*, A&E Television Networks, 29 Aug. 2017 https://www.history.com/news/the-father-of-modern-gynecology-performed-shocking-experiments-on-slaves.

Consenting Surgical Procedures

Sims claimed that all of his subjects consented to his experiments. According to the article, Why a Statue of the Father of Gynecology Had to Come Down,[2] he allegedly promised one slave owner, " If you will give me Anarcha and Betsey for experiment, I agree to perform no experiment or operation on either of them to endanger their lives."

He also purportedly asked his enslaved subjects if he could test on them before he did. He wrote that they "willingly consented." Yet as slaves, women like Anarcha, Betsey, and Lucy could *only* consent. As property, what other choice did they have? Today, medical ethics standards require informed consent – which Sims could not have obtained from a slave.

As he went on to open the first Women's Hospital in New York, he routinely used anesthetics on his paying White patients a benefit that his Black slaves never received or could have afforded. In fact, like other 19th-century physicians, Sims assumed that Black people simply had higher pain tolerances than White people and therefore, didn't require painkillers for these immensely uncomfortable surgeries. But as he treated these White, affluent women with the care ALL patients should have received, history Whitewashed his success, erasing the years of trauma, pain, and suffering he caused to so many Black lives.

Black Bodies Used and Abused

Historically, as shown with Dr. Sims, medicine has used Black bodies, without consent, for its own advancement; while, medical theories, technologies, and institutions were used to reinforce systems of oppression. This is racial discrimination in healthcare. And while many of these discriminatory practices may have begun with slavery, they did not end there.

There are countless examples of the ways Black people, and Black women in particular, have been abused by the healthcare profession. And though these atrocities began during slavery, as Black people were deemed "less than," were disregarded, were treated as no better than animals, and were altogether dehumanized, many have continued far too long into modern times.

One shocking, but widespread, example of the many ways Black women have been mistreated in the healthcare community, is through the practice known as the "Mississippi appendectomy." MSNBC reports[3] that "During the 1970s sterilization became the most rapidly growing form of birth control in the United States, rising from 200,000 cases in 1970 to over 700,000 in 1980. It was a common belief among Blacks in the South that Black women were routinely sterilized without their informed consent and for no valid medical reason. Teaching hospitals performed unnecessary hysterectomies on poor Black women as practice for their medical physicians. This sort of abuse was so widespread in the South that these operations came to be known as 'Mississippi appendectomies.' These practices [however] were not limited to Mississippi."

The Mississippi Appendectomy

As the "Mississippi Appendectomy" came to be so widespread, involuntary sterilization became legalized in the United States. The article What the 'Mississippi Appendectomy' says about the regard of the state towards the agency of Black women's bodies[4] states that, "This, of course, was passed as state law under the pretense that the sterilization was only provided to those with disabilities or those that were deemed to be too 'promiscuous' or 'feebleminded' to have children. This was the case with Elaine Riddick, a 14-year-old Black girl whose social worker decided it was best to sterilize her due to her falling pregnant after having been raped and assaulted by her neighbor." A young child was raped, impregnated, and then had all her reproductive rights forcibly removed as a result, with zero consent or permission. And this was just considered legal healthcare for Black people in America.

The last state (North Carolina) to repeal their law that allowed for involuntary sterilization, did not do so until 2003. Unfortunately, sterilization of Black bodies did not stop there. MSNBC[3] continued their report to say, "the Center for Investigative Reporting found that the California Department of Corrections sterilized nearly 150 female inmates from 2006 to 2010." From Dr. Sims, to the Mississippi Appendectomy, the history of Black relationships with reproduction rights has been steeped in abuse and racism.

These are the dangers of perpetuating illegal, dehumanizing and illegitimate practices of non-consenting experiments and operations on Black people. Sadly, only recently have these wrongs begun to be exposed and addressed.

A Long Overdue Victory

In 2006, the University of Alabama at Birmingham removed Sims from their display of the "Medical Giants of Alabama."[5] Twelve years later, New York removed the J. Marion Sims statue from Central Park, relocating it to Sims's burial site in a Brooklyn cemetery.[2] The city also replaced the original plaque that only told of Sims's medical achievements. And in its place,

---

2   Serwer, Adam. "Why a Statue of the 'Father of Gynecology' Had to Come Down." *The Atlantic*, Atlantic Media Company, 19 Apr. 2018, https://www.theatlantic.com/politics/archive/2018/04/why-a-statue-of-the-father-of-gynecology-had-to-come-down/558311/.

3   Kugler, Sara. "Day 17: Mississippi Appendectomies and Reproductive Justice." *MSNBC*, NBCUniversal News Group, 27 Mar. 2014, https://www.msnbc.com/msnbc/day-17-mississippi-appendectomies-msna293361.

4   Tafesse, Kidi. "What the 'Mississippi Appendectomy' Says about the Regard of the State towards the Agency of Black Women's Bodies." *The Movement for Black Women's Lives*, Black Freedom Struggles, 1 May 2019, https://BlackwomenintheBlackfreedomstruggle.voices.wooster.edu/2019/05/01/what-the-mississippi-appendectomy-says-about-the-regard-of-the-state-towards-the-agency-of-Black-womens-bodies/.

the new plaque recognizes the roles of his slaves, and others in the history of medicine.

Dr. Sims perfected his surgical skills by operating on enslaved Black women in the 1840's, taking sharp, cutting objects to perform invasive and deep surgical procedures without the use of anesthesia. Sims proved he had no respect for Black women or the "diseases of women" in general. According to Sarah Zhang's article, The Surgeon Who Experimented on Slaves,[5] he even once wrote, "If there is anything I hated, it was investigating the organs of the female pelvis." His hatred of the female organs rang true as he violently pierced, severed and degraded so many Black slaves throughout his life's work.

Race-Based Medicine

After reading about Dr. Sims, one cannot help but to step back and ask many questions related to the dehumanized treatment toward human life. Such questions may range from:

- How can someone in the medical profession allow another human being to endure so much pain and trauma for their own professional advancement?
- Why would one believe they are justified to enslave a free life?
- On what basis does one take up the privilege to look down on others and feel they are justified?

It is these types of questions that have haunted me to my core for most of my adult life. Moreover, these inquiries, and so many more, are answered in the hidden histories of science, politics, journalism, misogynistic cultures, traditions, medicine, philosophy and shared ignorance.

I am delighted that I had the privilege to attend a life changing and transforming webinar on July 20, 2023 hosted by Cherished Futures for Black Moms & Babies, titled Building Skills for Implementation. One of the main objectives of this workshop was to develop the understanding of how race-based medicine impacts the Black community and how it is still in play today.

I was most impacted by Asaiah Harville's presentation on race-based medicine, and am eager to share my take-aways from this transforming engagement. Much of her references and research came from the works of author Dorothy E. Roberts, and her book entitled Fatal Inventions: How Science, Politics, and Big Business Re-create Race in the Twenty-First Century.[6]

TAKEAWAY #1: In her book, Roberts discusses how biological differences were used to rally support for the political categorization of race. She explains that race is not biological, but it was used in a political way to create certain systems that we still see in place today. For example, in order to try and justify enslaving another human being, slave owners would use biology in their arguments, even if it was grossly absurd and ridiculous.

Asaiah expounded on Roberts' claims, noting how if enslavers, lawmakers, criminal systems and even physicians, or those with positions of power (whether in politics or socially) have the control, then they can define disease and health status however they want to - including in racial terms.

TAKEAWAY #2: Unfortunately, because those doing the justifying were also the ones in positions of power, they were able to manipulate different sources of academia to try and support their argument. For example, Asaiah also referenced the use of Crania America during this time to try to dehumanize Black people by comparing their skulls to those of apes. The images used were designed to show the supposed differences and similarities between the skulls of individuals of different races in order to determine whether Black people were "fully human". White skulls were used as the "default," and were spared from any animal comparisons.

TAKEAWAY #3: Asaiah went on to explain how these erroneous claims to race-based biological differences were often used as ways to justify political systems, such as slavery. For example, high ranking politicians, such as Thomas Jefferson, used these tactics as well. In a letter to visiting French dignitaries, Jefferson tried to justify America's use of slavery by saying Black people were "inferior" because they "slept more." Rather than equating the exhaustion of Black slaves to the most logical reason - that they were forced to work long, physically laborious days with little nutrition and inhumane conditions each day, causing extreme fatigue - he instead tried to manufacture biological differences to support his claims, referencing "a difference of structure and pulmonary apparatus," to try and imply that Black slaves had larger, "emptier" skulls, causing them to sleep more.

I left the workshop with many reflections, not least of which Dorothy Roberts' compelling argument that race is not a biological construct, it is a political one and a social one, inspired by the selfish aspirations of man.

TAKEAWAY #4: When we broaden this lens, we can also surmise that it is a very convenient privilege to be able to ignore the structural conditions in which Black Americans lived during this time, and then use the diseases they developed as a result of these conditions, to try and justify them. In other words, the oppressors at the time chose to argue that Black people were innately unequal biologically, and that is why there was an unequal system that was composed of whole persons (White) and their biological inferiors (Black), rather than to admit that they created an unequal system based solely on skin color simply for their own benefit, at the expense of their fellow humans.

As this webinar so brilliantly described, race-based medicine is derived historically from racist individuals who dehumanized the Black person, and hence the Black body, in order to gain

---

5   Zhang, Sarah. "The Surgeon Who Experimented on Slaves." *The Atlantic*, Atlantic Media Company, 16 Aug. 2021, https://www.theatlantic.com/health/archive/2018/04/j-marion-sims/558248/.

6   Roberts, Dorothy E. *Fatal Invention: How Science, Politics, and Big Business Re-Create Race in the Twenty-First Century*. The New Press, 2012.

some sort of advantage - whether medically (in the case of Sims), politically (in the case of Jefferson), or economically (in the case of slavery as a whole). It must stand to reason, then, that America is a country born of systems plagued with inherent racism, that has continued to trickle down and infect our greater society today - where the fields of health and medicine are certainly not immune. **At no time in history have these atrocious medical, political and economic findings ever been formally retracted by the dominant culture.**

NURTURING EQUITY MINDED EXERCISE #1

Using the practices of Dr. Sims as a case study, contemplate his actions, untruths, and thoughts about the female body. Sit with them before dividing into groups to express your feelings and thoughts.

Discuss your response to Dr. Sims' views on women, and how the Black slaves that he experimented on were treated.

Do you agree with the removal of his statue from the park to his gravesite? Discuss why or why not.

NURTURING EQUITY MINDED EXERCISE #2

1. Why is it important to have a respectful, dignified and honorable philosophy of patient consent?

2. What have we learned from Dr. Marion Sims as it relates to patient shared decision making and patient informed consent?

3. Do we still see practices without informed consent today or shared decision making?

4. Create a mission statement and philosophy of consent according to your values and convictions.

5. As you break into your small groups and come up with a patient consent statement that speaks to how you will protect your patients' boundaries and include their voice in all care.

6. How do you feel about Dr. Sims' philosophy about Black women having a higher pain tolerance and not needing as much pain management as White counterparts?

7. What should be done to medical books, journals and articles that perpetuate Dr. Sims' philosophy?

CHAPTER NINE
The Origins of Midwifery

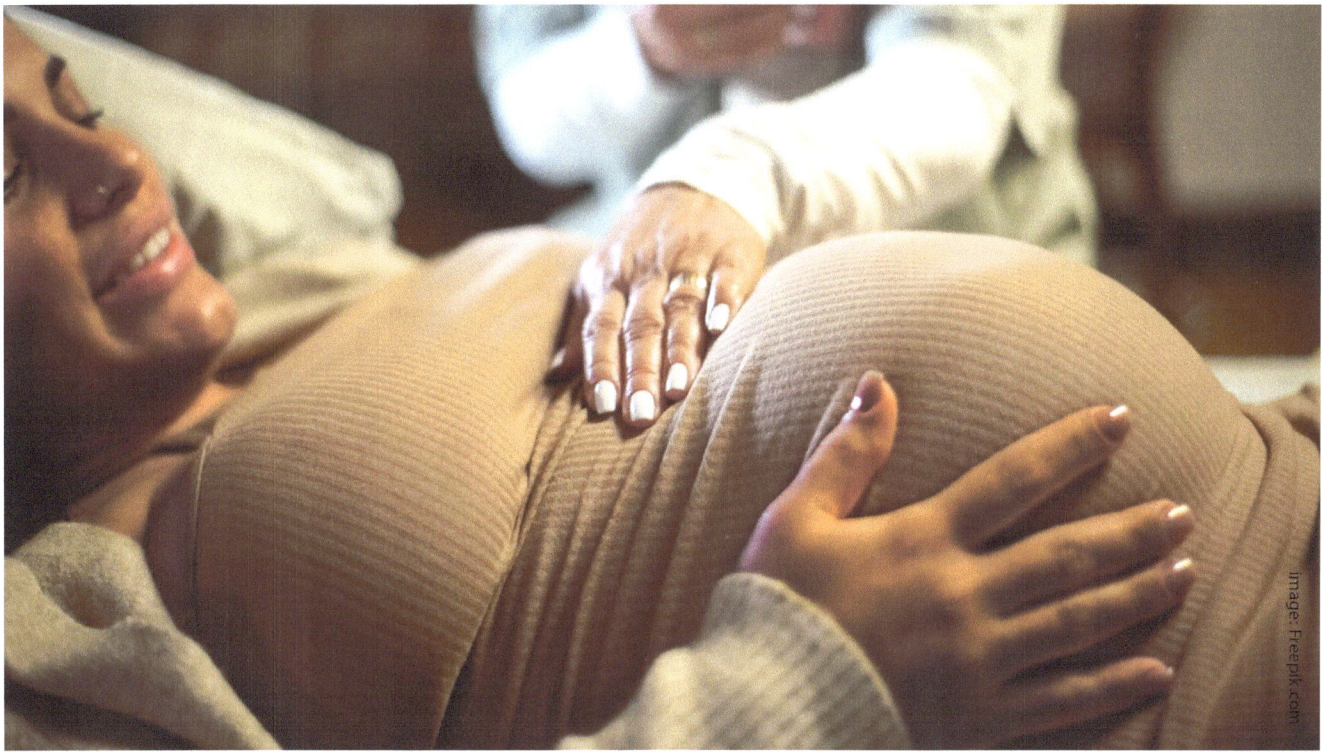

The Making of Midwives

Historically, midwives were the first to deliver babies. As is only natural, women knew how to help guide other women in their deliveries, taking the lead in birthing until the 1800s.

According to the article The Origins of Midwifery,[1] "The practice of midwifery can be traced back to the paleolithic era (40,000 B.C.), where pregnancy and childbirth required women to give birth in challenging and often life-threatening environments. Women supported themselves during birth based on knowledge and skills they learned from observing other mammals."

As women learned more about their own bodies, either from their own intuition, or from the observation of others, they began to build a foundation of child bearing knowledge. This valuable information has continued to be passed on from one generation to the next, as women from around the world have continued to share their knowledge and support each other through one of life's greatest miracles: childbirth.

---

1   ICM. "The Origins of Midwifery." *International Confederation of Midwives*, LDSC, 1 Feb. 2022, https://www.internationalmidwives.org/icm-news/the-origins-of-midwifery.html.

Tug-of-War: Midwives vs. Doctors

In this section, we will review many evidence based articles and narratives related to Midwifery. As we reflect on this subject, I will also share some of my learnings and editorial perspectives from my personal experiences.

For professionals that are passionately engaged in birth equity, you will benefit greatly from the article, How did birth move from the home to the hospital, and back again?,[2] which highlights learnings by Margaret Marsh, a Professor of History at Rutgers University.

Marsh skillfully articulates the timeline of home births, their history and benefits. She discusses how tensions later began to develop over where births should take place, and who was best qualified to be in the room. Professor Marsh showcases the historical power struggle between midwives and doctors and their battle for the final word on birthing care.

Despite this tug-of-war history, my experience has shown me that doctors and midwives do not need to be at odds with each other. In fact, the California Maternal Quality Care Collaborative (CMQCC) has recently found that the most successful births come from a team-based care approach in which doctors and midwives work together.[3] What's more, this chapter will look at how having midwives present during hospital births (specifically Black midwives when caring for Black mothers) can help save lives.

Benefits of Diversity: The Critical Role of Black Midwives

In the article, Black History Month: The Importance of Black Midwives, Then, Now, and Tomorrow,[4] the authors reflect that, "Midwives and specifically Black midwives, for *centuries*, have played a critical role in improving the care and outcomes for Black families. At the same time, Black midwives have also faced extra, unnecessary, and often extreme and insurmountable challenges to practicing and serving the families in need of their care."

Doula and midwife expert, Shafia M. Monroe, asserts that, "One of the darkest moments in US history was the systematic eradication of the Black midwife from her community, resulting in a legacy of birth injustices."

She further asserts, "Expanding the culturally diverse doula workforce is a necessity to improve birth outcomes in ethnically diverse communities, because culturally diverse doulas understand the needs of their community, and clients have trust with doulas who reflect their ethnic and cultural values…That is family-centered care."

Furthermore, according to the CMQCC,[3] midwifery and doula services can result in: shorter labors, reduced Cesarean sections, reduced medical interventions, reduced use of regional anesthesia, higher breastfeeding rates in the first hour after birth, greater patient confidence and control, and an increased feeling of satisfaction for the mother/ birthing person and father.

Doulas, known for providing support to women during childbirth, have a long history, but their role became more formalized and recognized in the 20th century. Here's an overview of how the role of doulas evolved during this period:

---

[2] Scott, Maiken. "How Did Birth Move from the Home to the Hospital, and Back Again?" *WHYY*, PBS, 13 Dec. 2013, https://whyy.org/segments/how-did-birth-move-from-the-home-to-the-hospital-and-back-again/.

[3] "Harnessing the Power of Team-Based Care: Medicine and Midwifery as Partners in Care." Presented by Holly Smith, et al., YouTube, California Maternal Quality Care Collaborative, 7 Feb. 2023, https://www.youtube.com/watch?v=Nsf6MGXs4m0.

[4] Terreri, Cara. "Black History Month: The Importance of Black Midwives, Then, Now and Tomorrow." *Lamaze International*, 14 Feb. 2020, https://www.lamaze.org/Connecting-the-Dots/Black-history-month-the-importance-of-Black-midwives-then-now-and-tomorrow-1.

EARLY TO MID-20TH CENTURY

From Traditional Birth Support to Medicalization of Birth

Before the mid-20th century, birth support was typically provided by female relatives and community members. This informal support network was crucial, especially in rural areas where professional medical assistance was not always available.

As childbirth began to move from homes to hospitals in the early to mid-20th century, the role of traditional birth attendants declined. The medicalization of birth led to a more clinical and less personalized birth experience.

1960S TO 1980S

The Revival of Natural Birth and Formation of Doula Organizations

In the 1960s and 1970s, there was a growing movement towards natural childbirth and a backlash against the highly medicalized birth practices. This period saw the re-emergence of the desire for more personalized birth support.

In the 1980s, organizations dedicated to training and certifying doulas began to form. One of the most notable is DONA International (originally Doulas of North America), founded in 1992. These organizations helped formalize the role of doulas and set standards for practice.

LATE 20TH CENTURY

Increased Recognition and Diversity of Roles

By the late 20th century, doulas gained more recognition and respect within the medical community. Research began to show the positive impact of doula support on birth outcomes, including reduced rates of cesarean sections, shorter labor, and higher satisfaction with the birth experience.

The role of doulas expanded beyond just birth support to include postpartum doulas, who assist families in the weeks following birth, and even antepartum doulas, who support women with high-risk pregnancies.

Overall, the 20th century saw a significant transformation in the role and recognition of doulas, evolving from informal community-based support to a professionalized and respected component of maternity care.

Midwives and Doulas: What's the Difference?

Midwives and doulas both play crucial roles in supporting women during pregnancy, childbirth, and the postpartum period, but their functions and training differ significantly. Here's a detailed comparison:

MIDWIVES	DOULAS
ROLE AND RESPONSIBILITIES:	
Medical Care: Midwives are trained healthcare professionals who provide medical care to women during pregnancy, childbirth, and the postpartum period. They can conduct physical exams, prescribe medications, and perform medical procedures. **Primary Care Providers:** Midwives can act as primary care providers for low-risk pregnancies, managing prenatal care, labor, delivery, and postpartum care. **Holistic Approach:** While midwives offer medical care, they often emphasize a holistic approach to childbirth, focusing on the physical, emotional, and social aspects of maternity care.	**Non-Medical Support:** Doulas provide non-medical support, focusing on emotional, physical, and informational support before, during, and after childbirth. They do not perform medical procedures or provide clinical care. **Birth and Postpartum Support:** Birth doulas assist during labor and delivery, helping with comfort measures such as breathing techniques, positioning, and pain relief methods. Postpartum doulas support families in the weeks following birth, helping with newborn care, breastfeeding, and adjustment to parenthood.
TRAINING AND CERTIFICATION:	
Education: Midwives undergo extensive training, which can include a Bachelor's or Master's degree in midwifery. In many countries, midwifery is a regulated profession requiring formal education and clinical training. **Certification:** Certification varies by country. In the U.S., for example, Certified Nurse-Midwives (CNMs) are registered nurses with advanced training in midwifery, certified by the American Midwifery Certification Board. There are also Certified Professional Midwives (CPMs) who are trained through apprenticeship and accredited programs.	**Education:** Doulas are trained through various certification programs offered by organizations such as NBDA (National Black Doulas Association) Leadership Academy, DONA International, CAPPA, and others. Training typically includes childbirth education, labor support techniques, and postpartum care. **Certification:** Certification requirements vary by organization but usually involve completing a training program, attending a certain number of births, and adhering to a code of ethics.
WORK ENVIRONMENT:	
Settings: Midwives can work in hospitals, birthing centers, clinics, or attend home births, depending on their training and certification.	**Settings:** Doulas work in various settings, including hospitals, birthing centers, and homes. They are often hired directly by families seeking additional support.

Summary

Midwives: Provide medical care, can act as primary care providers for pregnancy and birth, have extensive medical training, and are certified healthcare professionals.

Doulas: Offer non-medical support, focus on emotional and physical comfort, have specific training in support techniques, and are not certified to provide medical care.

Together, midwives and doulas can complement each other, with midwives handling the medical aspects of childbirth and doulas providing continuous emotional and physical support. Let's look now at the specific ways that doulas, a role which is becoming increasingly more common, support a birthing person during and after their birthing process.

NURTURING EQUITY MINDED EXERCISE

When looking for some of the common causes around Black maternal mortality, it is important to be made aware of the dangers. Please review each cause and discuss their importance. Also add one more cause that you feel should be part of this list.

- Ignoring Black women's plea for medical attention.
- The unconscious bias against Black women.
- Dismissing the health care needs of pregnant and postpartum Black women.
- Not believing Black women when they say, "something is wrong."
- Allowing Black postpartum mothers to die
- Social determinants
- _____

_____

"Simply put, for example, when Black families are cared for by Black health professionals, like midwives, they are better heard, seen, respected, understood, and get their needs met, which relates directly to health outcomes."[4]

Discuss with your group: Why did you choose the cause you listed above? Is there a "case study" you are thinking of that your group could discuss?

CHAPTER TEN
Doulas

The availability of Doulas and their accepted role in the birthing process has only grown in the past few decades. A 2023 study by Nova Southeastern University of Medicine, titled "The Effect of Doulas on Maternal and Birth Outcomes: A Scoping Review," states that, "doula guidance in perinatal care was associated with positive delivery outcomes including reduced cesarean sections, premature deliveries, and length of labor. Moreover, the emotional support provided by doulas was seen to reduce anxiety and stress. Doula support, specifically in low-income women, was shown to improve breastfeeding success, with quicker lactogenesis and continued breastfeeding weeks after childbirth."[1]

As we look to provide culturally-sensitive support for birthing persons, the role of Doulas can be an incredible opportunity for well-rounded and comprehensive support. The following chapter is full of practical steps for Doulas to consider their patient's birthing process, co-written by Dr. Candace Kelly and Felicia Francis-Edwards, CLES, CD.

Felicia is an empathetic birthing professional with over 30 years of experience, dedicated to supporting people of color, specifically African American women, in achieving safe births. She began her career at the Watts Health Foundation, where she provided Doula support, case management, and health education for over 16 years. Fluent in English and some Spanish, she educated pregnant parents on childbirth, lactation, and infant care.

---

1 https://pmc.ncbi.nlm.nih.gov/articles/PMC10292163/

After her time at Watts, Felicia transitioned to Youth and Family Services and the CAL-LEARN program, advocating for 30 clients and helping them access critical resources. She completed her Doula training at DONA (Doula of North America) in 2012 and continued her work through Healthnet's Doula program and the AAIM Doula Pilot. Throughout her career, she has supported over 200 births, providing education and advocacy for both pregnant and postpartum clients.

Felicia's vision is to train new Doulas and act as a safe mentor, particularly with the start of the medical Doula reimbursement initiative. She is committed to achieving equitable maternal and infant care for all people of color, especially Black mothers, to ensure optimal outcomes in safe birthing environments. Felicia also serves as Chief Operating Officer for Still Resilient Redefining Maternal and Infant Health, a nonprofit organization providing equitable empathy education and training to institutions, universities, hospitals, and birth workers. Felicia firmly believes that every mother deserves equity, and postpartum process, and she strives to be an empathetic birthing professional and advocate for every mother she serves.

9 PILLARS OF ENTERING THE SACRED SPACE

By Dr. Candace Kelly & Felicia Francis-Edwards

Every Doula must embrace the 9 Pillars of entering the sacred space of a client.

Here are nine ways to enter a client's space as a Doula, each defined to emphasize the importance of creating a supportive and trusting environment:

1. HUMILITY

Doulas must approach each client with a sense of humility, recognizing that every birthing experience is unique and that you are there to support them, not impose your beliefs or experiences.

Listen actively to your clients' needs, acknowledging their expertise in their own bodies and experiences. This creates a safe space where they feel valued and heard..

2. CURIOSITY

Cultivate a genuine sense of curiosity about your client's individual needs, preferences, and experiences.

Ask open-ended questions to better understand their desires for labor and delivery. This encourages them to share their thoughts and feelings, helping you tailor your support to their specific situation.

3. RESPECT

Show deep respect for your client's choices, values, and cultural beliefs, acknowledging their autonomy throughout the birthing process.

Validate their feelings and decisions without judgment, ensuring they feel empowered to make informed choices about their care and experience.

4. ADVOCACY

Advocacy involves supporting and empowering the birthing person in expressing their preferences, desires, and rights within the healthcare system.

Be a voice for the birthing person's preferences, desires, and needs. Educate them on their options and rights within the healthcare system, empowering them to make informed decisions. During labor, communicate effectively with the medical team, ensuring the birthing person's wishes are clearly expressed and respected.

5. GENTLENESS

Approach your clients and their situation with gentleness, both in your demeanor and your actions.

Use a calm and soothing voice, gentle touch, and mindful movements to create a peaceful atmosphere. This helps to ease tension and anxiety, allowing clients to feel more relaxed and supported.

6. DIGNITY

Treat every client with dignity, recognizing their inherent worth and the importance of their experience.

Ensure their privacy and comfort, respect their boundaries, and address them with kindness and compassion. This helps to foster trust and rapport, making clients feel valued and respected.

7. EDUCATION

Provide education and information to empower clients in their decision-making process, fostering a sense of confidence and understanding.

Share evidence-based information about pregnancy, labor, and postpartum care while respecting their individual choices. Encourage questions and discussions to ensure they feel informed and involved in their care.

8. ACTIVE LISTENING

Engage in active listening, giving full attention to your clients and showing empathy towards their feelings and concerns.

Use verbal affirmations and non-verbal cues (like nodding and maintaining eye contact) to show that you are fully present. Reflect back what they say to confirm understanding, which helps clients feel validated and heard.

9. TRUST

Build a foundation of trust with your clients by being reliable, honest, and transparent in your communication.

Establish clear boundaries and follow through on commitments, ensuring clients feel secure in your presence. Encourage open dialogue, reinforcing that their feelings and choices are respected and valued.

By incorporating these nine principles—Humility, Curiosity, Respect, Advocacy, Gentleness, Dignity, Education, Active Listening, and Trust—Doulas can effectively enter and support their clients' spaces, fostering a positive and empowering environment that enhances the birthing experience.

TIMELINESS

Critically important in showing up in the sacred space as a Doula is a focus on timeliness, which is essential for creating a supportive and empowering environment for the birthing person. Here are some key practices to ensure you embody this principle effectively:

PREPARE BEFORE THE BIRTH

Keep track of the estimated due date and have a plan in place to be available around th at time. Maintain communication with the birthing person and their support team to understand any signs of labor onset, preferences, or concerns. Have your doula bag ready with essentials like comfort items, educational materials, and tools to support the birthing process, ensuring you can leave quickly when needed.

COMMUNICATION

Discuss timelines, preferences, and emergency contacts during your prenatal meetings, ensuring everyone understands your role and availability. Maintain open lines of communication with the birthing person, providing updates and reassurance as the due date approaches.

TIMING YOUR ARRIVAL

Be aware of the stages of labor and know when to arrive. For early labor, check in frequently and assess if you need to be there, balancing your presence with their need for privacy. Trust your instincts about when the birthing person might need you most, being sensitive to their energy and needs.

BEING PRESENT IN THE MOMENT

Ground yourself through mindfulness techniques to remain fully present and focused when you arrive, enhancing your ability to support the birthing person. Be prepared for changes in plans or timing, maintaining a calm demeanor to help the birthing person feel secure and supported.

AFTER THE BIRTH

Offer continued support in the immediate postpartum period, assisting with breastfeeding, bonding, and the transition into parenthood as needed. After the birth, take time to discuss the experience with the birthing person and their partner, allowing them to share their feelings and thoughts, reinforcing the sacredness of their journey.

REFLECTION AND GROWTH

Follow up after the birth to see how they are doing, reinforcing your ongoing support and connection. Reflect on each birth experience to improve your timeliness and presence for future clients.

Learn from Each Experience: Reflect on each birth experience to improve your timeliness and presence for future clients.

By prioritizing timeliness and presence, you create a sacred space for the birthing person, allowing them to feel safe, supported, and empowered throughout their journey. Your role as a Doula is to honor the unique experience of each birth while being adaptable to the needs of the birthing person.

COLLABORATING WITH HOSPITALS AND BIRTHCARE CENTERS

The following is a Doula's essential guideline on how to effectively partner with a medical team while honoring their own respective boundaries.

GUIDELINES FOR DOULAS PARTNERING WITH A MEDICAL TEAM

Understand Your Role: Clearly define your role as a Doula. Understand that you are there to provide emotional, physical, and informational support to the birthing person, not to provide medical care or intervene in clinical decisions.

Establish Communication: Open lines of communication with the medical team before labor begins. Introduce yourself and explain your role to ensure everyone is on the same page regarding your involvement.

Respect Medical Protocols: Familiarize yourself with the hospital or birthing center's policies and procedures. Respect the medical team's protocols and work within their framework while advocating for the client's preferences.

Build Collaborative Relationships: Foster positive relationships with healthcare providers. Show appreciation for their work, and be respectful and cooperative, which can help create a collaborative environment.

Maintain Professional Boundaries: Clearly define your boundaries as a Doula. Communicate these boundaries to both the client and the medical team to ensure everyone understands your role and limitations.

Advocate, Don't Interfere: Advocate for the birthing person's wishes and preferences respectfully. Use effective communication skills to express their desires without undermining the medical team's authority or decisions.

Stay Calm and Positive: Maintain a calm and positive demeanor, especially during stressful situations. This helps to create a supportive environment for both the client and the medical team.

Document Important Information: Keep a record of the client's preferences, any important discussions with the medical team, and any significant changes during labor. This documentation can help facilitate communication and ensure continuity of care.

Encourage Teamwork: Foster a spirit of teamwork among the medical staff and the client. Encourage the client to express their feelings and concerns to the healthcare team, creating an environment of mutual respect.

Reflect and Debrief: After the birth, take time to reflect on the experience. If possible, have a debriefing session with the medical team to discuss what went well and what could be improved. This not only fosters relationships but also enhances future collaborations.

When following these guidelines, Doulas can effectively partner with medical teams while honoring their boundaries and providing the best possible support for the birthing person.

NURTURING EQUITY MINDED GROUP EXERCISE

Think of a situation you have recently experienced in your healthcare setting in which a Doula was present to the birthing experience. Using this as a case study, answer the following questions:

1. How did this Healthcare Center/Birthcare Center/Hospital respond? Was it a Doula-friendly facility?
2. Did the patient experience any barriers to her care?
3. How were any barriers mitigated by the Doula?
4. How did the Doula partner with the medical team?
5. How could care have been different for this mom from the Doula or Medical team?
6. Describe how the care the mother and family received was positively impacted by the Doula's work.

CASE STUDY

1. Jessica Ramierez is a thirty-one-year-old first time mother who was born in Mexico and has lived in the United States for the past three years. For her birthing experience, she found a Doula who was able to support her in a culturally-affirming role, advocating for specific needs she may have and easing her discomfort in giving birth with less community or familiar support. Fortunately, the hospital staff respected this desire and were able to incorporate the Doula's role smoothly into the birthing process. Jessica credits having a Doula around as the biggest factor in her positive and empowering birthing process.

    a. How did this Healthcare Center/Birthcare Center/Hospital respond? Was it a Doula-friendly facility?
    b. Did the patient experience any barriers to her care?
    c. How were any barriers mitigated by the Doula?
    d. How did the Doula partner with the medical team?
    e. How could care have been different for this mom from the Doula or Medical team?
    f. Describe how the care the mother and family received was positively impacted by the Doula's work.

2. In this same hospital, a woman named Jennifer Bridges is giving birth and is also utilizing the services of a naturopathic Doula. Unfortunately, throughout the course of the birthing process, the Doula and the hospital staff clash over roles and patient needs, causing extra stress during this already stressful time. Instead of bringing comfort and support, Jennifer found herself overwhelmed.

    a. How did this Healthcare Center/Birthcare Center/Hospital respond? Was it a Doula-friendly facility?
    b. Did the patient experience any barriers to her care? How could this have been resolved?
    c. How did the Doula partner with the medical team?
    d. How could care have been different for this mom from the Doula or Medical team?
    e. Describe how the care the mother and family received was positively impacted by the Doula's work.

CHAPTER ELEVEN
Wet Nursing & Breastfeeding Disparities

Breastfeeding as the Best Source of Nutrition and Addressing Barriers in Black Communities

Breastfeeding is universally recognized as the optimal source of nutrition for infants, offering unparalleled health benefits for both babies and mothers. Breast milk provides essential nutrients, strengthens the immune system, and fosters critical bonding between mother and child. The World Health Organization and the American Academy of Pediatrics recommend exclusive breastfeeding for the first six months of life, followed by continued breastfeeding alongside complementary foods for up to two years or beyond.

Despite these proven benefits, breastfeeding rates remain disproportionately low in Black communities due to a myriad of systemic, cultural, and socio-economic barriers. Historical trauma, lack of access to culturally competent healthcare, limited workplace support, and deeply ingrained formula marketing have created significant challenges for Black mothers. Furthermore, the lingering effects of systemic racism within healthcare systems have eroded trust, often leaving Black women without adequate breastfeeding education or support.

This chapter aims to explore the multifaceted benefits of breastfeeding while addressing the barriers that hinder its adoption in Black communities. By acknowledging these obstacles and working towards equitable solutions, we can help empower mothers to make informed choices for their families and support the health and well-being of the next generation. Below are traditional barriers to breastfeeding in traditionally marginalized communities.

Lack of Representation and Support: Many Black women do not see breastfeeding normalized or celebrated in their communities. The lack of culturally competent lactation consultants or mentors can make breastfeeding feel inaccessible.

Workplace Challenges and Inadequate Pumping Accommodations: Black women often work in environments with inflexible schedules, inadequate maternity leave, and limited access to private, sanitary spaces for pumping breast milk. Without proper accommodations, balancing work responsibilities with breastfeeding can be extremely challenging.

Misinformation and Myths: Common myths, such as breastfed babies not getting enough nutrition or formula being "better" or more modern, persist in some communities, discouraging breastfeeding.

Healthcare Disparities: Bias and lack of support from healthcare providers may lead to insufficient education about breastfeeding or limited encouragement to breastfeed during prenatal and postpartum care.

Social Pressures and Lack of Family Support: Some Black women face resistance from family members or partners who believe formula feeding is more convenient or appropriate, creating pressure to choose formula over breastfeeding.

Body Image and Personal Choice: Concerns about breastfeeding's impact on physical appearance, discomfort with the process, or simply feeling that it is not the right choice for them can influence some Black women to resist breastfeeding.

Sexual Connotations and Stigma: Breastfeeding can sometimes be sexualized in society, leading to discomfort or embarrassment for some women. The fear of being perceived as overly sexual or being judged for breastfeeding in public can discourage Black women from choosing to breastfeed.

Historical Trauma and Cultural Perceptions: The legacy of slavery, where enslaved Black women were forced to breastfeed white children (wet-nursing), has left generational trauma and cultural stigma associated with breastfeeding.

Aggressive Marketing of Formula in Developing Countries: Companies like Nestlé have historically promoted infant formula in developing countries through aggressive marketing tactics. They often target vulnerable communities by presenting formula as superior to breastfeeding, sometimes exploiting trust in Western products. These campaigns can undermine confidence in breastfeeding and lead to widespread reliance on formula, despite the financial and health challenges it poses.

Health Impacts: In areas with limited access to clean water, formula feeding can expose infants to life-threatening illnesses such as diarrhea and malnutrition. Breastfeeding, on the other hand, provides essential immunity and nutrition.

Economic Strain: Formula feeding imposes a financial burden on families in low-income settings, often diverting limited resources from other criticalneeds.

Cultural Shift: Such marketing campaigns can contribute to a cultural shift away from breastfeeding, portraying it as outdated or inferior. This perception can persist across generations, further discouraging breastfeeding practices.

HOW DO WE ADDRESS THE BARRIERS?

Global organizations like WHO and UNICEF have pushed for initiatives like the International Code of Marketing of Breastmilk Substitutes, which aims to regulate formula advertising and promote breastfeeding as the healthiest option for infants. Increased education, regulation, and community support are vital to counteract the negative impact of aggressive marketing by formula companies.

Addressing these barriers requires a holistic approach, including:

Culturally Sensitive Education: Providing accurate information about the benefits of breastfeeding and dispelling myths within Black communities in our homes, our communities, clinics and our healthcare organizations.

Enhanced Workplace Policies: Ensuring that workplaces offer flexible schedules, adequate maternity leave, and private, comfortable spaces for pumping while normalizing the value and importance.

Healthcare Provider Training: Training healthcare professionals to offer unbiased, supportive breastfeeding guidance for black and brown patients.

Community Support Systems: Building strong support networks through community programs, peer support groups, and mentorship from experienced breastfeeding mothers to provide in-service, education and training in our hospitals.

Challenging Stigmas: Promoting visual positive representations of breastfeeding to combat sexualization and normalize breastfeeding in all settings. Images of black and brown mother's are highly encouraged in our hospital systems.

By addressing both the historical and contemporary challenges, Global and Domestic, society can better support Black women in their breastfeeding journeys, ensuring that they have the resources and encouragement needed to make informed and empowered choices.

THE TRAUMA BASED HISTORY OF WET NURSING: BLACK WOMEN SLAVES WHO NOURISHED A NATION

Historically, Black mothers were forced, at their owner's threats, to breastfeed their owner's children at the neglect of their own. Many historians date wet nursing to the early 1600s.

Over time, this practice of not breastfeeding their own children became a social status for White women. Thus, it eventually became historically known as a symbol of wealth and status to have a wet nurse. According to Kamna Kirti's article, The Tragic Plight of Enslaved Wet Nurses,[1] "This had a trickle-down impact on not only racial but also the psychological, financial, and political fabric of the society throughout the Black community."

According to Kirti, "Wives of slave owners timed their pregnancies with that of their slaves and then forcefully separated enslaved new mothers from their infants to serve as wet nurses for their children."

This practice was a form of exploitation, as these women were compelled to nourish and care for the infants of slave owners, often at the expense of their own children.

'Dehumanizing' is an understatement for this forceful act. Words cannot adequately capture the degradation of these insidious acts upon human life. To deny another mother from feeding their own child, to beat them like animals, to milk them like cows, and to separate them from their own families in order to feed their owners' babies, can only be seen as the most heinous of acts.

The use of enslaved women as wet nurses had a detrimental impact on their own children, who were sometimes left without adequate nourishment. In some cases, enslaved mothers had to wean their children early or leave them in the care of other enslaved women who were not nursing this separation added emotional trauma to the physical exploitation, as mothers were deprived of the opportunity to bond with and care for their own babies.

Kirti continues by saying, "Even in the best of circumstances, wet nursing, like all slave labor, was difficult and dehumanizing. Wet nursing existed for many centuries dating as far back as the biblical days. However, in history, only slave mothers were forced into the act."

Post-Emancipation

After the abolition of slavery, the practice of wet nursing by black women continued in some parts of the United States, but the dynamics shifted somewhat. Black women who became wet nurses after emancipation did so under different economic arrangements, often working as paid domestic help.

However, the legacy of exploitation persisted, as black wet nurses often received low wages and faced discriminatory practices in the labor market.

"Liquid Gold"

"Liquid gold" is a term often used to describe colostrum, the first form of milk produced by the mammary glands immediately following the birth of a newborn. This milk is rich in antibodies, nutrients, and growth factors essential for the newborn's development and immune system.

In many cultures, colostrum has been revered for its health benefits. Historically, some societies have even used it for medicinal purposes beyond infant feeding. The term "liquid gold"

---

1   Kirti, Kamna. "The Tragic Plight of Enslaved Wet Nurses." *Medium*, Lessons from History, 8 Sept. 2021, https://medium.com/lessons-from-history/the-tragic-plight-of-enslaved-wet-nurses-b1c80b73f290.

underscores the preciousness and value placed on this early milk by healthcare professionals and mothers alike.

Modern Awareness

With increased awareness of the benefits of breastfeeding, healthcare providers often emphasize the importance of colostrum. Campaigns and educational programs encourage new mothers to breastfeed immediately after birth to ensure their babies receive this vital nutrition. It is important to understand the history of wet nursing so we can be sensitive to this topic and its implications today. We must recognize the tragedy that wet nursing created, in exploiting Black mothers to feed other children the precious nutrients that should have been their own. May history never return to this kind of treatment. Today, we should work to advocate for the benefits of breastfeeding for all Black and Brown mothers and children. Let's discuss this more in the following pages.

The Structural Roots in Racism in Lactation

In Erin V. Thomas's article "Why Even Bother; They Are Not Going to Do it?" The Structural Roots of Racism and Discrimination in Lactation Care,[2] she interviews 36 International Board Certified Lactation Consultants (IBCLCs) who assist mothers with breastfeeding.

In her study, she documents race-based discrimination against Black patients during lactation care and links implicit bias to disparities found in breastfeeding. Further, she uncov- ers patients of color receiving unequal care and overt racist remarks made directly to, or behind their backs.

Implicit Biases

Assumptions played a vital role in the discriminatory belief that women of color will not breastfeed, which resulted in them receiving less lactation attention and consultation, according to Thomas.

Thomas found additional factors that contributed to these acts of discrimination against Black mothers. These included the advertisement of White dominated imagery in breastfeeding resources, instances of Black mothers being more likely to receive prescriptions for long-acting birth control, and higher rates of referral to social workers.[3]

Breastfeeding in the NICU: Does Race Matter?

Research claims that African American women are 2.5 times less likely to breastfeed than Caucasian women, and are more likely than most minority groups to provide formula supplementation by 2 days of life. The causes of this variation are not well understood.

A study was conducted by Danisha S. McCall, MD, and Antoine Soliman, MD, at the Neonatology Division, Department of Pediatrics, University of California Irvine, Orange, CA; and the Miller Children's and Women's Hospital Long Beach, Division of Neonatology, Long Beach CA. Their goal was to gain insight into breast milk feeding rates during an infant's neonatal intensive care unit (NICU) hospitalization, and to identify if breastfeeding rates in VLBW infants treated and discharged home from 2012 to 2016 was congruent with racial disparities in the breast milk rates reported in the literature for term and preterm newborns in the United States, and if so, reasons for these disparities.

---

2   Thomas, Erin V. "Why Even Bother; They Are Not Going to Do It?" The Structural Roots of Racism and Discrimination in Lactation Care." *Qualitative health research* Vol. 28,7 (2018): 1050-1064. doi:10.1177/1049732318759491. https://pubmed.ncbi.nlm.nih.gov/29557297/.

3   Bartick, Melissa, et al. "Disparities in Breastfeeding: Impact on Maternal and Child Health Outcomes and Costs." *The Journal of Pediatrics,* Nov. 10, 2016; Vol. 181, P49-55.E6. DOI: 10.1016/j.jpeds.2016.10.028 https://www.jpeds.com/article/S0022-3476(16)31096-4/fulltext.

Using a retrospective review of rates of any breast milk feeding at the time of hospital discharge, standard maternal and infant demographics, and a sampling of in hospital morbidities, a 10 question prospective survey was sent out to all participant families of VLBW infants discharged from the MCWHLB NICU from January 2012 – June 2016.

Their conclusions showed that African American women with eligible VLBW infants discharged Their conclusions showed that African American women with eligible VLBW infants discharged home from MCWHLB NICU between January 2012 to June 2016 were:

- Younger and less exposed to antenatal steroids than other races/ethnicities
- 3 times less likely to provide breast milk at the time of discharge than White mothers
- 21% less likely to provide breast milk at the time of discharge than any other race/ethnicity.

Break into your small groups and discuss: have you seen these disparities at work? How might you advocate for a different outcome?

Barriers to Breastfeeding

Among the co-authors to the Journal of Pediatrics' study entitled <u>Disparities in Breastfeeding: Impact on Maternal and Child Health Outcomes and Costs</u>,[4] is Alison Stuebe, an MD, Distinguished Scholar, and associate professor of OBGYN at UNC. Through this study, she and her co-authors report on the disparities that reflect barriers to breastfeeding, such as lack of paid leave and outdated maternity care.

The UNC School of Public Health further cited this study in their article, <u>Lack of optimal breastfeeding may cause alarming disparities in infant deaths</u>,[5] in which they also interviewed Stuebe herself on these alarming findings. Stuebe suggests that these disparities are correctable if we as healthcare professionals stand in the seat of advocacy and equal consultation, stating, "we can reduce health disparities by protecting each birthing person's right to breastfeed her children."

If birthing people of color do not receive the proper education or consultation prior to discharge, due to implicit bias and erroneous assumptions, their babies remain vulnerable and at a grave disadvantage. Stuebe continues, "It is recom-mended that women exclusively breastfeed each of their children for the first six months of life, followed by continued breastfeeding for the duration of the first year while comple- mentary foods are introduced." The study's authors defined this practice as "optimal breastfeeding."

---

4   Bartick, Melissa, et al. "Disparities in Breastfeeding: Impact on Maternal and Child Health Outcomes and Costs." *The Journal of Pediatrics*, Nov. 10, 2016; Vol. 181, P49-55.E6. DOI:
10.1016/j.jpeds.2016.10.028 https://www.jpeds.com/article/S0022- 3476(16)31096-4/fulltext.

5   "Lack of Optimal Breastfeeding May Cause Alarming Disparities in Infant Deaths, Study Finds." *UNC Gillings School of Global Public Health*, University of North Carolina, 23 Nov. 2016, https://sph. unc.edu/sph-news/study-lack-of-optimal-breastfeeding-may-cause- alarming-disparities-in-infant-deaths/.

B.E.N.E.F.I.T.S. of Breastfeeding

Some patients may be hesitant to breastfeed. Below is a helpful acronym to remember when speaking to patients about the B.E.N.E.F.I.T.s of breastfeeding:

B - Baby. Remind your patient that the motive behind encouraging breastfeeding is simply about thinking of what is best for the baby.

E - Education. Help provide your patient with the resources necessary for them to understand the research behind the importance of breastfeeding.

N - Nourishing Value. The richest resources for your baby can be found within your own amazing body. Breast milk, and especially colostrum, can be an invaluable source of nourishment to your baby.

E - Empathy. Remember to use an empathic lens when discussing breastfeeding with patients. Not everybody has the same background or understanding when it comes to breastfeeding, and it is important not to judge any differing views, but to approach them with compassion and empathy.

F - Foundation. Breast milk provides an important foundation to a baby's immune system. It can help prevent diseases and allergies, while supplying many other healthcare benefits.

I - Inclusion. It is important to approach all mothers with the same information. It is not up to us to determine who is more likely to use the information, we simply do our best to provide it to all mothers.

T - Talk about it. Be a willing and engaging advocate for breastfeeding by continuing to talk about it with patients - especially Black mothers, due to the disparity rates. Make sure to provide them with all the information and resources.

S - Safety. Breastfeeding is a safe and natural way to provide optimum nutrition and immunity for your baby.

NURTURING EQUITY MINDED GROUP EXERCISE

Break into groups of two and begin a role play in which you explain to your patient the benefits of breastfeeding using the acronym B.E.N.E.F.I.T.S.

Create an equity-minded plan of approach, should the patient be hesitant.

What did you learn?

ADDITIONAL RESOURCES:

Recommended Books by Black Authors

For Black mothers, advocates, and healthcare providers, these books provide valuable guidance, support, and insights into overcoming breastfeeding barriers:

1. Breastfeeding: A Parent's Guide by Amy Brown and Kathleen Kendall-Tackett
   This guide covers evidence-based practices for breastfeeding and addresses challenges specific to Black communities.
2. The Black Woman's Guide to Breastfeeding: The Definitive Guide to Nursing for African American Mothers by Katherine Barber
   A culturally specific guide designed to empower and educate Black mothers about breastfeeding.
3. Mother of Milk: Breastfeeding Resources and Support for Black Mothers by Andrea Freeman
   This book dives into the systemic barriers Black women face and provides strategies for overcoming them.
4. Reclaiming Our Traditions: The African-American Breastfeeding Experience by Kimberly Seals Allers
   A powerful exploration of breastfeeding through the lens of Black history and culture.
5. The Big Letdown: How Medicine, Big Business, and Feminism Undermine Breastfeeding by Kimberly Seals Allers
   A deep dive into how systemic issues affect breastfeeding rates, with a focus on marginalized communities.
6. Lactation Support in the African American Community by Katherine Barber
   A resource for lactation consultants and healthcare providers to better support Black mothers.
7. It's Only Natural: Black Women and Breastfeeding by Wambui Bahati
   A practical and empowering book that breaks down myths and builds confidence for breastfeeding Black mothers.

Addressing These Barriers

In addition to culturally sensitive education and workplace accommodations, promoting the works of Black authors helps normalize breastfeeding, dispel myths, and build a robust community of informed and empowered Black mothers. By integrating these resources into support networks, Black women can feel better equipped to navigate their breastfeeding journeys.

CHAPTER TWELVE
Weathering & Epigenetics: Social Determinants

COMMENTARY OF EPIGENETICS, CULTURAL TRAUMA, COLLECTIVE MEMORY AND WEATHERING

By Robert L. Stevenson. Jr., PhD.
Assistant Instructional Professor,
African American Studies, UNIVERSITY of FLORIDA.

"Why don't they let the past be the past?" "Why do they keep harping on slavery?" "Can't they just move on and move forward? Nobody owes them anything, won't they just get over it?" These are the voices of many white Americans who cannot stomach the pain of our past.[1]

Dr. Candace Cole-Kelly has produced an insightfully well researched discussion on epigenetics and its effect on Black people. Health scholars have identified the disproportionate rate of

---

1 Cole-Kelly, Candace. *Nurturing Equity Minded Healthcare Providers*. Cole Publishing. 2023.

morbidity in Black and minority populations. One of the indicators of these unhealthy conditions can be explained via epigenetics.

Let me begin with a definition of epigenetics followed by an analysis of how it works, how it is transmitted, and how it affects the psyche of those who are affected by the phenomena.

Epigenetics is the study of how one's behavior and environment can cause changes that affect the way a person's genes work. Unlike genetic changes, epigenetic changes are reversible and do not change your DNA sequence, but they can change how your body reads a DNA sequence.

Dr. Joy Degruy poses this same argument in her book titled *Post Traumatic Slave Syndrome.* Both Cole-Kelly and DeGruy wrestle with the same issue but from different starting points. What those who decry this discussion and one's like it fail to realize is the role of generativity on the psyche of oppressed people. Author and researcher Raycene Nevils-Karakeci, refers to this phenomenon as "weathering."[2] Just as we pass on physical genetic traits there are also generational psychotic traits that can be passed on from one generation to the next.

What most people fail to realize is that one of the problems faced by Black Americans is the history of disrespect and experimentation upon us without consent that, to this day, plagues the medical field and the Black community.

In other words, epigenetics would be like using a pink highlighter to give precedence to the DNA that is most affected, or needs to be given preferential attention. Though the gene is modified (by being highlighted) in the above mentioned sequence, the genetic code stays the same and the epigenetic influence can be reversed.

I argue in my analysis that one of the reasons that many white Americans don't experience the same DNA corruption is because the sense of oppression (that can be attributed to epigenetics) is far from their psychological standing in American society. This means that even if a person of Caucasian descent is impoverished financially or intellectually, the benefits inherent in white privilege prevent them from feeling totally excluded from the ruling class. Therefore, the epigenetic influence is not experienced.

One further concern in the epigenetic discourse, is the traditional and historical role of racially influenced misdiagnosis of people of African descent by medical professionals.

"For example, mistrust of doctors amongst Black Americans can be traced to the Tuskegee Syphilis Experiment, in which the U.S. government ran a decades-long study on the effects of untreated syphilis in the black male without the knowledge (much less consent) of the participants."[3]

The Tuskegee Syphilis Trial was one in the line of long lasting miscalculations about the humanity of Black people. Many Black people know of the horrid misappropriation of trust by Black people with the health profession. But even before Tuskegee, even more egregious uses of power and influence were used to degrade and abuse black bodies. The following examples further explain how and why epigenetic discussions are warranted in this day and age of healthcare's racial biases and abuse.

Dr. James Marion Sims is often referred to as the "Father of Gynecology," however the controversy surrounding his medical practices are rooted in the revealing accounts of him using African women forced into slavery for his experiments. It is alleged that Dr Sims performed surgeries on his subjects without anesthesia. He argued that the operations were not painful enough to warrant any form of anesthesia, because Negro women don't feel the pain. Racially motivated under-education, in medicine and historiography have been and continue to be perpetrated to support notions of white supremacy.

"There is an undeniable optimism to the work of epigenetics and collective memory as it relates to providing equitable outcomes in healthcare. As our eyes are opened to some of these underlying causes of injustice in our society, we begin to understand that it is not our people who are evil, but our systems. And just as we learn to deconstruct the way these evil systems were inherited, we are given the opportunity to right these wrongs."[11]

Therefore, as Dr. Cole-Kelly explains, collective memory plays a major role in the unwillingness of people of African descent to place their trust in the healthcare profession. But there is hope, if the field is willing to take this present research seriously, and make the necessary changes in training to accommodate the needs of Black people.

---

2   Nevils-Karakeci, Raycene. "Collective Memory: Are We the Sum of Our Ancestors' Experiences?" Interesting Engineering, 18 May 2020, interestingengineering.com/health/collective-memory-are-we-the-sum-of-our-ancestors-experiences.

3   Newkirk, Vann R., II. "The Tuskegee Study and Black Culture." *The Atlantic*, 20 June 2016, www.theatlantic.com/politics/archive/2016/06/tuskegee-study-research-Black-experiences/487646.

Illustrations of Weathering

Weathering in the Earth: Weathering is the process of being broken down or worn out through exposure to the atmosphere. It includes dissolving of rocks and minerals on the Earth's surface through erosion.

Weathering in Healthcare: The hypothesis that "the health of African-American women may begin to deteriorate in early adulthood as a physical consequence of cumulative socioeconomic disadvantage."[4]

Dr. Arline Geronimus Profound Research Findings

In 1992, Dr. Arline Geronimus, a professor at the University of Michigan, developed the term "weathering" to refer to the idea that Black people, specifically young Black women, may

develop physical health problems as a direct consequence to disadvantages in their social determinants.[5]

Weathering is a concept relevant to our study when discussing the relationship between health disparities and social determinants for Black persons birthing babies and infant loss.

When Dr. Arline Geronimus, now a Doctor of Science in Behavioral Sciences, was in her first year at Princeton University in the mid-1970s, she was hired by an urban high school for pregnant girls to help try and curb teenage pregnancies.

At that time, she was considered part of the "solution." The "problem" was the girls themselves, those expecting and those treated at the school's Planned Parenthood clinic. Or so it seemed.

Dr. Geronimus soon found two surprising incongruities[6]:

1. These girls — young, mostly Black and Latina — were not unhappy to be pregnant. Some, she recalls, had even tried to get pregnant deliberately.
2. And although they were in roughly the same age group, these young women seemed far older and sicker than what Geronimus calls her "healthy and advantaged" Princeton peers. Her pregnant students were battling ailments, such as high blood pressure and diabetes, that usually affect older people.

Psychological Implications – Jane Elliott Experiment: Day 1

In April of 1968, school teacher Jane Elliott had just received news of Dr. King's assassination. Wishing to do something in response, she began an experiment in her classroom, to try and teach her students about the effects of discrimination. Mrs. Elliott conducted many similar experiments over the years as an elementary school teacher, and one such year this experiment was filmed as part of the documentary by PBS, A Class Divided.[7] The film depicts how, in her classroom of 3rd graders, Jane Elliott used this experiment to illustrate the effects of racism and learned discriminations to her class. The following is based on that film.

On Tuesday morning Mrs. Elliott told her class that blue-eyed people were "better," "smarter," and would get certain privileges. They would get to drink from the drinking fountain, go to

---

4 Sandoiu, Ana. "'Weathering': The Health Effects of Stress and Discrimination." *Medical News Today*, MediLexicon International, 26 Feb. 2021, https://www.medicalnewstoday.com/articles/weathering-what-are-the-health-effects-of-stress-and-discrimination.

5 Sandoiu, Ana. "'Weathering': The Health Effects of Stress and Discrimination." *Medical News Today*, MediLexicon International, 26 Feb. 2021, https://www.medicalnewstoday.com/articles/weathering-what-are-the-health-effects-of-stress-and-discrimination.

6 Geronimus, A T. "The weathering hypothesis and the health of African-American women and infants: evidence and speculations." *Ethnicity & disease* vol. 2,3 (1992): 207-21. https://pubmed.ncbi.nlm.nih.gov/1467758/.

7 FRONTLINE PBS, Official. "A Class Divided (Full Documentary) | FRONTLINE." *YouTube*, 18 Jan. 2019, www.youtube.com/watch?v=1mcCLm_LwpE.

recess first, and receive constant praise. Brown-eyed children were denied these privileges. What's more, they were made to wear collars denoting them as "inferior," were not allowed to play with the blue-eyed children, and were constantly belittled. Mrs. Elliott would even go so far as to point out any negative behaviors, such as "moving slowly," in the brown-eyed children, and attribute it to their "inferior" eye color.

By that afternoon, the blue-eyed children were calling the others "brown-eyes" in a derogatory fashion, and children that had been loving friends at the start of the day were getting into altercations over name-calling, and stereotypes based on their differing eye colors. The children with brown-eyes felt dejected, unintelligent, and less than, noting that they felt like they "didn't even want to try to do anything" and that "everything bad happened to [them]" because of the way they were being treated that day.

Jane Elliott Experiment – Day 2

The next morning, Mrs. Elliott reversed the experiment. She said she had lied to the class and in fact, brown-eyed people were "better" and "smarter." She had the brown-eyed children put their collars onto a blue-eyed peer, and brown-eyed people were to earn special privileges now such as extra recess, etc. The brown-eyed children could not get rid of their collars fast enough, and the blue-eyed children seemed less than happy to be receiving theirs.

Throughout the day, Mrs. Elliott again pointed out certain negative behaviors, such as "forgetfulness" or "naughtiness," in the blue-eyed children, and attributed them to their eye color. By Wednesday afternoon, results were completely reversed, including academically. The brown-eyed children had taken 5 minutes to complete a group task on Tuesday, but only 2 minutes on Wednesday, with nothing changing in the task other than that they were now being treated as "superior people." When asked why they were so much slower the day before, they replied "we had those collars on…we just kept thinking about those collars." Similarly, the blue-eyed children had completed the task in only 3 minutes the day before, but with their collars on, and the belief that they were therefore inferior in some way, it took them 5 minutes on Wednesday.[8]

By the end of the second day, the children were eager to remove all collars, and end their experiment on discrimination. They felt it had been "horrid" and "unfair" and ultimately created untrue stereotypes around eye color that greatly affected them. They learned an important lesson that day on not judging a fellow human based solely on how they looked - whether that be their eye color, or the color of their skin.

Jane Elliott Experiment – Results

By the end of the experiment, the children had learned a life-long lesson on discrimination, and the effects of racism, that would continue to stay with them well into adulthood - and this was after only 2 days. Now imagine the multitude of effects this kind of treatment would have after a year, ten years, a lifetime, or across multiple generations. What kinds of harmful, and untrue, messages would those who have been treated as "inferior" be receiving and believing about themselves - and how would it keep them from succeeding? What kind of privileges and benefits would those who have always been treated as "superior" receive - and how might they grow to believe they are entitled to them, even when unearned? Reflecting on how just wearing collars, and the implications that came with it, caused a decrease in the students' abilities to focus or perform academically, think about how discriminatory implications around skin color might seep into ALL the aspects of a person's life, including those less straightforward.

Jane Elliott herself explains it best. After news of her classroom experiments spread, she had many people write in about how "appalled" they were at her work. "'How dare you try this cruel experiment out on White children,' one said. 'Black children grow up accustomed to such behavior, but White children, there's no way they could possibly understand it. It's cruel to White children and will cause them great psychological damage.' Elliott replied, 'Why are we so worried about the fragile egos of White children who experience a couple of hours of made-up racism one day when Blacks experience real racism every day of their lives?'"[9]

Janet Elliott Experiment – Aftermath

The publicity Elliott received due to this exercise did not make her popular in her home town of Riceville, Iowa. Of all her co-workers, only one continued to speak to her. The co-workers claimed they did not support Elliott's cruel treatment of the children during the exercise. However, when interviewed as adults, none of the children expressed resentment at being treated poorly for one day, and instead mentioned feelings of immense gratitude for having been taught such an invaluable lesson at a young age. In fact, when Malinda Wisenhunt, a former student from the experiment ran into Mrs. Elliott many years later, she told her "'I've never forgotten the exercise… It changed my life. Not a day goes by without me thinking about it, Ms. Elliott. When my grandchildren are old enough, I'd give anything if you'd try the exercise out on them.'"[6]

As news of her exercise spread, Mrs. Elliott appeared on television shows and started to repeat the exercise on professional training days for adults. In December of 1970, she was invited to demonstrate the experience to adult educators at a White House conference on children and youth.[6]

Today, having retired from teaching years ago, she now travels frequently throughout North America and abroad, giving lectures.

---

8 "Jane Elliott 'Blue Eyes - Brown Eyes' Experiment Anti-Racism." *YouTube*, uploaded by chel.by.the.seas, 18 June 2020, www.youtube.com/watch?v=dLAi78hluFc.

9 Bloom, Stephen G. "Lesson of a Lifetime." *Smithsonian Magazine*, 1 Sept. 2005, www.smithsonianmag.com/science-nature/lesson-of-a-lifetime-72574306.

NURTURING EQUITY MINDED GROUP EXERCISE

1. Reflect on the Social Determinants and Social Drivers of Black Women:

    a. Social Determinants of Health (SDOH) are the complex, integrated, and overlapping social structures, policies, and economic systems that affect health and quality of life outcomes.

    b. SDOH are the conditions in which persons live, work, play, and access care.

    c. SDOH can also be a major cause of health inequities, particularly when populations do not have access to the same resources.

    d. Examples of SDOH include, but are not limited to: racism, sexism, education disparity, income inequality, housing insecurity, transportation access, health systems and service access, social isolation, food insecurity, unemployment, and public safety concerns.

2. Discuss and create a tool for promoting health equity for marginalized populations.

3. What, if any, sensitivities did the Jane Elliott experiment (and the responses to it) bring up for you? How do the results of the experiment further support the idea of weathering?

EPIGENETICS: INHERITED MEMORIES

The Impact of Collective Memories

"Why don't they let the past be the past?" " Why do they keep harping on slavery?" "Can't they just move on and move forward? Nobody owes them anything, won't they just get over it?" These are the voices of many White Americans who cannot stomach the pain of our past. It is comments like these, and others, that reveal people's ignorance of the power of epigenetics, and how traumatic experiences like slavery, oppression and marginalization to a particular group can be passed down from one generation to another.

Similar to the concept of weathering), "Collective memory is a term that refers to shared experiences and knowledge passed on within a social group or society, " explains author and researcher, Raycene Nevils-Karakeci, in her article Collective Memory: Are We The Sum of Our Ancestors' Experiences?.[10] These experiences are devastating and deeply wounding. The memory that is passed on could be positive or negative. Usually when we are dealing with "collective memory," it is also associated with cultural trauma.

Karakeci states that, "This [collective memory] is a popular term in history, sociology, and psychology that has recently gained relevance in the field of genetics. According to social sciences, the concept of collective memory is centered on the sharing, constructing, and passing of experiences around groups and through generations."

How Collective Memory is Shaped

In the article, Karakeci also addresses the origin of healthcare distrust widely known amongst Black people and people of color toward doctors. She exposits, "mistrust of doctors amongst Black Americans can be traced to the Tuskegee Syphilis Experiment, in which the U.S. government ran a decades-long study on the effects of untreated syphilis in the Black male without the knowledge (much less consent) of the participants."[7]

This horrid experience tainted the credibility, character and reputation of the healthcare system. It's no wonder that this Tuskegee experience is firmly planted in the collective memory of Black people between them and doctors who treated them as guinea pigs.[11]

Similarly, Black women have historically been experimented on, without their consent, and sometimes without even their knowledge. Whether it was through the experimentation on Black slaves without their consent ; the collection of Henrietta Lacks' cells that were obtained without her consent, knowledge, or fair compensation, but that are still being used in cancer research today[12] or the way some hospitals segregate patients of color to be "practiced on" by physicians , Black

---

10 Nevils-Karakeci, Raycene. "Collective Memory: Are We the Sum of Our Ancestors' Experiences?" *Interesting Engineering*, 18 May 2020, interestingengineering.com/health/collective-memory-are-we-the-sum-of-our-ancestors-experiences.

11 Newkirk, Vann R., II. "The Tuskegee Study and Black Culture." *The Atlantic*, 20 June 2016, www.theatlantic.com/politics/archive/2016/06/tuskegee-study-research-Black-experiences/487646..

12 "Henrietta Lacks: Science Must Right a Historical Wrong." *Nature - The International Journal of Science*, Springer Nature Limited, Vol. 585, No. 7823, Nature Portfolio, Sept. 2020, p. 7. https://doi.org/10.1038/d41586-020-02494-z.

people have continuously been used as subjects for experimentation in the name of medical science.

It is nothing but understandable, then, that generations of Black people have absorbed a rational mistrust of the healthcare system in America through this collective memory.

How Does the Epigenetics Science Address Slaveowner Descendants?

When we hear people say, "I never owned slaves," or "I'm not racist," or "I don't act like my fore parents," we must understand that they are not just denying any part in these negative attitudes, but are also failing to realize how they have inherited an entire system of privilege that their fore parents have established on the backs of slaves, indigenous or marginalized people.

Consider the fact that there are many people who may not necessarily agree with, or have originated some of the thoughts below, but instead are victims of epigenetics. What type of people:

- Believe it is okay to take another human being's freedom, enslave them, and purchase them like property?
- Can stomach a man or woman being lashed on their backs 100 times, or more, and feel no remorse?
- Rape slaves to breed more slaves?
- Mandate slaves to neglect their own babies in order to breastfeed their slave masters' White babies?
- Pride themselves on desegregating a race by "legally" stealing their land and reinvesting capital to enhance its use for themselves?
- Deny Blacks bank loans and deny them living next door to Whites because of their color?
- Hang men and women and children from trees?
- Teach their children's children that their race is superior while others are inferior?
- Serve as peace officers but will shoot a Black man after pulling him over for a broken headlight?
- (In healthcare) Provide necessary consultations and referrals to maximize the life of a White man but send the Black man home to die?
- Believe that medical experimentation on a marginalized group of people for their own gains is acceptable?
- Are non-sympathetic about severe maternal mortality/infant loss in Black mothers?

What kind of inherited feelings might be latent in the genetics of those descended from these individuals? And what psychological mindsets are being passed down through each generation?

The Heart of Collective Memory

My answer to this points back to collective memory. I argue that the same epigenetic science which has proven how traumas (such as slavery, famine, and war) committed on groups of people are inherited through collective memory also applies to the oppressor who oppresses. What has been passed down from the oppressors to their children's children? I strongly suggest that science works in the same way that it does for the victims of traumatic histories. Their acts are also inherited through the same system of collective memory passed to their descendents.

This means you have little choice in the matter of what you have inherited, but you do have a choice to discontinue the mindsets, attitudes and actions that demean and discount another race's values and contributions.

Having understood the power of epigenetics in both groups, we can move toward healing the heart of collective memory.

CASE STUDY

Instructions: Divide the group into teams of 2 and have each team consider the following scenario. One team member acts as Doris, and the other as the health care provider, and once the lesson is complete the team members should reverse roles to see if additional feelings and emotions are revealed.

Doris is a 36 year old Black woman. She has had 1 previous still birth 2 years ago. Her 15 year old son was shot and killed by police 5 years prior. Her husband is at work. She comes to her prenatal appointment 30 minutes late, again. Doris is 6 months pregnant.

What is your initial response as the health care provider? Consider both your thoughts and your actions. Are you quietly annoyed? Are you visibly annoyed? Do you remind Doris that she is constantly late? Do you make sure she feels guilty for being late? Do you ask her why she's late, or even tell her this time you need to reschedule her appointment? List other thoughts, feelings, and reactions.

Doris begins to apologize, breaks down in tears and tells you she needed to rely on a relative to babysit her other children (who are home sick with colds) and the relative was late in arriving at her home. Also, she had trouble starting her car, and was therefore forced to take a bus to town to get to this appointment.

Does this change your attitude towards Doris? How do your thoughts and responses change? Are you compassionate? What do you say to Doris to make her feel more comfortable? Is compassion reflected on your face? Do you apologize for her struggles this morning?

What self-preparation might you consider utilizing as you realize the struggles patients endure? Your medical clinic is in a heavily urban population. Should you expect situations to occur that you can be prepared in advance for? Might it be helpful to refer patients to a health care provider with more experience in dealing with situations involving weathering? What is your suggestion?

Identify areas of weathering and epigenetics in Doris' story.

CHAPTER THIRTEEN
Leading Causes of Death in Black Maternal Mortality and Infant Mortality

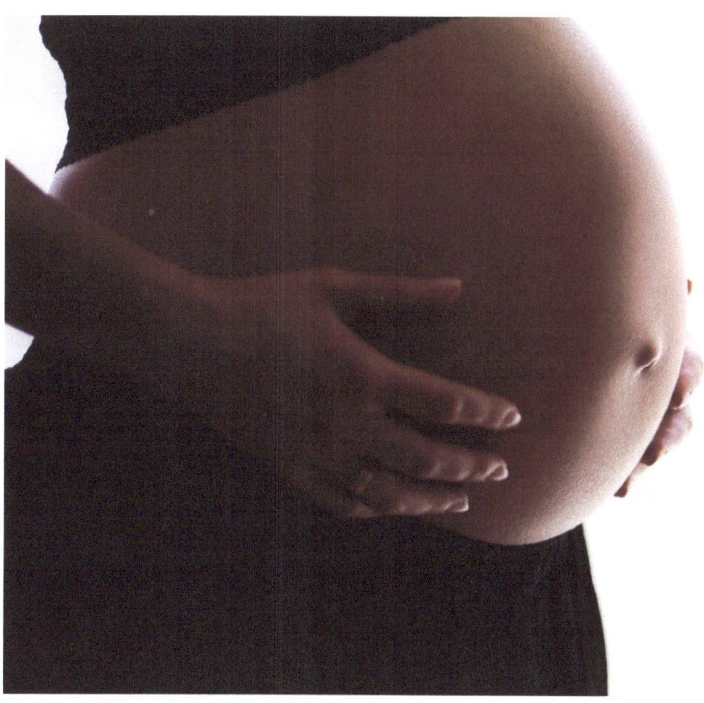

BEWARE OF COMMON BIASES WHEN PROVIDING PATIENT CARE

**By Dr. Lauren Yu, MD, OB-GYN
Medical Director**

The purpose of the sharing below is to highlight biases that can occur when providing patient care. The goal in presenting the case is to encourage reflective thought as individuals address patients and team members with the aim of improving patient care. Each of us has biases that we carry into our daily interactions regardless of whether they are recognized and named or not. It is the hope that as we continue in the journey of decreasing biases within healthcare that we would move to a better place and way of practice. The sharing below contains information related to true events however all factual identifiers have been changed for the purpose of protecting privacy.

The time is 0900 and the start of the day is well underway. The Obstetric team has already completed the first scheduled cesarean section of the day with three additional cases to follow. There is a palpable relief that all went well given that risk factors of obesity and prior surgical history always present challenges. The prior surgeries can pose the threat of scar tissue within the abdomen and difficulty visualizing tissue planes. The relief is short lived for experienced staff, as those privy to high volume and high acuity know the next phase- post-operative recovery- is a critical space. This can be a space where guards are let down. Rest and relief can be traded for vigilance.

The time is 1105 and the nurse caring for the above patient calls the Obstetric on call team. The nurse reports concern and requests for the patient to be evaluated. An overview of the course and vitals is provided: the patient is 2 hours post repeat c-section and tubal ligation. Quantified blood loss during the case was 1.5 liters. Blood pressure is 80/50, heart rate 130, temperature 97.5 degrees and patient without fever. There has been minimal vaginal bleeding since completion of the case however the patient has needed blood pressure support with medications. The pressor medications to maintain blood pressure are running at a high rate to maintain her blood pressure. There is a brief pause and moment of silence that is full of unspoken words and grave concern. Immediate evaluation is necessary and the Obstetric team briskly walks towards the post-operative recovery unit.

The time is 1110 and the multi-disciplinary team consisting of nursing staff, Obstetric and Anesthesiology physicians are at bedside. On physical exam the patient is sitting up, alert and oriented reporting mild abdominal discomfort. Her abdomen is moderately distended and mildly tender without signs of an acute abdomen. Review of the hospital course is completed and there is a suggestion made that alters the next steps in a monumental way. The suggestion referred to the reported blood loss being lower than what was actually reported. When the amniotic fluid is collected during a cesarean section there is often an estimation of fluid loss. This estimation can affect the total reported fluid and blood lost leading to an underestimation of blood loss. Labs are ordered to aid in the evaluation. Her hemoglobin results as 6 which is a life threatening value. Two units of blood are ordered to be transfused and ultrasound of her abdomen is completed. A large amount of fluid in seen in her abdomen outside of the uterus. It is clear that there is ongoing bleeding into her abdomen, a concealed hemorrhage which is a surgical emergency.

The patient's glow and previously rich brown hue began to fade. She was no longer alert and orientated however waxing and waning during conversation. The weight of it all was felt as the team put all the facts together. The abnormal vitals, the low hemoglobin and now change in mentation were due to massive hemorrhage not seen on physical exam. There was immediate need for action. The patient was consented for a second surgical procedure and massive transfusion protocol was activated. She was moved to the operating room. Upon entering the abdomen the evidence spilled over into the surgical field. Two liters of blood had collected in her abdomen from a bleeding site on the uterus. The site was repaired and her abdomen was closed. The patient was moved back to the post-operative recovery unit, this time with a vigilance from the team who was fully aware that the outcome could have been tragic but was instead a save.

Concealed hemorrhage can be lethal. There have been many cases that have been under diagnosed and missed. There is no associated red flag of vaginal bleeding. The patient can present with nondescript symptoms of abdominal pain or discomfort. This particular type of hemorrhage can be difficult to diagnose and requires a broadened differential from the team caring for the patient. Listening ears are required. Mindfulness of one's own biases is necessary. A global awareness of vitals and the patient's hospital course is key. It is my hope that this sharing sheds light on a rare but serious issue as we care for patients through a multi-disciplinary lens.

Leading Causes: Obstetric Hemorrhage

When we read that most of our Severe Maternal Mortalities (SMM) are preventable, it makes our hearts hurt. Where are we missing it? Why are we continuing to see these unnecessary deaths occur? Deaths that affect not just all their loved ones, but deaths that leave vulnerable children to be raised by a single parent, or even orphaned.

According to California Maternal Quality Care Collective (CMQCC),[1] "Obstetric hemorrhage is one of the leading causes of severe maternal morbidity and mortality in California. The California Pregnancy-Associated Mortality Review has repeatedly identified hemorrhage as one of the causes of potentially preventable maternal mortality and morbidity, a life-threatening complication during pregnancy. CMQCC has been working with hospitals to standardize care and improve their readiness, recognition, response and reporting of obstetric hemorrhage… CMQCC has launched statewide outreach collaboratives focused on implementation of patient safety bundles for hemorrhage." It is impressive to note that hospitals that collaborated and partnered with their key stakeholders benefited by participating in CMQCC's programs resulting in improved outcomes for their patients.[2]

Postpartum hemorrhages are clearly a primary cause in maternal deaths after delivery. But many Black mothers are victims of other leading causes of maternal mortality as well, such as: cardiovascular hypertensive disorder, diabetes, and the after effects of Cesarean-sections.

Leading Causes: Hypertensive Disorder

According to the National Library of Medicine's article Hypertensive Disorders of Pregnancy,[3] "Hypertension is the most common medical problem encountered during pregnancy, complicating 2-3% of pregnancies. Hypertensive disorders during pregnancy are classified into 4 categories [of] High Blood Pressure in Pregnancy: 1) chronic hypertension, 2) preeclampsia-eclampsia, 3) preeclampsia superimposed on chronic hypertension, and 4) gestational hypertension."

As it relates to maternal mortality, CMQCC provides the following education: "Hypertensive disorders of pregnancy (HDP) are one of the leading causes of pregnancy-related mortality and leading contributors to premature birth. Following the California Pregnancy-Associated Mortality Review, preeclampsia-related deaths were determined to have a significant chance of prevention."[4]

So while having hypertension is not uncommon during pregnancies, the number of deaths that result from it should not be nearly as high as they currently are, having a high opportunity for prevention. And so, to help healthcare providers implement best practices for early recognition and treatment of hypertensive disorders of pregnancy, CMQCC recently published the "Improving Health Care Response to Hypertensive Disorders of Pregnancy toolkit."[5]

---

1   "Obstetric Hemorrhage." *California Maternal Quality Care Collaborative,* Center for Academic Medicine, Neonatology, 2023, https://www.cmqcc.org/content/obstetric-hemorrhage.

2   Main, Elliott K et al. "Reduction of severe maternal morbidity from hemorrhage using a state perinatal quality collaborative." *American journal of obstetrics and gynecology,* National Library of Medicine, Vol. 216,3 (2017): 298. e1-298.e11. doi:10.1016/j.ajog.2017.01.017, https://pubmed.ncbi.nlm.nih.gov/28153661/.

3   Mammaro, Alessia et al. "Hypertensive disorders of pregnancy." *Journal of prenatal medicine,* National Library of Medicine, Vol. 3,1 (2009): 1-5. https://www.ncbi.nlm.nih.gov/pmc/articles/PMC3279097/.

4   "Hypertensive Disorders of Pregnancy." *Hypertensive Disorders of Pregnancy | California Maternal Quality Care Collaborative,* Center for Academic Medicine, Neonatology, 2023, https://www.cmqcc.org/content/hypertensive-disorders-pregnancy.

5   "Hypertensive Disorders of Pregnancy Toolkit." *Hypertensive Disorders of Pregnancy Toolkit | California Maternal Quality Care Collaborative,* Center for Academic Medicine, Neotology, 2023, https://www.cmqcc.org/resources-tool-kits/toolkits/HDP.

Leading Causes: Maternal Heart Failure

Authors Rachel A. Bright, Favio V. Lima, Cecilia Avila, Javed Butler and Kathleen Stergiopoulos write in the Journal of the American Heart Association[6] that, "Heart failure (HF) remains the most common major cardiovascular complication arising in pregnancy and the postpartum period."

In fact, there is an increased risk of death with mothers who develop HF along with other adverse cardiac and obstetric outcomes. In order to help prevent these deaths from HF, the American Heart Association advises that "Detection, access to care, insurance barriers to extended postpartum follow-up, and timely patient counseling are all areas where care for these women can be improved."

While these strategies can be used to prevent HF in all patients, it must be noted that certain populations are more prone to developing maternal HF in the first place. According to the American Heart Association, "demographic risk factors for the development of maternal HF include Black race, older age, tobacco use, alcohol use, drug use, and insurance under either Medicare or Medicaid." Due to these demographic predispositions, Black women are twice as common to encounter heart failure than their White counterparts. Special attention must, therefore, be paid to Black patients who are most at risk of developing maternal HF, and subsequently dying, as a result.

C-Sections: A Complex National Problem of Black Maternal Deaths

While C-sections can sometimes be life-saving procedures, any obtrusive surgery can result in increased complications, and mortality, and should therefore, be used only as a last resort. But more often than not, this is not the case, as ulterior motives can sometimes come into play.

Senior Paralegal and Advocate, Janet Sasser, cites a provocative learning from the documentary film Aftershock,[7] during which Dr. Neel Shah, MD, Harvard School of Medicine, is interviewed. Dr. Shah stated that, "2018 was the first year the Federal government started tracking the history of maternal death rates as they relate to Cesarean rates. The number of C-sections performed have increased over 500% between the years 1970 to 2019." Black moms are disproportionately the recipients of these C-sections.[8]

In her commentary for the birth equity consulting group Still Resilient,[9] Sasser asserts that, "One contributing factor for the growth in C-sections is that vaginal births take anywhere from 8 to 12 hours, whereas C-sections take approximately 45 minutes, i.e. delivery takes far less time. Even though C-sections take far less time, hospitals receive 50% more insurance payments when they do C-sections. Translation: less time, more money."

CDC - Complex National Problem

Sasser goes on to say, "Dr. Shah also stated during the interview that C-sections are considered major surgery and therefore can be dangerous due to their contribution to organ injury, infections, and hemorrhaging. With these threats occurring in major surgeries, C-sections contribute to maternal death rates three times higher than vaginal births."

---

6   Bright, Rachel A., et al. "Maternal Heart Failure ." *Journal of the American Heart Association*, American Heart Association, Vol 10, 14 (14 July 2021), https://www.ahajournals.org/doi/10.1161/JAHA.121.021019.

7   Eiselt, Paula and Tonya Lewis, directors. *Aftershock*, Hulu, 19 July 2022, https://www.hulu.com/movie/aftershock-c1414fdf-0741-4bd2-b62c-554db3d8f643.

8   Holmes, Laurens Jr et al. "Implication of Vaginal and Cesarean Section Delivery Method in Black-White Differentials in Infant Mortality in the United States: Linked Birth/Infant Death Records, 2007-2016." *International Journal of Environmental Research and Public Health*, National Library of Medicine, Vol. 17,9 3146 (30 Apr. 2020), doi:10.3390/ijerph17093146, https://www.ncbi.nlm.nih.gov/pmc/articles/PMC7246527/.

9   "Commentaries" *Still Resilient*, Still Resilient Consulting, 2023, https://www.stillresilient.com/commentaries

In the article Why Do Black Women in the US Have more C-Sections than White Women?,[10] Published by *Open Democracy,* author Joni Hess, observes that, "Despite these risks – and despite what the Centers for Disease Control and Prevention (CDC), the US health protection agency, calls a 'complex national problem' of Black maternal deaths – the evidence is clear. Black mothers consistently undergo caesareans more than White mothers, even in low-risk situations. And as a result, Black mothers are more likely to suffer for longer after birth, to struggle to fully recover, or to die."

NURTURING EQUITY MINDED GROUP EXERCISE #1

What went well in this case?

In which ways could patient care and patient interaction been improved here?

What are the biases presented here?

How could have biases affected this patient's care?

How do you plan to integrate learning from this case into your daily practice of patient care?

---

[10] Hess, Joni. "Why Do Black Women in the US Have More C-Sections than White Women?" *OpenDemocracy*, 13 July 2021, https://www.opendemocracy.net/en/why-do-Black-women-us-have-more-c-sections-White-women/.

NURTURING EQUITY MINDED GROUP EXERCISE #2

1. How might hospitals begin to mitigate the leading cause of preventable deaths in maternity: hemorrhaging?

2. Hypertensive disorders during pregnancy are classified into 4 categories [of] High Blood Pressure in Pregnancy. Using the section below, list the 4 classifications:

   A. _____
   B. _____
   C. _____
   D. _____

3. According to the American Heart Association, what are some ways to help improve, or prevent, maternal heart failure?

   _____
   _____
   _____
   _____

NURTURING EQUITY MINDED GROUP EXERCISE #3

As we have read, C-Sections are an intrusive surgery that can lead to many complications, including death. As such, they should not be considered a common course of action, but rather, only used as a last resort, after serious consideration.

Keeping this in mind, discuss amongst yourselves in groups of 2 or 4, what would be the last resort causes that might make you call for an emergency C-Section? List 2 reasons:

   A)

   B)

Conversely, what are some reasons a C-Section might be suggested, that you feel could be prevented? List 2:

   A)

   B)

Section III

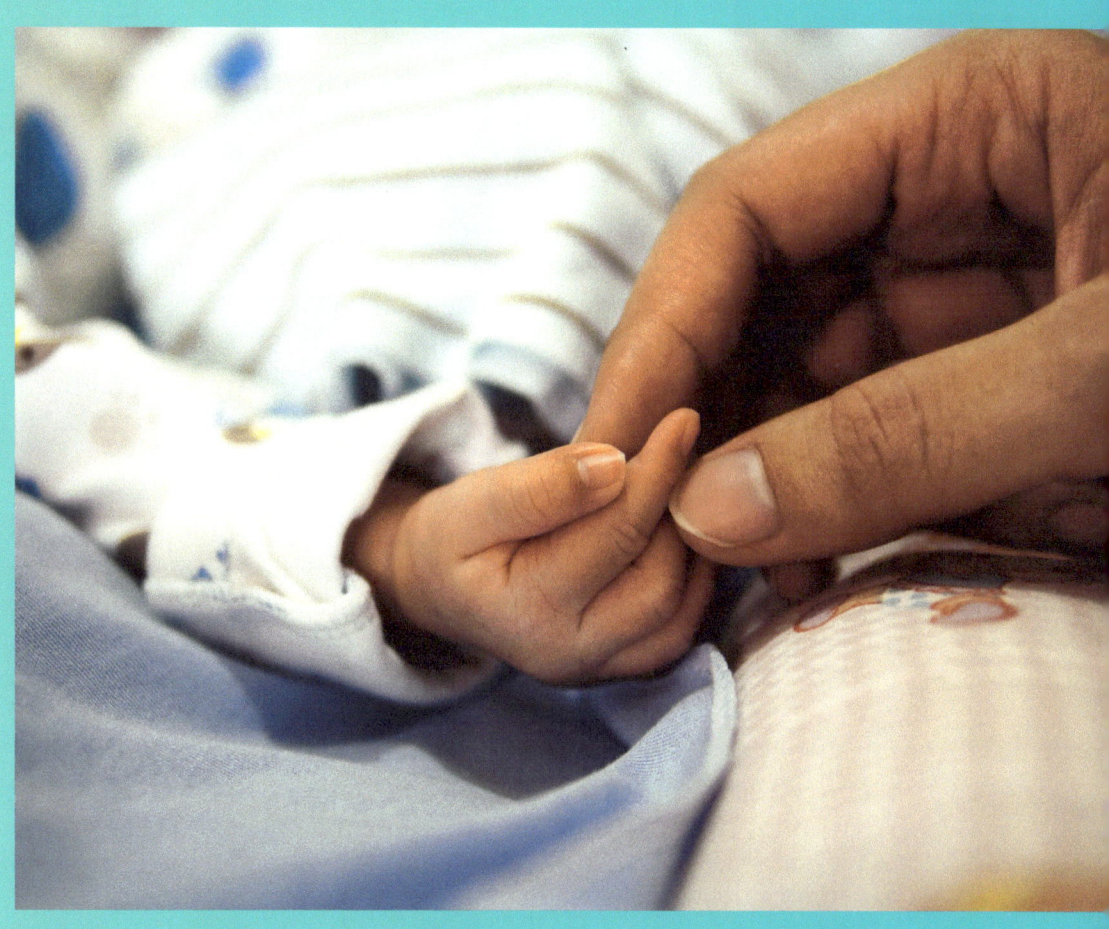

HEALTH INEQUITIES IN THE NICU

OVERVIEW OF SECTION III

WHAT YOU WILL LEARN (AND DO) IN THIS SECTION:

Chapter 14: Health and Racial Inequity in the NICU: Learn how the presence of racism in NICUs causes disparities amongst people of color, based on their socio-economic status, race and ethnicity. Consider how even the most innocent and vulnerable of our population are at risk.

Chapter 15: Belonging in the NICU: Creating a compassionate NICU environment requires intentional efforts to prioritize empathy, clear communication, and family-centered care. By doing so, healthcare providers can transform the NICU from a place of fear and isolation to one of hope, healing, and connection.

Chapter 16: Family-Centered Care in the NICU: Explore the growing body of evidence on the benefits of Family-Centered Care, and reflect on the two patients you care for in the NICU. Evaluate how these principles could help you in preparing families for discharge and improving long-term outcomes.

Chapter 17: Trauma-Informed Care in the NICU: Emerging research on NICU stays highlight the extremely traumatic event it is for both infants and their families. In this chapter, we will examine our Automated Nervous Response and the ways we can help infants and families heal. By creating systems where caregivers are able to access this place of calm and safety, and by giving children enough positive moments of connecting with these caregivers, the negative impact of traumatic experience can be cushioned and eventually integrated into a more adaptive and resilient view of the world.

Chapter 18: Infant Mental Health: Can infants experience mental health problems? What about positive mental health? Infant mental health is a growing field in psychology as we learn fascinating truths about babies' brains and the amazing ways in which they experience the world, even in utero. From the very beginning, parents, caregivers, and providers play a critical role in helping build good mental health for a child.

Chapter 19: Compassionate Language and Communication: EDiscuss the impact of language and communication in caring for medically fragile infants and their families.

Chapter 20: Caring Beyond Beliefs: The Complexity of Supporting Same-Gender Loving Couples in Healthcare: We are called to meet people in their most vulnerable moments—not with judgment, but with empathy and excellence. In this chapter, we will discuss the barriers many LGBTQUI+ couples and parents face in a healthcare setting, and how we respond with equity and compassion.

INTRODUCTION: WHAT DOES COMPASSIONATE CARE LOOK LIKE IN THE NICU?

Families and infants who experience a stay in the NICU face a unique set of stressors, traumas, and therefore opportunities for equitable and compassionate care. While some of the most painful experiences in a NICU cannot be avoided, many of the long-term impacts of these experiences can be mitigated with the right level of trauma-informed care and interventions. In addition, the painful experiences of disparities that often arise due to factors such as race or culture can always be mitigated when we are given the tools to do so.

Because of structural racism, Black and Brown families face disparities in the proportion of children who spend time in the NICU, as well as their experience while there. In this Section, we'll focus specifically on what equitable family-centered care looks like, including trauma-informed care and infant mental health from experts in NICU settings. We'll also hear from NICU mothers and healthcare providers to discuss compassionate and equitable communication among providers and their patients.

CHAPTER FOURTEEN
Health and Racial Inequity in the NICU

(NEONATAL INTENSIVE CARE UNIT)

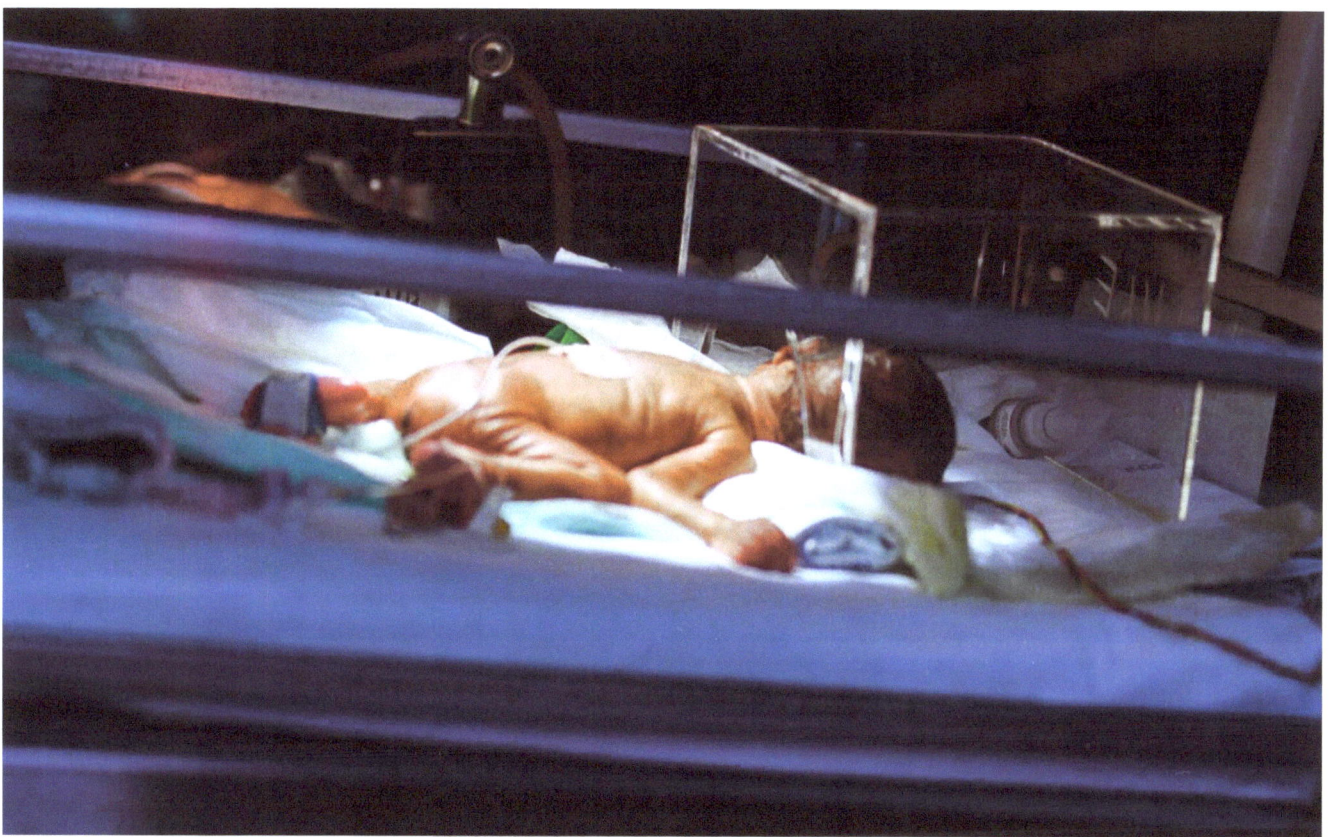

Discrimination in the NICU

Throughout this workbook, we have examined the various ways in which racial inequalities have, and continue to, play a part in all aspects of healthcare disparities. Unfortunately, these inequalities begin from the very moment a new baby is born into our world, as those with darker skin are often already at a disadvantage when it comes to healthcare. Sadly, a baby's race, insurance, socioeconomic status, etc. will have a major impact on the care they receive (higher or lower quality of care). In other words, a baby might experience their first taste of racial discrimination at the most vulnerable time of their life - when they do not have a voice, or a choice.

In this chapter, we will examine the ways in which racial inequalities affect care, even at the NICU level.

Quality Care Based on Race

In the article Overcoming Racial Disparities in California Neonatal Intensive Care Units,[1] published by Stanford Impact Labs, author Sarah Jane Staats describes how current data about NICU care was indicating that "fewer Black and Hispanic babies survive and thrive than White babies in the same hospitals." Based on these findings, neonatologist and epidemiologist, Henry Lee, in collaboration with The California Perinatal Quality Care Collaborative (CPQCC), began work on studying the disparities in NICU care across the state of California.

In the article, Lee explains how "he wasn't initially focused on disparities in care, but as an epidemiologist, there comes a point when you look at neonatal outcomes—including mortality rates and the quality of care—and the thing that sticks out is racial disparity. 'There's no biological reason these disparities exist,' says Lee. 'We recognize that even as we've advanced medical care, we need to address the social determinants of health and our own process of care.'"

The extent to which public policies, access, and choice for minority women and their infants decides their quality of care, and whether these precious babies will receive best practices and heroic interventions is not only atrocious but creates a health crisis as well. The inequities at play in these glaring results continue to persist. Since the data proves there are no biological factors supporting these results, we must conclude structural racism is at the helm, steering the boat.

Racial Disparities in Pre-Term Births

Though Black mothers and infants may represent the lowest population in any one service line, they continue to have the highest overall mortality rates.

These disparities must not be dismissed - no matter how few Black patients might come through any particular clinic. It is the responsibility of ALL providers, everywhere, no matter the number of Black patients treated, to do the work in eradicating these devastating inequalities, often perpetuated by a system that has long overlooked these gaps in care for marginalized communities.

The authors of Ignored and Invisible: Perspectives from Black Women, Clinicians and Community-Based Organizations for Reducing Preterm Birth,[2] argue, "Preterm birth (PTB) is a leading contributor to infant mortality and morbidity in the U.S. Furthermore, racial disparities persist in PTB rates with Black women disproportionately impacted by adverse birth outcomes. While the PTB rate in the U.S. declined in 2020 for the first time in several years, the rate for Black women did not change significantly. The same 2020 data found Black women experience a PTB rate that is 50% higher than women of other races."

Research Based Findings

These findings reflect a reality that has often been felt by minority communities, though never before backed by evidentiary support in such clear and concise ways. In August of 2017, the CPQCC published a study on the racial and ethnic disparities of NICU care among 134 hospitals in California. The study used "Baby-MONITOR" (Measure of Neonatal Intensive Care Outcomes Research) scores to determine NICU care quality (see next page for study results). According to their analysis of Disparities in NICU Care,[1] from the CPQCC website, the results indicated that Black and Hispanic infants "received worse care overall when compared to White infants" and that "hospitals that scored high on overall quality of care tended to treat more White infants and those with poorer quality of care primarily Black and Hispanic infants." The research laid forth the findings in clear data that cannot be refuted - Black infants are often segregated into receiving worse quality care, meaning they are more likely to die if they are born with serious health complications.

The article Overcoming Racial Disparities[3] goes on to address how many of these disparities are due to socio-economic factors - such as unequal paid leave, financial privileges, and communication barriers. The article asserts that "clinicians are not always aware of how these policies affect what happens in the NICU" and that clinicians would do well to learn from the research and data, as well as from listening to real patient stories. Lee goes on to say "We see how much the social environment affects [infant] care in the NICU and what happens afterwards. It's not a technological problem; it's a human one. And so it needs a human solution. Just getting people in the same room to listen to each other's stories can change the response." Once again we find how leading with compassionate care can not only mitigate the heartbreaking racial disparities we see in healthcare, but can ultimately save lives.

---

1   Staats, Sarah Jane. "Overcoming Racial Disparities in California Neonatal Intensive Care Units." *Stanford Impact Labs*, Stanford University, 5 May 2021, impact.stanford.edu/article/overcoming-racial-disparities-california-neonatal-intensive-care-units.

2   Smith, Kendra M., et al. "'Ignored and Invisible': Perspectives From Black Women, Clinicians, and Community-Based Organizations for Reducing Preterm Birth." *Maternal and Child Health Journal*, vol. 26, no. 4, Springer Science+Business Media, Jan. 2022, pp. 726–35. https://doi.org/10.1007/s10995-021-03367-1.

3   "Disparities in NICU Care." *California Perinatal Quality Care Collaborative*, Center for Academic Medicine Neonatology - Stanford University, 2023. www.cpqcc.org/analysis/our-research-priorities/disparities-nicu-care.

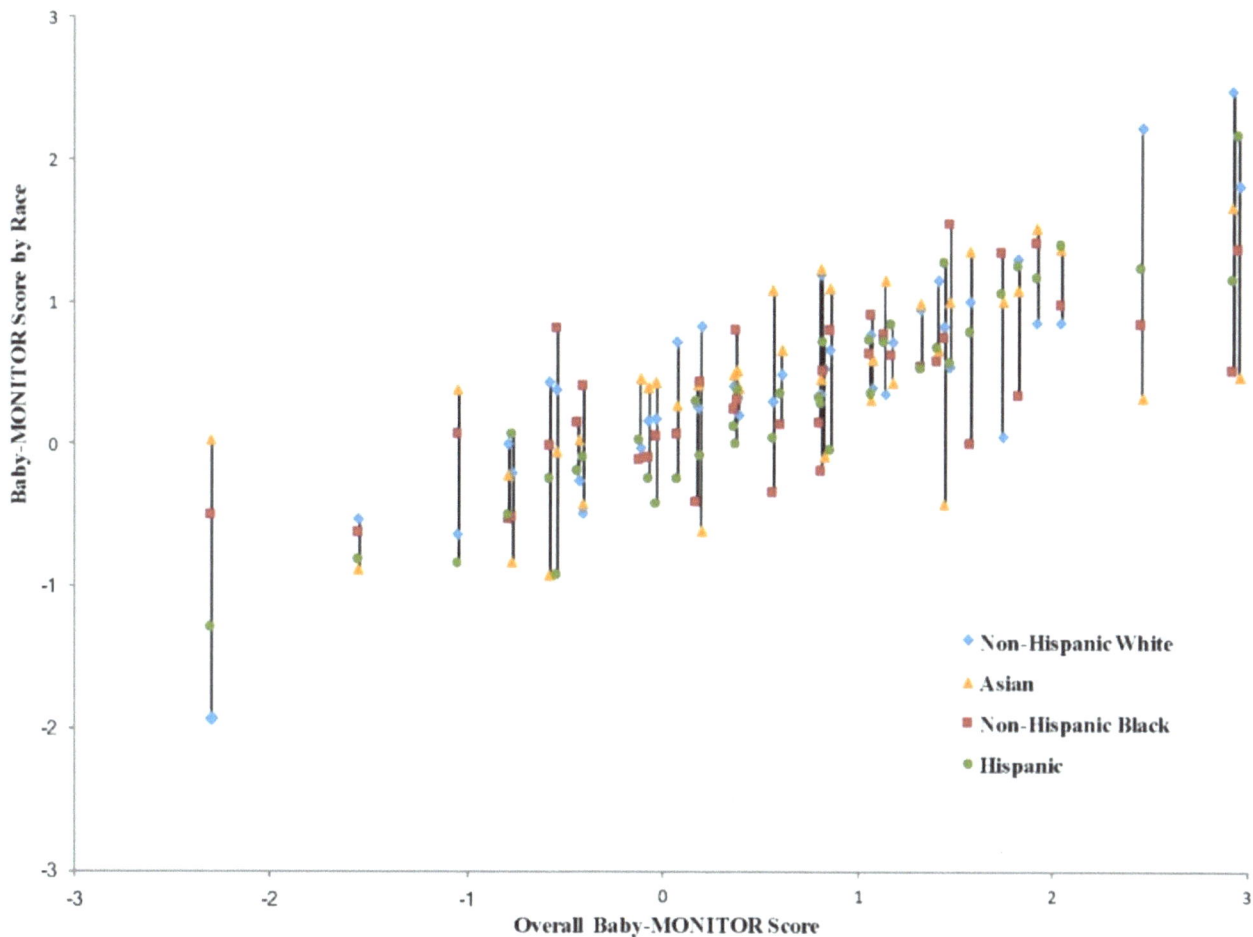

Racism in Nursing: A National Crisis

As we've seen above, racism in healthcare is a national crisis that poses a safety issue for patients and families - but it does not stop there. Recent studies reveal an unsettling undercurrent in the nursing profession, despite its longstanding reputation as the most trusted profession.

Nearly 2 in 3 nurses (63%) said they have experienced an act of racism in the workplace, either from peers (66%) or a manager (60%).

More than half (57%) said they challenged racist treatment in the workplace, but 64% said it made no difference.

Almost all Black nurses surveyed (92%) said they have personally experienced racism at work, and 70% said it came from leaders, while 66% said it originated from peers.

Over 75% of Black nurses report being negatively impacted in their professional well-being due to racism.

"Even our Black patients have bought into believing that Black nurses are less than and cannot provide qualified care," another nurse told the commission.

Racism in nursing includes acts of exclusion, incivility, disrespect, and denial of opportunities. This is a crisis that affects both care provider and care recipient. Toxic cultures that ignore or downplay racism can lead to disparity in patient care, as patients of color will likely receive the same treatment. As we saw in the chapter above, the lives of birthing women and their children are at stake. It is up to us to address racism in healthcare head-on and find a new path forward.

NURTURING EQUITY MINDED GROUP EXERCISE #1

Discuss with your small group: Have you seen these disparities at work within the NICU or other maternal and infant care settings?

How might you advocate for different outcomes? Are there structural issues you need to address?

NURTURING EQUITY MINDED HEALTHCARE EXERCISE #2

Discuss ways that you can use your privilege to promote allyship in advancing marginalized staff.

As a White professional in management, how would you feel if your White boss retired and, in light of your organization working to diversify the workforce, her position was filled by a Black professional woman: How would you feel?

Take a moment to take it all in: Reflect on how you would honestly receive this new change. Speak from a place of authenticity, rather than what you think might be the "right thing to say." There has never been a Black Director in the history of your organization. Are you on guard or are you celebrating the history making moment?

CASE STUDY: Rachael, NICU Chaplain

Rachael is a bi-racial Chaplain. Her heart is broken after attending a meeting with a family she met 3 days earlier. She is passionate about working with NICU/Pediatric populations, and regrettably has seen race issues up close and personal. She shares her excruciating experience with her colleague as a way to process a very emotional meeting. The following is her retelling of that encounter:

"I just sat with a father after a family meeting and listened to his heart-wrenching interpretation of care from the NICU medical team. The father said, 'I begged and begged - please keep fighting for my son (while they just stared at me emotionless), go back in there and do something, please.' Tears flowed down this father's face, as he felt powerless and had no control or ability to change their minds.

They repeatedly told him, 'sir, we are sorry, but there is nothing more we can do for your son.' At one point he asked how and why did this happen to his son? The primary doctor blurted out, without thinking, 'it was just bad luck.' The palliative care team just sat in silence - the bedside nurse stared at the physician who had delivered such an emotionless and insensitive reply to the family. I could feel his heartbreak. He stood there watching heroic measures being done for 2 White babies 10 feet away from his own baby's isolette. Those babies had been in the NICU 3 weeks. His son had only been in the NICU 3 days. He learned of the durations of the other families when he and the fathers met at the sink while scrubbing in to see their sons. 'Why are they giving up on my baby so soon?' he asked me. I had no reply for him, but his response left me speechless. His interpretation was 'if I had more than medicare, perhaps that would qualify my baby to live, qualify for them to care more.'"

NURTURING EQUITY MINDED GROUP EXERCISE

Break into small groups and discuss the following questions:

1. How does learning the information that Black and Hispanic infants in NICUs "received worse care overall when compared to White infants" make you feel?

2. Considering that Black infants are disproportionately treated with worse quality NICU care, due to their socio-economic disadvantages, what does that indicate about the chances of survival for a Black infant born with serious health complications?

3. What are some best practices your hospital can implement in their NICU to help combat these disparities?

Re-read the Case Study on the NICU Chaplain, Rachael, found on the previous page, then consider the following questions:.

4. How might this father's experience have been different, had the NICU team not dismissed him so quickly? To help you formulate your answer, consider reading Chapter 29 on Supporting Partners.

5. Knowing that an infant has no voice to advocate for itself, who can be an advocate for the baby instead, and how might they do so? Consider the fact that, though the baby cannot speak, it is still a patient that must be prioritized and cared for with compassion and dignity. How could the outcome for this baby have been different, if the NICU team had treated the baby as such?

CHAPTER FIFTEEN
Belonging in the NICU

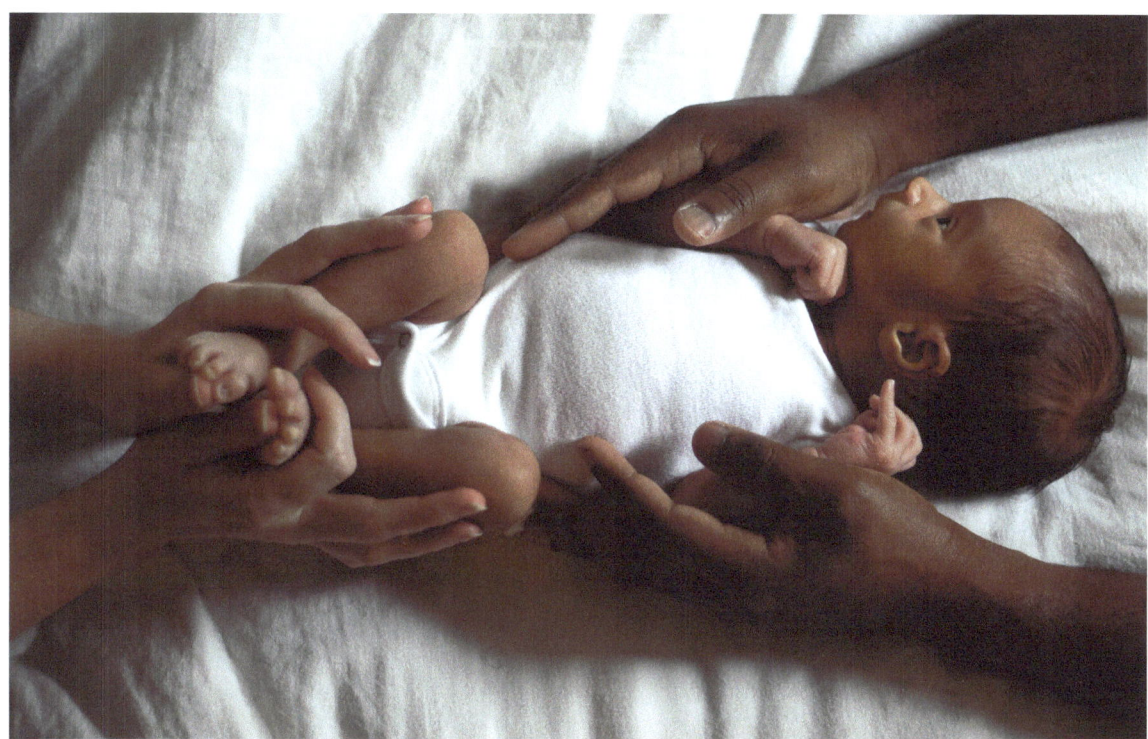

Introduction

The birth of a child is often imagined as a joyous and celebratory event. However, when parents are unexpectedly thrust into the Neonatal Intensive Care Unit (NICU), the experience can be devastating and deeply traumatizing. Instead of the anticipated warmth and bonding moments, they are met with the sterile and clinical environment of the NICU, where their infant's survival may be uncertain. This sudden shift places parents in a Level 1 trauma state, characterized by intense fear, anxiety, and emotional vulnerability.

In this fragile state, every subsequent interaction becomes critical. How healthcare professionals engage with parents can either exacerbate their trauma or provide a pathway toward healing. A compassionate sense of belonging is not just a courtesy but a necessity in this environment. When interactions are inviting, respectful, helpful, and collaborative, parents are more likely to feel valued and supported. This sense of inclusion fosters trust and empowers them to take an active role in their infant's care, improving both parental well-being and infant outcomes.

Creating a compassionate NICU environment requires intentional efforts to prioritize empathy, clear communication, and family-centered care. By doing so, healthcare providers can transform the NICU from a place of fear and isolation to one of hope, healing, and connection.

Evidence-Based Practice: Creating the Essential Sense of Belonging in the NICU—The Missing Vital Sign

The sense of belonging is increasingly recognized as a critical yet often overlooked component in the care provided within Neonatal Intensive Care Units (NICUs). This "missing vital sign" significantly impacts the emotional well-being of parents, staff, and, ultimately, the developmental outcomes of infants. Evidence-based practices (EBP) can foster this essential sense of belonging, improving family-centered care and patient outcomes.

Studies show that a strong sense of belonging reduces parental stress, anxiety, and depression, which are common in the NICU environment. Parents who feel included and respected are more likely to actively participate in their infant's care, enhancing bonding and attachment. Evidence suggests that when staff foster belonging, their own job satisfaction and emotional resilience improve, reducing burnout.

Parental involvement in care has also been linked to better neurodevelopmental outcomes for preterm infants. Kangaroo Care, skin-to-skin contact, and parental presence during medical rounds positively influence infant stability and growth.

The following EBPs have proven to be effective in family centered- communication which fosters a sense of belonging in the NICU and improves health outcomes.

Family-Centered Communication

EBP: Structured family conferences and daily bedside updates involving both medical staff and parents.

Evidence: Regular communication improves parental understanding of their infant's condition and fosters trust.

Environmental Design

EBP: Create private and family-friendly spaces within the NICU for bonding and caregiving.

Evidence: Studies show that family-integrated spaces reduce stress and enhance parental participation.

Cultural and Spiritual Inclusivity

EBP: Tailor care plans to respect diverse cultural and religious values.

Evidence: Inclusive practices lead to greater parental satisfaction and a deeper sense of respect and belonging.

Peer Support Programs

EBP: Establish parent-to-parent support groups led by NICU alumni families.

Evidence: Peer mentorship reduces isolation and provides emotional validation for current NICU families.

Staff Training in Compassionate Care

EBP: Ongoing training in active listening, empathy, and trauma-informed care.

Evidence: Compassionate care training improves patient satisfaction and creates a supportive, inclusive environment.

Parental Role in Care

EBP: Encourage and train parents to perform caregiving tasks (e.g., feeding, diaper changes, and holding their infant during procedures).

Evidence: Parent participation enhances self-efficacy and strengthens the parent-infant bond.

Metrics for Measuring Belonging as a Vital Sign

Certain metrics can also aid a healthcare setting in measuring how effective their efforts are in creating a sense of belonging for patients and caregivers. The following four metrics are key to measuring belonging as a vital sign:

1. **Parental Satisfaction Surveys, which** measure perceived inclusion, respect, and emotional support.
2. **Infant Developmental Outcomes, which** track weight gain, neurodevelopment, and length of hospital stay.
3. **Staff Retention and Burnout Rates, which** monitor job satisfaction and emotional well-being of NICU staff.
4. **Parental Engagement Metrics, which** evaluate the frequency of parental visits and participation in caregiving activities.

Creating a sense of belonging in the NICU is essential for promoting the well-being of infants, families, and staff. By adopting evidence-based practices such as family-centered communication, inclusive care, and staff training, NICUs can address this "missing vital sign" and foster a compassionate, supportive environment. Continuous evaluation and feedback from families and staff will ensure the sustainability and effectiveness of these practices.

SAMPLE: NICU PARENTAL BELONGING SURVEY

This survey is designed to assess your sense of belonging in the NICU. Your feedback will help improve our efforts to create a supportive, inclusive, and compassionate environment for you and your baby. Please complete this survey weekly.

General Experience

1. On a scale of 1 to 5, how welcomed and included do you feel in your baby's care?
   - ☐ 1 = Not welcomed at all
   - ☐ 2 = Slightly welcomed
   - ☐ 3 = Neutral
   - ☐ 4 = Mostly welcomed
   - ☐ 5 = Completely welcomed

2. How comfortable do you feel asking the NICU staff questions about your baby's care?
   - ☐ 1 = Not comfortable at all
   - ☐ 2 = Slightly comfortable
   - ☐ 3 = Neutral
   - ☐ 4 = Mostly comfortable
   - ☐ 5 = Completely comfortable

3. Do you feel respected and valued as a parent by the NICU staff?
   - ☐ 1 = Not at all
   - ☐ 2 = Rarely
   - ☐ 3 = Sometimes
   - ☐ 4 = Often
   - ☐ 5 = Always
   - ☐ Communication

4. How effective is the communication between you and the NICU staff?
   - ☐ 1 = Not effective at all
   - ☐ 2 = Slightly effective
   - ☐ 3 = Neutral
   - ☐ 4 = Mostly effective
   - ☐ 5 = Extremely effective

5. Do the NICU staff provide clear and understandable explanations about your baby's condition and care?
   - ☐ 1 = Never
   - ☐ 2 = Rarely
   - ☐ 3 = Sometimes
   - ☐ 4 = Often
   - ☐ 5 = Always

Emotional and Practical Support

6. How supported do you feel emotionally by the NICU staff?
   - ☐ 1 = Not supported at all
   - ☐ 2 = Slightly supported
   - ☐ 3 = Neutral
   - ☐ 4 = Mostly supported
   - ☐ 5 = Completely supported

7. Are the resources and information provided by the NICU helpful in managing your baby's care?
   - ☐ 1 = Not helpful at all
   - ☐ 2 = Slightly helpful
   - ☐ 3 = Neutral
   - ☐ 4 = Mostly helpful
   - ☐ 5 = Extremely helpful

Parent Involvement

8. How often are you encouraged to participate in your baby's care (e.g., feeding, bathing, holding)?
   - ☐ 1 = Never
   - ☐ 2 = Rarely
   - ☐ 3 = Sometimes
   - ☐ 4 = Often
   - ☐ 5 = Always

9. Do you feel confident in your role as a caregiver for your baby in the NICU?
   - ☐ 1 = Not confident at all
   - ☐ 2 = Slightly confident
   - ☐ 3 = Neutral
   - ☐ 4 = Mostly confident
   - ☐ 5 = Completely confident

Overall Belonging

10. On a scale of 1 to 5, how strong is your overall sense of belonging in the NICU?
    - ☐ 1 = No sense of belonging
    - ☐ 2 = Slight sense of belonging
    - ☐ 3 = Neutral
    - ☐ 4 = Strong sense of belonging
    - ☐ 5 = Very strong sense of belonging

Optional Comments:

Please share any suggestions or specific experiences that could help us improve your sense of belonging in the NICU.

Thank You for Your Feedback!

Your responses will help us enhance the care and support provided to families in the NICU.

CASE STUDY

Break up into three groups and assign each group one of the following case studies to discuss. Then, share what you discussed with the rest of the class.

CASE STUDY #1: *A Sense of Belonging: The Missing Vital Sign*

Background

Maria and José Ramirez, a young Hispanic couple, were eagerly anticipating the birth of their first child, Sofia. At Maria's 32-week prenatal checkup, an ultrasound revealed a diagnosis of gastroschisis, a condition in which the baby's intestines protrude through a hole in the abdominal wall. Sofia was delivered prematurely and immediately admitted to the NICU for surgical intervention and intensive care.

The couple's initial excitement was replaced with shock, fear, and helplessness as they found themselves in an unfamiliar and intimidating environment. Neither Maria nor José had any prior knowledge of the NICU, and the sight of their tiny baby hooked to various tubes and monitors heightened their trauma.

The Challenge: Trauma and Isolation

Maria and José felt overwhelmed and excluded in the NICU. Medical terminology was difficult to understand, and the highly structured routines left little room for their emotional needs. Additionally, language barriers and cultural differences created further isolation, leaving them unsure of how to interact with staff or participate in Sofia's care.

The couple's trauma was compounded by feelings of guilt and inadequacy, as they felt disconnected from their role as parents. José, in particular, felt his presence in the NICU was undervalued, exacerbating his anxiety and sense of helplessness.

Intervention: Creating a Compassionate Sense of Belonging

1. **Culturally Sensitive Communication**
   A bilingual NICU nurse, Ana, was assigned as their primary point of contact. She provided clear explanations of Sofia's condition and care plan in Spanish, ensuring that Maria and José fully understood each step of the process.

2. **Building Trust and Inclusion**
   Ana introduced Maria and José to the care team and emphasized the importance of their involvement. She encouraged them to participate in Sofia's care by helping with tasks such as hand hygiene before touching Sofia, providing gentle soothing, and participating in skin-to-skin contact.

3. **Empowering Parental Roles**
   The NICU staff implemented a trauma-informed care approach by creating a care schedule that included time for parent education. They taught the couple how to recognize Sofia's cues and respond appropriately, empowering them to feel more confident and competent in their caregiving role.

4. **Creating a Family-Friendly Environment**
   The staff provided a private space for the couple to bond with Sofia and offered culturally familiar comforts, such as playing soft Spanish lullabies. They also introduced Maria and José to a Hispanic parent support group to help them feel less isolated and more connected to others with similar experiences.

Outcomes

1. **Improved Emotional Well-Being**
   Over time, Maria and José reported feeling less anxious and more supported. They began to trust the care team and felt reassured by their consistent communication and encouragement.

2. **Strengthened Parental Confidence**
   As the couple participated more in Sofia's care, their confidence grew. José remarked that he felt like an integral part of Sofia's recovery, which strengthened his bond with his daughter.

3. **Enhanced Infant Outcomes**
   Sofia's recovery progressed steadily, aided by the nurturing environment fostered by her parents' active involvement. Maria and José's consistent presence and participation improved Sofia's stability and comfort.

Conclusion

This case highlights the critical importance of fostering a sense of belonging in the NICU. By addressing cultural, emotional, and practical needs, the care team transformed Maria and José's traumatic experience into one of empowerment and healing. This intervention demonstrates that belonging is not merely an emotional need—it is a vital sign that directly impacts both parental well-being and infant outcomes.

CASE STUDY #2: *A Sense of Belonging: Overcoming Distrust in the NICU*

Background

Lydia, a 28-year-old white woman, and her partner, Marcus, a 30-year-old Black man, were overjoyed to welcome their first child, Elijah. However, their joy quickly turned to anxiety when Elijah was born at 35 weeks and diagnosed with severe neonatal lung disease. He was immediately admitted to the NICU for specialized respiratory support, including mechanical ventilation and close monitoring.

The couple's experience in the hospital leading up to Elijah's birth had already been fraught with tension. Marcus was denied entry to the labor and delivery room by a staff member who questioned his identity as the baby's father, leaving him humiliated and angry. This incident created a deep sense of distrust toward the medical team, particularly for Marcus, who now felt anxious and judged in the NICU.

The Challenge: Overcoming Distrust and Anxiety

Marcus's distrust and feelings of exclusion were compounded by subtle microaggressions, such as staff avoiding eye contact, speaking to Lydia while ignoring him, or responding with hesitation to his questions. Lydia, though equally overwhelmed, felt torn between managing her own fears and supporting Marcus.

This atmosphere of discomfort and tension made it difficult for the couple to focus on Elijah's care, further isolating them during an already traumatic experience.

Intervention: Establishing Trust and Belonging

1. **Acknowledging Past Harm**
   The NICU social worker met privately with Marcus and Lydia to validate their experiences and apologize for the incident in labor and delivery. This open and honest conversation acknowledged the impact of systemic bias and helped Marcus feel heard.

2. **Assigning a Consistent Care Team**
   A diverse care team was assigned to Elijah, including a Black male respiratory therapist who could serve as a role model and point of connection for Marcus. This team consistently engaged with both parents, making an intentional effort to address Marcus directly and involve him in care decisions.

3. **Trauma-Informed Communication**
   The team implemented trauma-informed practices by using clear, respectful language and checking in frequently to ensure both Lydia and Marcus understood Elijah's care plan. They encouraged Marcus to ask questions and offered extra time to address his concerns.

4. **Involving Marcus in Care**
   Marcus was invited to participate in tasks such as diaper changes, hand-holding, and reading to Elijah. These small but meaningful actions helped him feel more connected to his son and more confident in his role as a father.

5. **Creating a Safe Space for Reflection**
   The NICU team facilitated a weekly family support group where parents could share their experiences. This gave Marcus a platform to discuss his anxieties and connect with other fathers, breaking down feelings of isolation and building a supportive network.

Outcomes

1. **Restored Trust**
   Over time, Marcus began to trust the care team, thanks to their consistent efforts to include and respect him. He expressed gratitude for the transparent communication and the steps taken to address his initial discomfort.

2. **Improved Parental Engagement**
   Both Lydia and Marcus became actively involved in Elijah's care, fostering a stronger bond with their baby. Marcus's confidence grew as he saw the positive impact of his presence and participation.

3. **Positive Infant Outcomes**
   Elijah's condition steadily improved with the support of his parents and the NICU team. The collaborative care approach ensured that both his medical and emotional needs were met.

4. **Strengthened Family Unit**
   The shared experience of overcoming adversity brought Lydia and Marcus closer together as a couple. They reported feeling more prepared to advocate for their family in the future.

Conclusion

This case study highlights the importance of addressing biases and fostering a compassionate sense of belonging in the NICU. By recognizing the unique challenges faced by bi-racial families and implementing trauma-informed, inclusive practices, the NICU team transformed a distrustful, anxious environment into one of empowerment and healing. Belonging is a vital sign that directly impacts family dynamics, parental engagement, and infant outcomes.

CASE STUDY #3: *A Sense of Belonging: Empowering a Mother's Role in the NICU*

Background

Angela is a 32-year-old mother of four whose 34-week preterm baby, Noah, was admitted to the NICU after birth for respiratory distress and feeding support. Angela's husband works full-time, and their car is currently in the shop, requiring her to take three buses to visit the hospital each day. She relies on a friend to babysit her three other children while she spends time with Noah.

Feeding time with Noah has become a cherished opportunity for Angela to bond with her baby and feel a sense of control and connection amidst the chaos of having a preemie in the NICU. Despite her challenging circumstances, she prioritizes being at the NICU during feeding times to maintain her presence in Noah's care.

The Incident: A Breaking Point

One morning, Angela's babysitter arrived late, causing her to miss her scheduled bus. She arrived at the NICU 15 minutes after Noah's feeding time, only to find a nurse bottle-feeding her baby. Exhausted, overwhelmed, and feeling defeated, Angela broke down in tears, crying uncontrollably.

When the nurse asked why she was late, Angela snapped, responding, "Why I am late is not the question. Why didn't you call me? And why are you feeding my baby when you know I want to feed my own baby?"

The Challenge: Emotional Distress and Miscommunication

Angela's emotional response stemmed from a deep sense of loss and frustration. Feeding Noah was one of the few ways she felt like a mother in the NICU, and being denied that opportunity left her feeling helpless and excluded. The nurse, while trying to follow NICU protocols, did not anticipate Angela's strong emotional reaction, creating tension in their interaction.

Intervention: Rebuilding Trust and Fostering Belonging

1. **Acknowledging Angela's Emotions**
   The charge nurse intervened, taking Angela to a quiet, private room where she could process her emotions. She listened empathetically as Angela shared her struggles and validated her feelings, acknowledging the difficulty of juggling multiple responsibilities and the significance of feeding Noah.

2. **Developing a Communication Plan**
   The NICU team implemented a new communication protocol, ensuring that Angela would receive a phone call if she was not present at feeding time. They also introduced a feeding preference plan that documented Angela's desire to feed Noah whenever possible.

3. **Providing Flexible Support**
   The staff arranged for Angela to have a feeding window instead of a strict feeding time, offering more flexibility in light of her transportation challenges. They also provided her with taxi vouchers to ease her commute to the hospital.

4. **Building Collaborative Relationships**
   The nurse who initially fed Noah apologized to Angela, explaining the NICU's protocols and expressing her understanding of Angela's frustration. Together, they discussed ways to ensure Angela felt more included and respected in Noah's care, fostering a more collaborative relationship.

Outcomes

1. **Enhanced Emotional Well-Being**
   With improved communication and support, Angela reported feeling more valued and understood by the NICU team. Her confidence in Noah's care improved, and her emotional outbursts decreased.

2. **Strengthened Parental Involvement**
   Angela became more engaged in Noah's care, participating in feedings, skin-to-skin contact, and learning about his medical needs. The feeding preference plan empowered her to maintain her role as Noah's primary caregiver.

3. **Improved Staff-Parent Dynamics**
   The NICU staff reported better interactions with Angela, appreciating her resilience and commitment. The collaborative care approach helped to rebuild trust and reduce tension.

4. **Positive Infant Outcomes**
   Noah's feeding tolerance and overall stability improved as Angela's consistent presence provided him with nurturing care and comfort.

Conclusion

This case underscores the critical importance of fostering a compassionate sense of belonging for parents in the NICU. By addressing logistical challenges, improving communication, and respecting Angela's role as a mother, the NICU team was able to transform a moment of emotional crisis into an opportunity for connection and healing. Recognizing the unique needs of each family and adapting care plans accordingly can significantly enhance both parental well-being and infant outcomes.

ADDITIONAL RESOURCES

List of Studies and Resources on Compassionate Belonging in the NICU

"Family-Centered Care in Neonatal Intensive Care Units: Evidence and Best Practices", Gooding JS, Cooper LG, Blaine AI, et al. Pediatrics, 2011

This study highlights the importance of family-centered care in reducing parental stress and improving infant health outcomes. It provides evidence-based recommendations for integrating families into caregiving practices.

"Trauma-Informed Care in the NICU: A Concept Analysis", Hall SL, Cross J, Selix N, et al., Advances in Neonatal Care, 2015

This paper explores the concept of trauma-informed care in the NICU, emphasizing the need for compassionate interactions to mitigate parental trauma.

"The Effects of Kangaroo Care on Parental Stress and Infant Outcomes in the NICU", Charpak N, Ruiz JG, Zupan J, et al., The Lancet, 2005

This study demonstrates the benefits of skin-to-skin contact (Kangaroo Care) in fostering emotional connection and reducing stress for both parents and infants in the NICU.

"The Role of Parental Empowerment in NICU Settings: A Systematic Review", Melnyk BM, Feinstein NF, Alpert-Gillis LJ, et al., Journal of Perinatal & Neonatal Nursing, 2014

This systematic review highlights the importance of empowering parents through education and collaborative care to foster a sense of belonging and improve outcomes.

"Compassionate Communication in the NICU: Supporting Families Through Crisis", Curtin M, Savage E., Journal of Neonatal Nursing, 2020

This article examines the role of compassionate communication in reducing parental anxiety and fostering trust between healthcare providers and families in the NICU.

CHAPTER SIXTEEN
Family-Centered Care in the NICU

Family-Centered Care is a model gaining increased recognition in healthcare settings due to its effectiveness in involving families in successful outcomes for them and their children.

It is easy to get wrapped up in the tasks and technology of the NICU. We as healthcare professionals must remember to center the personhood of the baby and their family. Staying connected with our shared humanity helps us make life-saving decisions from a place of equitable empathy and connectedness, suspending parental judgment at all cost.

Many experts in the field of Family Centered Care have provided valuable evidence-based education to support a growing, vibrant and effective NICU experience for patients and families. Some of those experts include Dr. Olubunmi Bakare, Neonatologist NICU FCC (Director, Miller Children's & Women's Hospital); Dharshi Sivakumar, MD; and Mia Malcolm, BS, CDFT, who have provided some of the best practices in obtaining leadership buy-in and recruiting diverse Family Partners.

- Actively reach out to diverse former NICU parents: begin relationships in admission and plant the seed during post-discharge phone call follow ups; reach out personally via email or phone number when it's appropriate timewise for those families to participate; or create pathways for parents/primary caregivers to self-identify. It's important to have multiple modes of recruitment because often we count on staff referrals which can be problematic for many reasons.

- Representation is important to create support for future NICU families. When inpatient NICU families see diverse Family Partners, that allows diverse representation to build upon itself. We need socioeconomic, gender, gestational age, language, geographical, etc. diversity as well as racial/ethnicity.

- The NICU needs to be a safe space for diverse populations initially in order to be able to recruit those families later on. We need to WANT to hear those perspectives that aren't always positive. We have to figure out how to stop shaming and labeling NICU parents.

- Allow families to contribute at whatever level works for them. This means we must consider how to remove barriers to participation, such as offering virtual/hybrid participation options outside regular working hours, etc.

- Science and research point to the fact that trauma occurs whether it was five minutes or five months, from the moment they walk through the NICU doors the disruption substantiates the impact of trauma. We are missing opportunities for NICU family representation and participation by putting limits on those who had a shorter length of stay.

- Be careful not to manage parent's lives for them by assuming their level of involvement. Don't make assumptions about who wants to be involved and who doesn't want to be involved. Keep the door open; communication and relationship is key.

- To get buy-in, present to your leadership council each year on what has happened, scores that have improved by utilizing FCC. Educate leadership on the importance of what your are doing; they may not even realize there is trauma for NICU families. Prioritize reaching your CEO & CFO, as they need to agree on change. Consider sending your unit's FCC communications (newsletter, shout outs, milestones) to C Suite leadership quarterly or bringing leadership onto the unit or to a PFAC/FCC Committee meeting so they can see the importance of the work for themselves.

- The truth is, the NICU is what contributes most to the bottom line through surgeries, therapy visits, follow-up visits, etc. Those don't happen if we don't get it right in the NICU. We have a responsibility to the entire hospital to provide FCC; NICU patients are the next generation of hospital patients and parents are making decisions about whether they want to utilize other facilities within your hospital during their time in the NICU. You have every right to ask about the business side of the NICU as a provider.

- Family Partners and PFACs need to be viewed as consumer panels and experts.

- Regularly review Press Ganey surveys/Top Box scores, specifically 'would you recommend this hospital?' questions; ask parents to fill these out by including them in discharge instructions and be clear that you're not interested only in good feedback. Make sure to access your hospital's Quality Dashboard to view patient recommendations, specifically NICU patient recommendations; these aren't usually separated out for review.

These insights and educational pieces will help cultivate a healthy, non-toxic NICU environment by integrating the wisdom and evidence-based practices offered by dedicated clinicians. Through this approach, we prioritize the well-being of both infants and their caregivers, fostering a space of healing, equity, and excellence in neonatal care.

A Plethora of Emotions - Normalizing our Mental Health Needs

What we know about children who have a history of premature birth is that there can be associations with significant challenges across their lifespan. Those early findings include cerebral palsy, vision or hearing differences, challenges with learning or autism, as well as "minor morbidities" that include challenges with executive function and attentional regulation, anxiety, depression, and learning disadvantages with visual-spatial learning and socio-emotional learning.

On July 25, 2024, I had the honor of gleaning from Paige Terrien Church, Family Centered Care Task Force, as she lectured on families in the NICU. Her insights should be heard around the world of those caring for the most vulnerable population.

There is so much to know and learn about life, medicine, diagnosis, and impact in the NICU. This can create an overwhelming sense of trauma by the sheer nature of being an ICU Unit. Paige Terrien Church rightly posits that we know that the NICU is a place of intense emotions. I would also add that we are all pouring in our hopes or biases, our fears, and our understanding of the situation or insights. But the parents also come and they add their hopes and their biases and their emotions and their understandings to this cocktail. It creates an environment that can be very challenging, particularly for parents.

They often feel like they are parenting "on stage", feeling like everyone is watching them come in with all their pre-existing challenges that may have nothing to do with the NICU but are added stressors that are going to constantly weigh on their family. It might be a lack of support, mental health conditions that pre-existed this pregnancy, other social stressors, prejudice, fatigue, families trying to work come in and see their babies, the exhaustion that certainly changes how you process information and how you learn and how you respond to trauma. Or it could be feeling a lack of control of your baby's or family's future, the loss of a dream and the identity crisis that comes with it.

So in this ICU setting, all of this is happening in the background for our families. Paige Terrien Church offered that studies show that upwards of 40 to 45% of parents leaving the NICU may experience mental health or post traumatic stress as a result of being a parent in the NICU.

BARRIERS FOR OUR FAMILIES

We also know that by even just arriving at the NICU, families face many barriers. We have outlined the following tool to help you understand some of the potential barriers that a **FAMILY** may be struggling with:

Fear of their child dying and surviving the NICU

Access to empathetic and equitable care while in the NICU

Money - the many unexpected costs of managing NICU visits, i.e. parking, gas, public transportation, taking time off from work, food, getting childcare, and parenting additional children

Infections from illnesses pose a frightening and traumatic barrier that results in isolating parents from their child.

Language is a huge barrier as parents navigate the NICU culture in all of its complexities, including understanding what is happening, why things are happening, and the foreign language they hear daily.

Yearning to provide the appropriate care for their child despite the learning curve of caring for a child with special medical needs, sometimes as a single parent.

All of this contributes to why parents may not want to come in or may struggle to be present to their child. As healthcare providers, we have to ask the question: Does the culture of our NICU staff judge these families harshly?

WE DON'T HAVE JUST ONE PATIENT

We actually have two patients: the infant and the parent(s). It is foolish for us to think that we don't have to care for both of them, because we really do. We've done such a good job with our science on developing nutritional bundles and respiratory bundles and all these bundles to help our babies grow. But we haven't come nearly as far at helping our parents to grow and recognizing that most of our parents are premature in this area as well.

Parents tend to cope with the trauma of a child in the NICU by trying to intellectualize: they want to learn, and they want to understand what's happening. They will go to resources like Google and books, trying to come up with information so that they can feel empowered. As clinicians, we too can improve

There is also the danger of attachment competition and comparison: when parents aren't attaching to their babies because they feel they cannot care for their child like we do. For example, they aren't able to feed their babies like the NICU team can. They aren't as capable of handling the crises that happen. Parents then feel that they have to step back, and the providers become the more attached figure to their babies. This is very unsettling because it's not our baby, and it's not supposed to be our baby. As providers, we must pay attention to the needs of both of our patients, rather than just the infant, and respond to both with **CARE:**

Compassion for parents who struggle with comparing themselves to the NICU team of nurses, gently bringing parents alongside the nursing team to empower and affirm. Being a compassionate nurse that identifies this fear present in a parent can be a gift that helps validate the parent's ability and capacity to care for their child.

Addressing any barriers to care for their babies that parents are facing with kindness and a sense of belonging.

Respecting parent's values, cultures, and beliefs as a way of supporting diversity and inclusion.

Equitable care for all parents, especially traditionally or historically marginalized parents who may need extra attention and resources for their baby.

So how do we do that?

The foundation of being more family centered and encouraging families to come in comes from Mary Copland's work with trauma informed care. But at the core of **this is this idea that we build trust.** We empower families, we collaborate with them, we offer them choices when possible, we make them feel safe, and we give them an environment that feels safe.

Nurturing an Integrated NICU that is Family-Centered

How do we accomplish this, and provide families with an opportunity to feel like they can be in the NICU and be understood? Often, parents experience a revolving set of clinicians, and their story can get broken as we hand off to each other, resulting in a negative impact on how they feel for clinicians, rather than respecting their personhood and personalizing their care.

In addressing this important attempt, many hospitals are using a tool embedded in their EPIC system which is called the Family Snapshot. It is a very powerful way to make families feel more centered and more involved in our day-to-day care quickly, placing vital information in a centralized place that we can scan in three minutes and get a sense of who this family is.

The questions are:

1. What are their values, what's important to them?
2. How do they see this going forward?
3. What are their supports that they have?
4. What are their important religious beliefs that I should be honoring?
5. What are the things that are keeping them from spending time with their baby?
6. What are the barriers in their life? race, economic, education, language,
7. What are their preferred pronouns?

This information personalizes each family, highlighting their uniqueness and their specific needs and perspectives. This provides an opportunity for families to share what they want you to know about them upfront, consistently in one place. This is a key fundamental piece of helping families feel that they can be a part of our care and that they are the center of our care, and that they belong.

LANGUAGE MATTERS

It cannot be overstated, we have to pay attention to how we communicate and what we say. Parents are coming into the ICU learning a whole new language. When they hear our language, such as "severe risk," "bad impairment," or "abnormal," they may interpret these differently than we intended.

One question to ask is: Is there a risk to having a child have a developmental outcome? What if a child could still go on to have friends and all the important things in their life? Many families would say, "no, I don't see that as a risk. I see that as a possibility." So what we say shapes their realities and their understanding.

INVOLVING PARENTS IN THEIR OWN GROWTH:
INTEGRATING PARENTS IN THE CARE AND PROGRESS OF THEIR BABIES

There are many evidence-based resources and approaches such as Kangaroo Care for both child and parent. The data shows that these children do better when they are hugged. We also know that these children are exposed to many, many, many procedures and moments where they are touched, and handled by providers who are not their parents and whose hands feel, touch, and smell differently.

Beyond the medical benefits, however, what Church has seen is that involving parents in their child's care is a powerful school for parents as they become more confident in caring for their medically fragile child. They have seen young parents go from being incredibly frazzled, shy and uncertain about their baby to being very powerful and very confident - but it didn't happen overnight. It took time to assist parents in making them feel like they were capable.

Building confidence in parents is very hard to do when you're in a NICU environment with a door or a curtain between you and an expert who knows your baby and can care for your baby "better." Even letting these parents do something on their own, such as take their baby for a walk, making decisions for their babies that do not include the team and the nurses, demonstrates that these parents were more connected to the children in more confident leaving. Which leads us to the next point…

PREPARING THEM TO LEAVE THE NICU

"I was now in charge of my child and it said it was up to me to decide how safe or not safe and to give myself a little bit of self confidence." This is how many parents feel. The lack of self confidence and knowledge of your own capabilities as a mother can emerge before discharge, because the normal parental relationship is stripped from parents in the NICU. Church found that in their program, which lets parents take their babies out in strollers, sometimes with a nurse supervising them at first, the parent demonstrated greater capacity and was more prepared and confident at discharge. It stretched the umbilical cord of the NICU to the parent, to let them start to experience parenting independently.

A helpful pre-discharge checklist for the multi-disciplinary team when graduating out of the NICU:

- ☐ All Provider Specialties
- ☐ Social Work
- ☐ Psychologist
- ☐ Spiritual Care/Chaplain
- ☐ Caseworker

FIVE STEPS TO PREPARE PARENTS

Below are 5 steps from JESS DAIGLE, MD, FAAP, and NICU parent, to ensure parents feel more prepared for the transition home:

Early Discharge Education: Start educating parents and family caregivers about their baby's diagnoses, care, and what the transition home will look like well in advance of discharge. Shift the culture in your unit to make early discharge education the expectation rather than the exception.

Hands-On Training: Involve parents in hands-on care under the supervision of NICU staff to build confidence and competence. Empower families to embrace their role as caregivers with the ability to handle their baby's care despite medical fragility.

Regular Updates: Provide consistent updates on baby's progress and expected discharge time more than 48 hours prior to discharge so parents can mentally prepare and get their home ready.

Comprehensive Discharge Checklist: Use a detailed discharge checklist covering all aspects of home care including feeding, sleeping, medication, and emergency contacts.

Post-Discharge Support: Arrange follow-up appointments and provide contact information for lactation consultants, pediatricians, perinatal mental health support, and NICU support groups.

Our families are our first wall of defense, and we need them so desperately to help us take care of their babies. The problem is that they are premature parents too, and we need to help them grow as well. In order to do that we need to create an environment where they feel safe, where they feel like they can explore their parenting at the point in their own development, and that they can develop their own capacity as parents to make their own decisions. This process is not easy, but it can result in a healthy, beautiful attachment to their child and the best outcome for everyone involved.

NURTURING EQUITY MINDED HEALTHCARE EXERCISE

As you reflect on the idea of Family-Centered Care, what questions arise for you? Discuss with your small group what benefits and challenges you foresee.

CASE STUDY: *Family-Centered Care in the NICU*

The Smith family consists of Jane (mother), Robert (father), and their newborn daughter, Emma, who is in the Neonatal Intensive Care Unit (NICU). Emma was born prematurely at 29 weeks and has a congenital intestinal malformation that requires surgical correction. The medical team has recommended the procedure as essential for Emma's survival and long-term quality of life. Jane agrees with the recommendation, but Robert, a Christian man who places great value on prayer and faith, is apprehensive about the risks and long-term effects of the surgery. After prayer and reflection, Robert begrudgingly agrees to the procedure, though he remains emotionally and spiritually conflicted.

Discuss as a team: How would you approach supporting the Smith family during this time? What are the most important elements you would focus on? What particular challenges do you foresee?

Steps for Family-Centered Care

Read through the following example of how your team might approach supporting the Smith family. At the end, discuss anything you feel is missing from this approach.

1. **Initial Assessment and Rapport Building**
   Nurse's Role: Conduct a detailed family assessment to understand Jane and Robert's emotional states, cultural and spiritual values, and specific concerns. Use active listening and empathy to validate Robert's concerns and honor his reliance on faith. Acknowledge Jane's support for the medical team's recommendation while recognizing her stress.

2. **Transparent and Collaborative Communication**
   Medical Team's Role: Host a family meeting with the pediatric surgeon, neonatologist, social worker, chaplain, and NICU nurse. Use clear, simple language to explain the procedure, its necessity, and potential risks. Provide visual aids, such as diagrams, to enhance understanding. Encourage open dialogue and allow both parents to voice their concerns and questions. Offer Robert time with the chaplain to integrate prayer and spiritual guidance into the decision-making process.

3. **Emotional, Psychological, and Spiritual Support**
   Chaplain Referral: The NICU staff refers Robert to the hospital's chaplain, who meets with him privately to provide spiritual guidance, prayer, and emotional support. The chaplain prays with both parents if desired, helping to create a sense of peace and trust in the process.
   Social Worker's Role: Meet with Jane and Robert separately to explore their individual feelings and coping strategies. Normalize Robert's fears and offer strategies for managing uncertainty.
   Psychologist Support: A psychologist is made available for family or individual sessions to help both parents process their emotions, manage anxiety, and improve coping mechanisms.

4. **Ensuring Participation in Care**
   Nurse's Role: Involve Jane and Robert in Emma's daily care routines, such as feeding, diaper changes, and soothing techniques, to foster bonding and

confidence. Provide education on how these activities will support Emma's recovery and strengthen her resilience post-surgery. Incorporate opportunities for Robert to pray over Emma during caregiving routines, respecting his spiritual practices.

5. **Decision-Making Support and Flexibility**
   Medical Team's Role: Allow time for the parents to fully process the information and make their decision without pressure. Offer a second opinion or consultation with another pediatric surgeon if Robert requests it. Reassure the family that their decision-making process is respected and supported.

6. **Building Trust Through Follow-Up**
   Post-Surgery Communication: The surgeon provides immediate updates after the procedure. The chaplain is present during post-surgery updates to offer prayer and reassurance to the family. A NICU nurse or social worker meets with the family daily to provide updates on Emma's recovery and answer any questions.
   Celebrate Milestones: Highlight Emma's progress and milestones to encourage positivity and confidence in the parents.

7. **Offering Additional Resources:** Provide information on peer support groups for NICU families. Ensure access to hospital-based lactation consultants if needed. Offer educational materials on premature baby care and post-surgical recovery. Schedule follow-up meetings with the family advocate and psychologist to discuss the transition home.

8. **Long-Term Support:** Create a comprehensive discharge plan for Emma's transition home, including follow-up appointments, at-home care instructions, and emergency contacts. Arrange for ongoing spiritual support with the chaplain or a local pastor of Robert's choosing. Provide access to mental health resources for both parents through counseling or peer group sessions.

Outcomes of Family-Centered Care

For Jane: She feels supported in her decision to advocate for Emma's surgery and is reassured by the medical team's clear communication and resources.

For Robert: He finds emotional and spiritual solace through prayer with the chaplain, gaining trust in the medical team and feeling reassured that his faith is respected.

For Emma: She benefits from a timely surgical intervention and a family that feels empowered and prepared to support her recovery.

By incorporating spiritual, emotional, and practical resources, family-centered care ensures the Smith family remains supported and engaged throughout Emma's NICU journey, fostering trust and collaboration that extends beyond the hospital stay.

CHAPTER SEVENTEEN
Trauma-Informed Care in the NICU

TRAUMA-INFORMED CARE - MARY COUGHLIN, MS, NNP, NCC-E

In the Neonatal Intensive Care Unit, every interaction can significantly impact the fragile lives of newborns and their families. Implicit bias—unconscious attitudes or stereotypes that affect our understanding, actions, and decisions—can subtly but profoundly undermine communication in this critical environment. Utilizing a trauma-informed framework is essential to recognize and mitigate these biases, ensuring that every family receives equitable care and support.

Implicit bias in the NICU can manifest in various ways; clinicians may communicate differently with families based on their backgrounds or they may make assumptions about a family's understanding and needs. For instance, a parent's concern might be dismissed due to stereotypical beliefs about their socioeconomic status or education level, leading to a breakdown in communication and care. Such biases can erode trust, create misunderstandings, and exacerbate the already high levels of stress and trauma experienced by NICU parents.

To combat this, NICU teams must be trained to recognize and actively address their biases.

Trauma-Informed Care principles emphasize safety, trust, healthy relationships, empowerment, and equity. Applying these principles can help create a more inclusive environment where every family feels heard, respected, and valued.

Equally important is the provision of early mental health services for NICU parents. The NICU experience can be deeply traumatic, and parents often struggle with a variety of feelings that can lead to anxiety, depression, and PTSD. With mental health support, parents can process their emotions, build a repertoire of effective coping strategies, enhance their decision-making capabilities, and foster healthy parent-infant attachment and bonding that ultimately enriches their baby's developmental outcomes.

By addressing implicit bias and offering robust proactive mental health support, we can improve communication and outcomes in the NICU, ensuring that all babies and families receive the compassionate, equitable care they deserve.

Over twenty years ago, Kaiser and the CDC launched a groundbreaking study of over 17,000 patients. The results showed a direct link between adverse childhood experiences, commonly known as ACEs, and long term health and wellness. When participants reported four or more ACEs, this corresponded to an increased chance for heart disease, cancer, or drug abuse. With six or more ACEs, life expectancy decreased by almost twenty years.

Because of the field I work in, I recently spent some time doing further research on Trauma in the NICU and its correlation to both healthcare and equity work. As part of this process, I came across many important resources, including work done by Dr. Mary Coughlin on Trauma and Nervous System using a polyvagal perspective.

Research shows the Automatic Nervous System (ANS) reveals enormous implications for the way we understand NICU spaces. It is widely noted that when we experience trauma and chronic stress as humans, it can keep our Automatic Nervous System (ANS) from functioning in a healthy, regulated and resilient way, and can keep us stuck in states of survival. For those with a history of trauma and chronic stress, the ANS detection system often becomes faulty, constantly signaling danger even when we are safe.

So what does this have to do with the NICU? Coughlin posits that it has to do with connection. Research also shows that childhood experiences don't just impact our health, they also keep us from connecting with others - which can be devastating for children, whose number one survival priority is to attach to caregivers.

When babies are living in chronic states of unsafety, their ANS doesn't get "wired" right. Imagine of your first taste of the world was in the NICU, a place often filled with frightening experiences - loud noises, strange people, unpredictability, sharp experiences of pain or discomfort...the list of ACES could go on and on. These traumatic experiences may unwittingly teach the child that the world is a dangerous place - which not only contributes to their long-term health, but their immediate health and wellbeing in our care.

Trauma also compromises our ability to engage with others, replacing the need for connection with the need for protection. As Coughlin reminds us, when there has been trauma, our ANS can no longer differentiate between our unsafe past and our now safe present. This means that even after the crisis has passed, children in the NICU (or who previously experienced a NICU stay) may be struggling to feel safe and regulated.

It is important for us to be aware of this as healthcare professionals. We must ask ourselves: How can we make the NICU the most trauma-informed space possible? How can we help these children survive and thrive through creating a sense of felt safety even in the midst of the necessary medical interventions? The last thing we want is for these children to graduate from the NICU, only to face years of further health and emotional challenges for the rest of their lives.

Retraining Our ANS

The good news is that science tells us that we CAN retrain our ANS to feel safe again, and that this is mainly done through co-regulation with others. Children's brains are amazingly adaptive, and with the right attachment to their caregivers (normally their parents), and enough experiences of attunement to their positive emotions, the brain will learn a sense of safety again, increasing its capacity for resilience and flexibility.

The most important thing to remember in the NICU is that we aren't required to give children a calm environment every moment. Rather, we need to help children develop a flexible and resilient nervous system that can accurately assess safety or danger and respond appropriately. By creating systems where caregivers are able to access this place of calm and safety, and by giving children enough positive moments of connecting with these caregivers, the negative impact of traumatic experience can be cushioned and eventually integrated into a more adaptive and resilient view of the world. And that, in the end, is what we want for all of our patients in our work towards equity, wholeness, and belonging.

NURTURING EQUITY GROUP EXERCISE

Gather into groups of two or three. If possible, make sure that at least one healthcare professional in your group has experience in a NICU setting. Discuss their experiences of the past week and make a list: on one side, list what experiences might set a child or caregiver's Automatic Nervous System into flight or fight. On the other side, list the positive experiences that would help a child and caregiver co-regulate and experience safety.

Discuss the following questions together:

1. Which list was longest? Why do you think this is?
2. Where do you see the inequity? Where are the disparities?
3. What do you think could be done to balance these lists for the wellbeing of the children in your care?
4. What does Trauma-Informed Care look like in the NICU setting?
5. List five action steps you can take this week to care for patients in a Trauma-Informed way.

CASE STUDY: *Trauma-Informed Care for a Single Parent with Kidney Failure and Dialysis*

Maria Lopez, a 32-year-old Hispanic single mother, suffers from kidney failure and undergoes dialysis three times a week. She was diagnosed with kidney failure several years ago and has struggled with managing her health alongside being a mother to her 6-month-old son, Antonio. During her pregnancy, Maria experienced significant depression and felt unsupported by family or friends. Her job recently laid her off, and now Maria is concerned about how she will care for her baby while managing her health and financial instability. Maria is a devout Catholic and finds solace in her faith. She feels isolated and overwhelmed, unsure of how to navigate her health issues and motherhood, especially in light of her financial struggles.

As a group, read through the following recommendations and discuss the questions at the end of each step together.

Steps for Trauma-Informed Care

1. **Initial Assessment**
   The first step in trauma-informed care is to conduct a compassionate, non-judgmental assessment that recognizes Maria's unique struggles and challenges
   Physical Health: Assess the status of Maria's kidney failure and dialysis treatments, ensuring she has access to necessary medical care. Check her dialysis schedule, health symptoms, and any complications that might arise. Review her postpartum health and ensure that she has access to maternal health care, addressing any lingering physical or emotional concerns from her pregnancy and childbirth.
   Mental Health: Conduct a mental health screening to evaluate Maria's current state of depression, stress, or anxiety. Given her previous experience with depression during pregnancy, assess whether she is experiencing postpartum depression or chronic stress related to her health, finances, and caregiving responsibilities. Acknowledge her history of depression and validate the impact it has had on her emotional and physical well-being.
   Social Support: Explore Maria's current support system, including any family or friends who may be able to assist her with childcare or emotional support. Recognize her isolation due to the lack of support during pregnancy and her current struggles, including her recent job loss.
   Spiritual Needs: Recognize Maria's Catholic faith as an essential source of comfort and strength. Allow space for her to express her spiritual needs and connect her with faith-based resources if desired.

Questions: What, if any, aspects do you feel are missing from this assessment? How can you ensure that racial bias does not play a part?

2. **Trauma-Informed Approach**
   A trauma-informed approach ensures that Maria feels safe, validated, and empowered during her care.
   Create a Safe and Respectful Environment: Show empathy by acknowledging the challenges Maria faces in a non-judgmental way. Avoid blaming her for her situation, and instead listen carefully to her concerns. Ask open-ended questions and provide a space where she feels comfortable expressing her fears, frustrations, and needs without fear of being dismissed or stigmatized. Build trust by providing consistent and clear communication about available resources and options.
   Empathy and Compassion in Interaction: Use active listening, allowing Maria to speak freely about her emotional and physical struggles. Validate her feelings, acknowledging the stress of being a single parent, facing health challenges, and dealing with a job loss. Emphasize that seeking help and utilizing resources does not equate to failure, but rather to strength and self-care.

Questions: What challenges do you foresee in creating this environment for Maria? What self-awareness will it require from you as a clinician?

3. **Resources and Support for Maria**
   The following are some possible resources you could refer Maria to for additional support.

   Physical Health Support:

   Dialysis Center Referral: Ensure Maria is connected to a local dialysis center with convenient access to treatments and follow-up care.
   Nephrologist Consultation: Refer Maria to a nephrologist for ongoing management of her kidney failure. Make sure she is receiving regular check-ups and treatment for any related complications.
   Pediatric Care: Ensure that Antonio is connected with pediatric care services for well-child visits, vaccinations, and infant care. Offer resources on infant care and support for new mothers.

   Mental Health Support:

   Psychological Counseling: Refer Maria to a mental health professional specializing in trauma, depression, and chronic illness. Therapy can help Maria address her postpartum depression, manage the emotional toll of chronic illness, and navigate her feelings of isolation.
   Support Groups for Single Parents and Chronic Illness: Connect Maria with support groups for single mothers, people dealing with chronic illness, and those who have experienced depression during pregnancy. These groups can help her build community, share coping strategies, and reduce her sense of isolation.

   Social Support and Advocacy:

   Catholic Charities Referral: Provide a referral to Catholic Charities for assistance with food, emergency financial support, or access to faith-based services. Many Catholic organizations offer support programs that can help Maria with childcare resources, food pantries, or financial aid during difficult times.
   Family Advocate/Case Manager: Refer Maria to a family advocate or case manager who can assist her in accessing additional community resources, including housing, childcare assistance, and benefits. The case manager can help her navigate public services and connect her to local programs that address her needs as a mother and an individual with chronic illness.
   Food Assistance: Provide information on food assistance programs such as SNAP (Supplemental Nutrition Assistance Program) or local food banks to alleviate financial stress.

   Financial Assistance and Employment Support:

   Unemployment Benefits Referral: Help Maria apply for unemployment benefits and offer guidance on other available financial assistance programs for people in her situation.
   Job Retraining and Placement Programs: Refer Maria to workforce development programs that focus on job retraining, resume building, and placement assistance to help her return to work when she is able.
   Childcare Assistance: Connect Maria to local subsidized childcare programs or resources for affordable daycare. This will allow Maria to care for herself and her health while having support for Antonio's care.

Questions: What, if any, supports are missing from this list? How can you make sure referrals are not weaponized?

4. **Equitable Empathy and Compassion**

    Equitable Empathy: Recognize Maria's Hispanic cultural background and Catholic faith as crucial aspects of her identity. Empathetic care should involve respecting her values and using culturally relevant language and practices. Ensure that all resources provided to Maria are equitable, meaning they take into account her specific needs as a single mother with chronic illness, while also considering the financial strain she is under. Provide resources in Spanish if necessary, to ensure that Maria can fully understand and access available support.

    Compassion: Demonstrate compassion by addressing all aspects of Maria's well-being—physical, emotional, social, and spiritual. Ensure that Maria is not only receiving healthcare but also emotional and spiritual support through counseling, faith-based resources, and community groups. Involve Maria in decisions about her care, ensuring that she feels empowered and included in her treatment plan. Acknowledge her concerns and preferences, particularly around her faith and cultural practices. For example, if she would like a chaplain to pray with her, make that a part of her care plan.

Questions: What was the healthcare provider's compassion level (1-10)?

5. **Plan and Referrals**

    Immediate Action Plan (Sample):
    - Maria will continue with her dialysis treatments and receive necessary nephrology care.
    - She will begin counseling sessions to address depression and emotional well-being.
    - Maria will be connected to Catholic Charities for food, financial support, and faith-based services.
    - A family advocate or case manager will be assigned to assist Maria with accessing local resources and addressing childcare needs for Antonio.

    Long-Term Plan:
    - Maria will engage in job training programs when her health allows and will be referred to additional support as her financial situation improves.
    - She will receive ongoing emotional and spiritual support, including access to a chaplain for prayer and faith guidance.
    - Maria will be supported with consistent check-ins, addressing her physical, emotional, and financial well-being as she moves forward with her care.

Questions: What resources were afforded and extended to Maria? Is there anything you would change about this action plan?

By providing trauma-informed care with an emphasis on equitable empathy and compassion, Maria receives holistic support tailored to her unique needs, ultimately improving her ability to manage her health, care for her son, and access the resources necessary to navigate her challenges.

In the following chapter, we will discuss what it looks like to care for Infant Mental Health in the NICU and other healthcare settings.

CHAPTER EIGHTEEN
Infant Mental Health

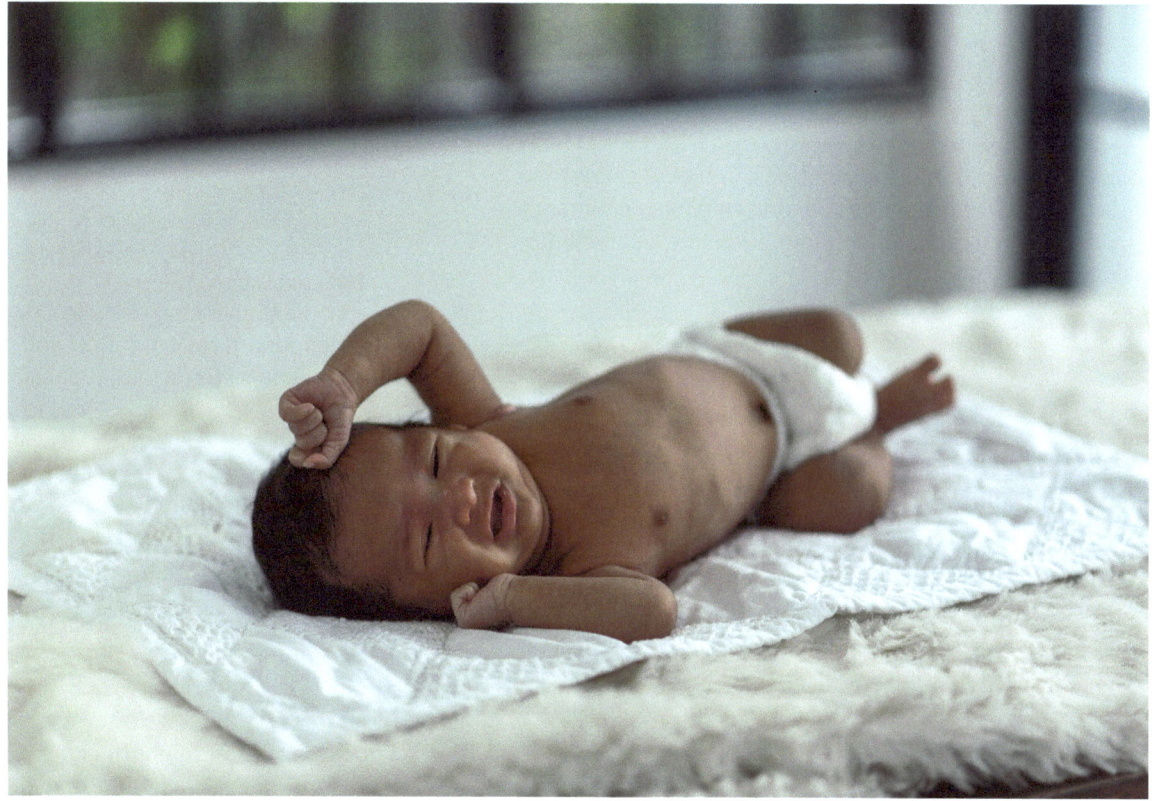

As we saw in the previous chapter, when we experience trauma and chronic stress as humans, it can keep our Autonomic Nervous System (ANS) from functioning in a healthy way, and keep us stuck in states of survival. This poses the question: can infants experience mental health problems? What about positive mental health?

Infant mental health is a growing field in psychology as we learn fascinating truths about babies' brains and how they experience the world, even before birth. In fact, it was long believed that newborns, due to their underdeveloped nervous systems, were not capable of feeling pain. However, research in the last few decades has shown that infants, even in the earliest stages of life, not only feel pain but also experience stress and emotional discomfort. Not only is their nervous system sensitive, but the brain pathways responsible for pain perception and emotional responses are active. Knowing this, it is critical that we respond to every opportunity to provide appropriate pain relief, comfort, and emotional support during medical procedures to protect their developing brain and promote healthy emotional and neurological growth.

The shift in understanding infant mental health is transformative not only for the field of healthcare but also for the way society views the emotional lives of young children. If we acknowledge that infants are capable of feeling and experiencing trauma, healthcare providers must then approach care with empathy, compassion, and awareness of the long-term impact of their actions. As we move forward, it is crucial that we continue to prioritize the emotional well-being of infants, integrating this knowledge into clinical practices that protect and nurture the mental health of our youngest and most vulnerable patients.

This new paradigm calls for a commitment to healing and preventing harm from the earliest stages of life, ensuring that all infants are given the best possible start in life—not just physically, but emotionally as well.

The Impact of Formative Experiences on Infant Mental Health

As mentioned, it was widely believed for many years that infants lacked the capacity for emotional responses or memory. Because of this, healthcare practices in neonatal care often focused on physical outcomes—such as survival rates or medical procedures. The emotional and physical distress these procedures caused had long-term effects on infants, especially when repeated without adequate pain relief or emotional soothing.

In reality, we now know that early traumatic experiences, such as excessive pain or prolonged stress, can disrupt the development of the infant's brain. Although their memories are not stored explicitly, every infant's brain still records implicit memories (emotional and physiological responses that are stored in their brains). Research proves that repeated painful experiences, without being followed by comfort or nurturing, may directly affect children's emotional health later in life.

With all of this information, we now have a much greater awareness about how integral infant mental health is to adult health and development. A newborn's emotional, psychological, and neurological needs are just as important as their physical. It is key that we learn to recognize the early signs of emotional distress in infants and to take action to mitigate the impact of procedures, as well as the impact of isolation and distress that can be caused by a long NICU stay.

Key Principles for Supporting Infant Mental Health

Remember that as we discussed in the previous chapter, when there has been trauma, our ANS can no longer differentiate between our unsafe past and our now safe present. Even after the crisis has passed, children in the NICU need our care in order to feel safe and regulated. Here are some of the key principles for you to remember:

Pain Management and Comfort: proper pain management during procedures could include using pain-relief techniques, minimizing the number of painful procedures, and providing comfort such as holding, swaddling, or gentle touch during and after procedures.

Reducing Stress: Prioritize reducing unnecessary noise, bright lights, and distressing stimuli. Where possible, avoid procedures that cause unnecessary distress.

Promoting Secure Attachment: Support and encourage bonding with primary caregivers by facilitating skin-to-skin contact, breastfeeding, and encouraging involvement in care.

Infant Mental Health as Part of Holistic Care: Infant mental health must be integrated into all aspects of neonatal and pediatric care. This includes training healthcare providers to recognize the psychological and emotional needs of infants and to work collaboratively with parents and caregivers to provide supportive, nurturing environments.

Social Determinants in Infant Health

From the very beginning, parents and caregivers play a critical role in helping build good mental health for a child and those they provide care for. Because brain development happens so rapidly (up to 1 million new neural connections per second), the quality of early care has a tremendous impact on a child.

We know from our discussion in Section One that poverty, racism, sexism, pollution, lack of nutrition, and many other social determinants all impact the environment and development of children. Fortunately, so do love, acceptance, encouragement, and unconditional positive regard. Many studies show that even for children who have experienced many ACES, having a secure and loving attachment to a caregiver can buffer much of the stress in their environment.

Babies in the NICU start off at a deficit when it comes to building good, healthy attachment. Families from historically marginalized communities face all these barriers and more, including environmental toxins, unstable housing, higher life stress, and many other factors. Weathering (see Section 2) has a huge impact on the birth experiences of Black and Brown women, directly resulting from structural racism. Our empathetic recognition and response to these disadvantages will determine the level of equitable healthcare we provide.

Because of this, it is critical that we provide empathetic and equitable care to parents and caregivers, in order for them to be able to best provide security and attunement for their child. Caregivers are who model for children how to respond adaptively to adversity and thrive. By being a trauma-informed environment for both patients, we can support parents and caregivers in their ongoing journey. And as healthcare providers, we must also practice our own regulation skills, in order to assist the infants in our care and protect them from absorbing our own stress at the bedside.

NURTURING EQUITY GROUP EXERCISE

Read the following case studies and discuss the questions below with your team. Then, report back to the group.

CASE STUDY

Lucille is a first-time mother of Hawaiian and African descent whose child is placed in the NICU right after birth. At first, they believe it will only be for a few days, but as the days stretch into weeks, you begin to notice signs of anxiety and hypervigilance in your interactions with Lucille, and wonder if there are ways you could help her find a greater sense of calm and safety.

Discuss with your team:

1. Knowing what you know about infant mental health, what is the best plan of action?

2. What resources are available to Lucille that you could refer her to?

3. What do you think is the best way to discuss what you observe with Lucille? How can you involve her in her own and her child's wellbeing?

4. How can you as a healthcare team build a sense of safety and regulation in your interactions with Lucille and her child?

ADDITIONAL RESOURCES

BOOKS

Dr. Jay L. Rosenbloom, *"Pain in Neonates"*

Dr. Rosenbloom's work focuses on understanding the neurological aspects of pain in neonates and how early-life pain can affect development. His research explores the pain processing systems in infants and emphasizes the importance of proper pain management in neonatal care.

Dr. Maria Fitzgerald, *"The Neurobiology of Pain in Infancy"*

Dr. Fitzgerald's groundbreaking work helped shift the paradigm in understanding that infants experience pain. Her research highlights how the infant brain processes pain, providing insights into how early pain experiences can affect long-term neurological development.

Dr. Ronald G. Barr, *"Pain in Infants, Children, and Adolescents"*

Dr. Barr's work is foundational in pediatric pain management. He explains how infants perceive pain and the critical importance of addressing pain early to prevent long-term psychological and neurological consequences.

Dr. Catherine A. Lord, *"Infant and Early Childhood Mental Health: A Neurobiological Perspective"*

This book provides a comprehensive exploration of infant brain development and the emotional experiences of infants. Dr. Lord's work examines the impact of early caregiving and medical interventions on mental and neurological health, stressing the interconnectedness of physical and emotional well-being in infancy.

ARTICLES

Dr. Susan J. L. H. Lee, *"Neonatal Pain and the Long-term Consequences of Early-life Pain"*

Dr. Lee's research addresses the neurodevelopmental consequences of untreated neonatal pain, including how early-life trauma and pain experiences shape emotional and neurological outcomes.

Dr. Nils Bergman, *"The Impact of Birth and Early Maternal Care on Infant Mental Health"*

Dr. Bergman's research emphasizes the importance of early bonding and nurturing care to prevent emotional and neurological distress in infants. He explores how early experiences shape emotional development and advocates for minimizing interventions that cause trauma during early infancy.

World Health Organization (WHO), Reports on Infant Health and Pain

The WHO has developed guidelines based on evidence that neonates feel pain and require appropriate management. These resources advocate for better practices in neonatal intensive care units (NICUs) and other medical settings to reduce trauma and pain in infants.

American Academy of Pediatrics (AAP) Guideline/Position Statement, *"Pain Relief in Neonates"*

The AAP recognizes the importance of pain management in newborns and calls for physicians to assess pain and distress in infants. Their guidelines reflect the current scientific understanding that infants can feel pain and that inadequate pain management can have long-lasting effects.

CHAPTER NINETEEN
Language and Communication

NEONATAL INTENSIVE CARE UNIT: (NICU) THE IMPACT OF LANGUAGE AND COMMUNICATION RELATING TO OUTCOMES FOR PARENTS

by Mia Malcolm, BS, CDFT

Anytime there is a group of NICU parents (e.g. at a conference, in a cafe, at the hospital), we, at some point, talk about our experiences in the unit. Primarily, we discuss the idea that while our babies were there fighting for their lives, we, like our babies, were also premature. Imagine that. Choosing those words, that language, to describe yourselves as adults. Imagine people that were moving through life with a plan to "adult" and yet were thrust into parenting prematurely. Except, no one sees you as premature. No one realizes that like you, like your babu, are not ready. They only see you as an adult. In the NICU, these people were medical professionals. Often, ones with little to no empathy for our newly found status of prematurity because they see us as fully functioning, fully informed (when it suits them), fully capable adults. So, they address us as such. Truth is: We are premature. We are overstimulated, overwhelmed, not ready, scared, incapable of language, in crisis, and in need of support. What we need is a lifeline via effective communication to provide us with hope, collaboration, and information.

Effective communication hinges on many things: <u>clarity</u>, consideration, context and intentionality, and listening. The "simplest" of the three, clarity (i.e. to speak plainly) is seemingly impossible from a parent point of view. Oftentimes, communication in the NICU comes to us as a foreign language of acronyms and medical jargon and is not centered on what we as parents need or understand. IVH, PDA, BPD, central line, umbilical line, and CBC. I was barely 12 hours postpartum, and I had entered a medical school program to which I never applied.

Even worse, while I did not understand most of these words, because no clarification was ever given, I did fully understand the part where they told me that my son was going to die. They were very clear that his chances of survival were extremely minimal and that if he did survive. he would likely be "blind, deaf, para/quadriplegic and unable to talk, live outside the hospital setting, or breath on his own…" Indeed, it was very clear that the people who took an oath to "first do no harm" had no hope for my son. No medical jargon could cover up that fact. So, when my father kneeled in front of me and grabbed my face and said, "you have to get discharged from the hospital and get over there with your baby." A dying little Black boy is who they experiment on…they are going to kill your baby. You can't leave him." I was clear. The lack of clarity by medical professionals regarding my son's care activated my need for effective communication, activated my trauma, and broke my trust.

Still, considering all the acronyms and medical speak, as a parent, the most interesting part of "medical language" is the word *failure*. Words on their own are not "good" or "bad." *Context* makes them so. For example, *positive* is good and negative is bad. That is unless you test positive for COVID or have a negative blood culture. Context is everything. It provides meaning to the message and helps avoid miscommunication.

Failure, like any other word, is not bad or problematic on its own. Indeed, I believe many things can fail inside of a hospital or NICU. Machines can fail, medicine can fail, we, as the adults in the room with all the information, can fail to do our jobs effectively. But babies, my baby, the patients, cannot fail. If the purpose was to convey that the treatment plan did not work, say that. Do not put the onus on the baby who had no choice in the matter. They are not failing the medicine that has been around since 400 B.C. They are not failing the machines. And, most importantly, they are not failing the practitioners of the medicine. They are not even supposed to "be born yet" most of the time – let alone doing much beyond existing and surviving. The word failure being used to describe our babies is not only hurtful, but it is harmful and adds to our trauma. Therefore, medical professionals must have consideration for the patients, who are babies, and their parents/caregivers when communicating with them, by being intentional with their words. We are in active trauma. Although I do not think that we take things out of context during this time, I do believe that miscommunication or lack of communication leaves too much room for the imagination. We as premature parents, are processing with the tools we have available while emotionally dysregulated and navigating trauma. So, if your explanations are lacking consideration for our present situation and you are not being clear or using intentional - language you are setting the foundation for miscommunication.

The imagination of a tired, stressed out, terrified, hangry individual, like a NICU parent, is a complicated place to be. Remember that for many of us, the reason that our babies are "failures" is because our bodies failed them. We do not need you to remind us. We are well aware. When medical professionals mentioned my son's "failure to thrive" or "failure to extubate" it may not have been their intention to also remind me of my body's failure to provide him with what he needed to thrive, but that was all I could hear. My need for effective communication had increased because of their lack of context, consideration, and intentionality. And so had my trauma.

Last, but not least, the key to effective communication is listening. As a NICU parent, I believe the main reason that communication in the NICU is so hard is because healthcare professionals do not know how to listen. Listening, on the surface, feels easy since we've been told to do it our entire lives. But the reality is that most of us do not do it well, if at all. Brene Brown, in her tv series *Atlas of the Heart*, points out that listening is a two-part process: humility and empathy. I think that health care professionals often miss the first part– hearing with humility. Humility means decentering oneself. It means that you, healthcare professionals, *are not the most important people in the room*. You are not the headline or center of this story. Your feelings, thoughts, etc. are not the biggest or most important thing. And sometimes that can be a hard concept to grasp.

I know that the nurses, doctors, respiratory therapists, physical therapists, occupational therapists, etc., all cared about my son. But no matter how any of them felt about him, they never felt more for him than we, his family, did. Their concern for him was never more than ours was. They were not more worried, scared, or happy. They didn't dream bigger or pray harder for him than we did, than I did. He, at the end of the day, was their patient. He is my child. I loved him before I knew him. Before I saw his face, before I knew his name, before I heard his heartbeat. I dreamed for him. He is my child. So whatever feelings they had, we were not the same. Our journeys inside that hospital were not the same. You trained for this. You prepared for these hard moments that were happening to your patient. **You are at work. I am in hell.** Listen to me because these words are intentional: I am in hell.

Your job is my hell. I am in hell while you are at work. We are not the same. So, hear me when I say that I am scared. When I say, "I didn't hear you" even though you have explained it 100 times, hear that I am swimming and drowning and meet me where I am instead of judging me for being in the sunken place. Because again I am trying to navigate hell for my heart, my child, with no GPS, no training, no preparation – I am premature. I am doing my best. I know it's hard to believe.

The second part of listening is believing people when they tell you about their experiences. With you. With life. With your unit. With *this*. This moment in their shoes. AND, this is the **hard part,** because real listening requires you to believe people even when, especially when, their experience doesn't reconcile or align with your own experiences of life, of your colleague, your unit or yourself. Believing families is what healthcare professionals do not do and it's usually the reason that they are called to task for not listening.

Brene Brown talks about the fact that we will ask people, "what is that like" or "what's wrong" or "how are things going" and they tell us about being "overlooked, ignored, or dismissed." In the NICU, we will tell clinicians or leaders about how they (the staff) have hurt us, how they have broken our hearts, our trust, about micro and macro aggressions, about not being heard. They ask and we tell them. But because our experiences are not their experiences, because they would never hurt *anyone*–perfect people could never–they don't believe us. Even though they asked us, even though they claimed to listen to what we, the families have said, they don't believe us. Why? Brene Brown says that because too much of what professionals have invested their time, energy, resources, and life in is threatened if that family is telling the truth of their experience. It is impossible to have effective communication with families and achieve true patient and family centered care and deliver hope to our families if we don't increase our compassion ceiling through empathy and true listening, which means BELIEVING FAMILIES WHEN THEY TELL YOU THEIR EXPERIENCES IN THEIR SHOES! When you don't believe us, trust crumbles and our trauma dam breaks.

Communication is the foundation of any relationship – language is what we build on. You cannot get anywhere in the NICU journey–to trust, healing, discharge, safety, planning, feeding, or diagnosis– without language and communication. Jay Z said in an interview once, that when words fail, disease sets in. When we take the time to be intentional with our words, cognizant of the impact, and committed to hearing others, we are able to understand or receive ideas and thoughts that may be different from our own. This is the foundation of collaboration with families.

Language, words, the ability to communicate – these are the most powerful tools you have. Regardless of who, what, when or where you come from, you use language –verbal, body, or visual–to express your feelings and thoughts to others. When you are abusive or arrogant with your words, trust is broken. When you are irresponsible, flippant, dismissive, or disrespectful with your words – you obliterate trust. Trust is lost in buckets and gained in drops. One word can throw gallons of trust out the window. That is the power of language. If the goal is to collaborate towards improved outcomes for families, it is imperative to pause and take inventory of your words and the power they have to impact trust, outcomes, and collaboration with families. Because, as I said, when words fail, disease sets in, and it may be an incurable disease if you are not careful.

UNDERSTANDING THE POWER OF WORDS IN CLINICAL SETTINGS

by Dr. Candace Kelly

When communicating with parents about their premature baby's health. the language clinicians use is more than just a means of conveying information. It can profoundly shape parents' understanding and emotional responses, potentially influencing their decisions and long-term perceptions. This phenomenon is partly explained by the concept of anchoring bias—a cognitive bias where individuals rely too heavily on the first piece of information they receive (the 'anchor*) when making decisions.

In their article, "NICU Language, Everyday Ethics, and Giving Better News: Optimizing Discussions about Disability with Families, authors Paige Terrien Church, Maya Dahan, Amy Rule, Annie Janvier, Jane E. Stewart, John S. Maypole, Darcy Fehlings. Jonathan S. Litt, and Rudaina Banihani, suggest that the Neonatal Intensive Care Unit (NICU) has a language and culture that is its own. For professionals, it is a place of intense and constant attention to microdetails and cautious optimism. For parents, it is a foreign place with a new and unique language and culture. It is also the setting in which they are introduced to their child and parenthood for this child. This combination has been referred to as an emotional cauldron. The neonatal ethics literature mainly examines complex ethical dilemmas about chitchening/drawing life sustaining interventions for fragile children.

In the context of discussing neurodevelopmental outcomes for premature babies, the language clinicians choose can anchor parents' expectations and perceptions, sometimes in unintended ways. For example, if a clinician uses a term like "severe impairment", this may create a lasting association in the parents' minds that heavily influences their understanding of their child's future, even if the actual prognosis is more nuanced.

The use of such language can lead to anchoring bias, where the initial description heavily influences the parents' subsequent thoughts and decisions, potentially overshadowing other relevant information. This is particularly problematic because once an anchor is set, it can be challenging to adjust parents' perceptions, even when presented with additional data or alternative perspectives.

Recommendations for Clinicians: Communicating with Care

To mitigate the effects of anchoring bias, clinicians should be mindful of the language they use when discussing neurodevelopmental outcomes with parents. Here are some recommendations:

Use Neutral Language: Avoid terms that might create a strong emotional response or set rigid expectations. Instead, use language that is descriptive but neutral, allowing room for a range of possible outcomes.

Provide Context: Ensure that parents understand the broader context of any prognosis. Explain that neurodevelopmental outcomes can vary widely and that early predictions are not always definitive.

Encourage Questions: Invite parents to ask questions and express their concerns. This helps ensure they have a clear understanding and can process the information more fully.

Follow-Up Communication: Recognize that initial conversations may set an anchor, but ongoing communication can help adjust and refine parents' understanding as their baby develops.

By carefully selecting words and being aware of the potential for anchoring bias, clinicians can provide information that supports parents in making well informed, balanced decisions about their premature baby's care.

HONEST AND RESPECTFUL COMMUNICATION: THE FOUNDATION

It has been said numerous times throughout this workbook that communication is the cornerstone of effective patient-family centered care, and that is what we should all be striving for.

In this chapter we will present three NICU Mothers that agreed to share their experiences, both highs and lows. They will also share valuable feedback for healthcare providers and how to provide family-centered care during NICU stays that dignifies and respects patients and parents. We will explore five family-centered drivers:

- The Prognosis
- What Did She Hear?
- The Challenges
- The Healthcare Provider's Growing Opportunities
- How Can We Work Together for Equitable Outcomes?

These raw stories have come from the depths of vulnerability, discouragement and struggle. Each of these mothers have come through their worst nightmares and triumphs, and now shares with us what we can do better as healthcare providers to communicate and use language that is honest, integrous, and hopeful even in the most traumatic prognosis.

Diane Ramierez and her son Beau (Hispanic Family)

The Prognosis

Beau has been diagnosed with Hypoxic-ischemic Encephalopathy (HIE), spastic quadriplegic cerebral palsy, Lennox-Gastaut Syndrome (LGS) which is a rare form of epilepsy, and a rare genetic mutation known as DHDDS.

Post-Discharge, these conditions have made Beau's life incredibly challenging, as he suffers from daily seizures - it started as 200+ a day, and has been managed to less than 20. His seizures, which began as infantile spasms and have since evolved into tonic -clonic seizures and LGS, have made his early years a continuous battle for stability and comfort.

What Did She Hear?

Diane was known in the NICU for readily asking questions when she did not understand the report-outs given by the bedside nurse to the medical providers during rounding. Curiously, she would ask, "Can you please break that down in layman's terms? I'm not a doctor and I'm not a nurse. I don't understand anything you just said. I need to understand what he's going through and I need to understand you."

At times, she was met with nonverbal resistance through body language. But this did not deter her or her continual ask for clarification. She and her partner were there every day without failure to support her child. Over the course of Beau's NICU stay, the parents were told many things such as, "You don't have to be at the bedside all day long. You should take advantage of down time or go on a date, spend some time away or take some personal time. "They didn't understand the trauma, the fear, of leaving your baby in a Neonatal unit in a critical condition - particularly when you were told your baby was not supposed to live after 48 hours, and you don't know if your baby will be there the next day, or the next.

Their presence at daily rounds were consistent, as difficult and hard as it was to hear what seemingly felt like no progress and constant failures. Their faith kept them faithing. There were times that tears would flow from their eyes during the most dismal report and the medical team or provider continued with nonstop medical information, until a kind voice spoke through saying, "I know this must be a lot to take in. Maybe we can pause." The provider who was reporting out stopped talking and looked with shock, not realizing both parents were in tears. The chaplain asked additionally, "Is there anything you need at this moment?" The father responded, "Thank you for your sensitivity. Can we just have a moment and you can come back to us?"

The Challenges

From the day Beau was born at 25 weeks, Diane and her partner were told he would die within 24-48 hours. She faced a mountain of discouragement and naysaying during their 249 day long stay in the NICU. As explained above, Beau's prognosis was rare and presented numerous and severe threats to his life. Yet Beau continued to confound the doctors by surviving, again and again. Just by being alive, he confounded all the science that said it was impossible, especially when he began to breathe on his own and his body began to be less rigid.

"As we prepared to leave the NICU, we received many well-wishes from NICU parents that we had befriended for life, and staff," said Diane. "Doctors came around and wished us well. Social work stopped by to assure us all equipment would arrive on time. Beau's primary doctor walked us near the elevator after the graduation celebration, held me close, and whispered, "I really, really hope the best for you and your family."

"Those last words haunt me from time to time because I feel she could have prepared me for what I didn't know I was headed toward, which was my resignation of my full-time job with benefits, my social life, and my freedom. I've had to learn how to care for a NICU baby who needs 24-hr care and who needs 3-4 doctor appointments a week, and who suffered 200 seizures a day until finally doctors were able to manage them to 20. I didn't know what I didn't know. As painful as this reality is as a parent, we have a right to know the truth about our future and what it looks like, and every doctor should be courageous enough and honest enough to tell their families this truth."

The Healthcare Providers' Growing Opportunities

Reflecting on her experience in the NICU, Diane described that she and her partner felt so alone at times, like this was a fight they had to fight all by themselves. At times, they felt guilty for "making" the healthcare providers work harder to keep their son alive. She expressed many "misses" in communication, where providers failed to explain the situation to her appropriately. Had they done so, she might have made different decisions at several points in Beau's journey.

How Can We Work Together for Equitable Outcomes?

What encouraged Diane and her partner was watching the medical team eventually, one by one, join "Team Beau," as she calls it. They began to cheer him on as he made unexplainable progress over and over again. She believes that clear, honest communication that takes the time needed for parents to truly understand their child's situation is key to the best outcomes for children in the NICU. Without adequate understanding and information, parents cannot make the most well-informed decisions, and relationships between providers and families can become strained or even tainted with suspicion and distrust. Although Diane, Felix and Beau's journey is still paved with challenges, Diane is grateful for all those who chose to hope with her in those uncertain days.

Diane and Felix offer the following suggestions:

1. When rounding, address parents with empathy and honest communication.
2. Accept a parent's hope, even if it doesn't line up with your values.
3. Discuss as much as in your power what the future care management looks like for this child and this family, i.e. frequent medical appointments, viableness, ability to speak and walk, neurological function.
4. Healthcare providers should work harder at being completely honest with parents about the realities they face - the long-term outcomes they may see, the way it will irrevocably change their lives forever. It is devastating to receive bad news, but also be taking a baby home without full knowledge of how to care for them, and realistic expectations of what they will face.

Monica Johnson (African American Family)

The Prognosis

Monica will never forget the day Nia was born. She arrived too soon, at just 35 weeks premature, but to her, she was perfect, her miracle, her little fighter. The doctors soon shattered her joy with devastating news: Nia had heart failure and severe neurological damage. They told Monica and her husband that Nia would never progress like other children and would likely never live beyond her early teenage years. They felt their whole world crumbling around them.

What did they hear?

After fourteen days, the hospital called them into a family meeting, one of those cold, clinical rooms that, in Monica's words, "feels like a prison when you're facing your worst fears." They sat there surrounded by doctors—cardiologists, neurologists, palliative care specialists—and nurses, all with their charts and somber expressions. The chaplain was there too at Monica's request for her support, sitting right next to her, already sensing the heartbreak that filled the room.

As the cardiologist spoke, explaining Nia's prognosis in cold medical terms, Monica felt like she was drowning with twelve subspecialists staring at her and her husband, overwhelmed and not able to fully absorb all of his words. "Heart failure." She heard that part. Next, the neurologist spoke for about ten minutes nonstop, ending with "she is severely neurologically impaired." She could feel herself grow numb. Each phrase struck like a physical blow. She wanted so desperately to hear something hopeful, something that would tell her they were wrong. But instead, it felt like they were reading a script for Nia's future that she hadn't agreed to. Why are there are there so many subspecialists at the same time in the same room, expecting us to understand and absorb all of this critical information? she wondered. Is this fair? Is this normal? Is this reasonable? Why can't they space it out more gently at different times?

The Challenges

She had been holding onto a tiny sliver of hope. She'd overheard one of the nurses earlier, in the hallway. The nurse didn't know Monica was listening. Monica heard her tell another nurse that she was "too optimistic, unrealistic, and overprotective" of her baby - as if wanting her daughter to have a chance was a crime. It stung her so deeply. She felt judged, like she was wrong to hold onto hope, wrong to protect her little girl as fiercely as she could.

When it was her turn to speak, Monica couldn't hold it in any longer. Her voice trembled, but she made sure they heard her. "I overheard a nurse say that I'm too optimistic, unrealistic, and overprotective of my baby," she said. "You all keep talking about what Nia won't be, what she won't do. But I have to believe in her. I have to hope for her because I'm her mother. Isn't that what I'm supposed to do?"

The room went silent. Her husband squeezed her hand, but no one else spoke. Monica saw the awkward glances between the doctors, and she could feel their discomfort. It felt like they were so used to seeing the worst-case scenarios that they forgot what it meant to be human, to have a mother's heart that just couldn't give up.

The Healthcare Providers' Growing Opportunities

Moncia's husband, his voice choked with emotion, asked the question that was burning in both of them. "What happened to our baby girl? Why did this happen to her?"

The cardiologist looked at them without a hint of warmth. "She just had bad luck," he said flatly.

Bad luck? Their beautiful little girl, their Nia, reduced to just bad luck. Monica couldn't stay in the room another second. She ran out of the room, tears blinding her as she stumbled into the stairwell. She collapsed onto the steps, sobbing so hard she could barely breathe. How could they not see the little girl she saw, the one worth fighting for?

It wasn't long before the chaplain came after her. She sat next to Monica on the steps, her presence calm and gentle, just letting her be. When Monica finally managed to speak, she looked at her, her face wet with tears. "They don't get it. I'm not stupid. I know what they're saying, but how can I give up on my own child? They've given me no hope, but she's still my little girl. How do I go on when they tell me she'll never be what I dreamed she'd be?"

The chaplain put her arm around Monica, her voice soft and full of understanding. "You're not wrong for hoping. You're her mother. No one can take that from you. Even in this pain, even with all the medical talk, your love for Nia is everything. You are her advocate, her protector, her comfort. They can talk about what she won't be, but no one can tell you how to love your child. That's yours alone."

Monica nodded, still hurting, still angry, but feeling a little less alone. She knew then that her hope for Nia, no matter how "unrealistic" it seemed to them, was the only thing keeping her going. She couldn't change what was happening, but she could love her fiercely, protect her, and hold onto every moment she had.

How Can We Work Together for Equitable Outcomes?

Reflecting on her experience, Monica acknowledged that what was most difficult for her was the loss of hope, the sense of being left with nothing to cling to.

She suggests:

1. It is important that providers include dignifying ways of inclusive love language that honors and acknowledges the worthiness of love for a mother's baby who has limited time.

2. Consider how overwhelming it has to be for parents to have twelve subspecialists in one room, and consider spacing out different meetings for the benefit of their emotional health.

3. Nurses should approach every situation with empathy, understanding, and a non-judgemental perspective, and should create safe and supportive environments where parents feel seen, heard, and respected regardless of their background, emotional responses, or coping mechanisms.

As we see in Monica's story, it is a mother's job to hope for, to love, and to protect their child in the best way that they can. We as providers need to acknowledge this unique and sacred role and support them in it, as we do our best to fulfill ours.

The Power of Effective Communication in the NICU

On July 11, 2024 this author attended the Family Centered Care Task Office Hours Webinar where Mia Malcolm was one of the guest speakers. Below are some important takeaways from her talk, The Power of Effective Communication in the NICU, that all healthcare providers caring for NICU babies should benefit from.

TAKEAWAY #1: What Mia Heard

"The stories that were told to me about my son for so long were the worst stories ever written in my mind, because they were devoid of hope," Mia says. "All I heard from the day after he was born is how he would die. I heard how sick he was. How he had continuously missed the mark because he failed all these things. I heard stories about myself - that I was delusional or absent or a bad mom, had an unwillingness to listen which would cost 'the patient,' my son, his life."

TAKEAWAY #2: The use of the word "failure"

Mia heard this word often when referring to her son, as in, he "failed" a procedure or a medication. And yet it seemed that things were being asked of him that he was obviously not physically ready for.

How is it that this baby could be such a "failure", for example, when he is in such a vulnerable state? Are there more helpful terms we could use, such as "this medication was not effective," or "this procedure did not work?"

TAKEAWAY #3: "Misbehaving"

"Misbehaving": Mia also heard nurses saying, "man, he is really misbehaving today." She would wonder, "Do they think he's doing this on purpose, just to make their lives more difficult?"

TAKEAWAY #4 "Absentee" or "Disengaged"

Out of the over 268 days that her son was in NICU, Mia missed only 10 because she was hospitalized. His dad was present every single day. However, in the notes during those days Mia was labeled as "absentee" or "disengaged."

TAKEAWAY #5: "Difficult"

Mia would often hear people talked about as being "difficult families". Later, she went around a unit and asked a variety of people with different job titles what they felt "difficult" really meant?

Some of the answers that she received were that "difficult families" were:

- The ones don't show up
- The ones that are always there
- The ones that don't trust us, ask too many questions
- Those that don't ask enough questions
- Those that never tried to build rapport with the staff
- Those that are not compliant
- Those that are always questioning everything we do
- Those that don't listen
- Those that are writing down every single thing that we're saying. They're listening too much.

She remembers thinking after that: *so in order for me to be a good parent, or at least just not be difficult, I need to show up just enough, blindly trust strangers with my child, ask the right number of questions, be willing to listen but not listen too much, and adjust all of these things depending on who I'm interacting with.*

Mia admits that during their time in the NICU, she was probably labeled a "difficult" parent. She knows this because she was hyper-vigilant about everything. But nobody seemed to notice these traits and realize that this was really just a trauma response, and an area she might need extra support instead of being labeled "difficult." Never mind being her best self - she couldn't even be her full self most days because Gavin was unstable and she was emotionally dysregulated. *She was without adequate support from the staff, rather, much judgment.*

TAKEAWAY #6: Privilege and Power

"I think that a lot of us are socialized to be sympathetic," Mia says. "But when it comes to effective communication, especially in trauma situations, trying to walk in someone's shoes can unintentionally minimize their experience and make it all about you.

"Brene Brown talks about sympathy, saying basically that you can't walk in the shoes of someone who doesn't share your privileges around certain things like education, class, race, access to resources, privilege or power. We all know that there is a really big power dynamic that happens in our NICU space. And when you try to walk in the person's shoes, many times you end up causing harm or pain, which leads to disrespect or mistrust." Mia reminds us that the stories we tell among ourselves as staff - in the hallway, in charts, during handoffs, in the break room, during rounds right outside of people's doors like the walls are soundproof (and they are not) - are powerful stories precisely because of power.

"You don't get it and it's okay. I don't need you to get it. Invite yourself out of my shoes because I promise I don't need you to walk in them. Sympathy is the thing that we are often doing when empathy is what we should actually be doing because that is a gateway to compassion."

TAKEAWAY #7: Listening

"Listening is hard and it's a two part process, and I think that sometimes we get lost in the idea of it. But the first part of listening is listening with humility. We have to understand that we're having a shared experience and we are both caring for this child," Mia reminds us.

"That patient of yours, my child, which I love beyond any comprehension, is sick, is hurting, all of these things you've told me. It's your patient and it is my child, and we are not having the same experience. So hear me when I say that I'm scared or that I don't understand, even though you've explained it a hundred times. Just hear that I don't get it, and I need you to help me get it. When I say that I'm angry, create space where that's okay. Just hear me and meet me where I am in a judgment free zone."

TAKEAWAY #8: Fostering Hope

Language is the first way we foster hope. Our ability to communicate ideas is the most powerful tool that we have, because regardless of who we are, where we come from, we use language in all of its forms to express our thoughts and our feelings to others. When parents are in active trauma spaces, it's a hard place to communicate. If you don't provide very clear context for the information you share, you may be spreading fear.

We have the power to change the narrative and give people hope that regardless of the moment that they're in at that time, it's gonna be okay - and that they can define and redefine what "okay" means, with compassion, empathy, and intentionality in our language and listening.

NURTURING EQUITY-MINDED HEALTHCARE EXERCISE #1

Reflecting on these two family stories, choose one and discuss it with a partner. Using their suggestions, how would you provide family-centered care in this situation?

NURTURING EQUITY-MINDED HEALTHCARE EXERCISE #2

Discuss the above article with your small group. For each recommendation above, list two ways you can put them into action within your work environment.

CHAPTER TWENTY
Caring Beyond Beliefs: The Complexity of Supporting Same-Gender Loving Couples in Healthcare

Healthcare is a sacred calling—a commitment to **care, advocate, and heal** without prejudice. Yet, within the walls of hospitals, clinics, and care facilities, we encounter complex dynamics that challenge not only our clinical skills but also our personal values, beliefs, and convictions. One such complexity arises when providing care for **same-gender loving couples, and LGBTQIA+** families.

These couples, like all patients and families, come to us in vulnerable circumstances, seeking hope, answers, healing, and a sense of belonging. They are navigating the same fears, anxieties, and heartbreaks that any family faces, especially in high-stakes environments like the Neonatal Intensive Care Unit (NICU) or critical care settings. Their love, commitment, and grief are no different. Yet, the care they receive can often be filtered through the lens of societal biases, systemic barriers, or even the personal beliefs of healthcare providers.

But here's the truth:

We did not enter this field to serve only those who reflect our own values.

We became healthcare professionals to uphold the sacred principles of **compassion, equity, and dignity of all people**—to be a beacon of hope for every person, regardless of who they love or how they identify.

The Challenge of Personal Beliefs in Professional Spaces

As we discussed in Section One, it is natural for healthcare providers to carry personal convictions shaped by culture, religion, or upbringing. However, when we step into our roles, we make an unspoken promise:

- **To provide care impartially.**
- **To advocate fiercely for every patient.**
- **To create a safe space for healing, free from judgment.**

Our personal beliefs should never become a barrier to the dignity of another human being. Whether we fully understand or agree with a person's identity is not the measure of our professionalism—**our ability to care for them with respect and excellence is.**

The Human Cost of Bias in Healthcare

For same-gender loving couples, healthcare can be a minefield of microaggressions, silent judgments, or even overt discrimination:

- Parents questioned about their legitimacy in decision-making.
- Couples ignored or dismissed in favor of a "biological" parent.
- Healthcare environments that feel cold, unwelcoming, or unsafe.

These experiences don't just harm emotionally—they can delay care, erode trust, and contribute to worse health outcomes. Bias, whether conscious or unconscious, can cost lives.

Re-centering Our Purpose

When we strip away the layers of politics, religion, or societal norms, what remains is our fundamental purpose:

- **To heal.**
- **To comfort.**
- **To protect.**

We are called to meet people in their most vulnerable moments—not with judgment, but with empathy and excellence. The dignity of every human being is not negotiable. It's the very foundation of ethical healthcare.

A Call to Action

As healthcare professionals, we must continually reflect:

- Are my personal beliefs affecting the care I provide?
- Am I creating a space where every family feels safe and respected?
- How can I challenge my biases to better serve my patients?

Let us be leaders in not just **clinical best practices** but in **human dignity.**

Let us advocate fiercely, care deeply, and treat impartially—because **every person deserves to be seen, heard, and healed.**

CREATING A SENSE OF BELONGING AND SAFETY FOR LGBTQIA+ PARENTS IN HEALTHCARE

Remember our discussion about having two patients in the NICU (Patient and Parents)? In today's diverse healthcare landscape, it is essential to recognize and affirm the unique experiences of LGBTQIA+ parents, particularly in high-stress environments like the Neonatal Intensive Care Unit (NICU). This child's wellbeing is dependent on the wellbeing, safety, and belonging of the parents. These parents come from varied backgrounds, family structures, and lived experiences, yet they all share one common reality—they deserve respect, dignity, and compassionate care as they navigate the challenges of caring for a medically fragile newborn.

LGBTQIA+ parents are not just recipients of healthcare—they are also healthcare providers, leaders, and advocates. Their presence in the healthcare system is both personal and professional, adding layers to how they experience and interact with medical spaces. Despite progress in LGBTQIA+ rights and visibility, many parents still face barriers such as discrimination, exclusion, or unconscious bias when accessing medical care for their children.

Providing a sense of belonging and safety goes beyond simply acknowledging these families. It requires an intentional, trauma-informed approach that honors the humanity of each parent, regardless of personal values, beliefs, or cultural perspectives held by healthcare professionals. This is not about agreement with individual identities or family structures—it is about upholding the core principles of healthcare: equity, empathy, and ethical care.

Key Principles for Inclusive Care:

- Respect Over Agreement: Affirming a parent's identity and role in their child's life is not an endorsement of personal beliefs; it's a commitment to professional respect.
- Safety Without Bias: Every parent should feel safe from judgment, discrimination, or microaggressions while in healthcare spaces.
- Belonging as a Standard of Care: Inclusion should not be an exception—it should be embedded in the policies, language, and practices of all healthcare settings.

When healthcare teams foster environments where all families feel seen, heard, and valued, it leads to better outcomes—not just for the parents, but for the babies who rely on them. Compassionate, trauma-informed care helps reduce parental stress, promotes stronger family bonds, and ultimately supports the holistic well-being of the entire family unit.

Below, we will explore practical strategies for creating inclusive NICU environments, addressing barriers LGBTQIA+ parents face, and ensuring every family receives the dignified, respectful care they deserve.

TRAUMA-INFORMED CARE FOR LGBTQIA+ NICU PARENTS

Understanding Trauma in the LGBTQIA+ Community

To show appropriate care and empathy, we must recognize that LGBTQIA+ individuals may face unique stressors, including discrimination, rejection, and social stigma, which can be re-triggered in healthcare settings. This means acknowledging historical medical mistreatment and biases that contribute to mistrust, and understanding intersectionality—how race, socioeconomic status, and gender identity compound trauma experiences.

We must take into consideration these core principles when providing appropriate care:

- **Safety:** Ensure physical and emotional safety by using inclusive language, respecting pronouns, and creating a welcoming environment.
- **Trustworthiness & Transparency:** Communicate clearly, explain procedures thoroughly, and involve parents in decision-making.
- **Peer Support:** Connect LGBTQIA+ parents with support groups or mentors who share similar experiences.
- **Collaboration & Empowerment:** Value parents' input in care plans, reinforcing their role as essential members of the healthcare team.
- **Cultural, Historical, and Gender Sensitivity:** Educate staff on implicit bias and cultural competency to provide respectful and affirming care.

Barriers Faced by LGBTQIA+ NICU Parents

It's important for us to recognize the barriers that many LGBTQIA+ parents face when entering NICU spaces. These include:

- **Discrimination & Bias:** Fear of judgment or mistreatment can deter engagement with healthcare providers.
- **Lack of Representation:** Few role models or visible LGBTQIA+ staff can make parents feel isolated.
- **Legal Challenges:** Non-biological parents may face hurdles in being recognized as legal guardians.
- **Misinformation:** Assumptions about family structures can lead to miscommunication and alienation.
- **Healthcare Mistrust:** Past negative experiences in medical settings can lead to anxiety and reluctance to seek care.

Providing Respectful, Dignified, and Compassionate Care

It's not enough to check our bias at the door. Once we recognize these barriers, we must take forward actions in order to truly provide equitable care to all. This includes using gender-neutral language when addressing parents and documentation; displaying visible signs of support, such as inclusive posters or pride symbols; training staff regularly on LGBTQIA+ issues; ensuring consistent, informed care across all departments; and validating parents' experiences and emotions without judgment. Only then can we foster an environment where diversity is celebrated, not merely tolerated.

Case Study: *Promoting a Sense of Belonging and Safety*

Jordan (non-binary) and Alex (transgender man) are new parents to a premature baby in the NICU. They feel overlooked when medical staff consistently refer to them as "mom" and "dad," despite sharing their preferred names and pronouns.

Discuss the following interventions with your partner. Do you think anything is missing? Is there anything you would do differently?

Intervention:

- **Inclusive Communication:** The charge nurse holds a staff meeting to reinforce the use of correct pronouns and names.
- **Personalized Care Plan:** Incorporate their preferences into the baby's chart to prevent repeated misgendering.
- **Support Network:** Connect them with an LGBTQIA+ parenting support group.
- **Empowerment:** Involve them in daily care routines, reinforcing their role as vital caregivers.
- **Safe Environment:** Display inclusive signage and provide private spaces for family bonding.

Intended Outcome: Jordan and Alex report feeling seen, respected, and actively involved in their baby's care, reducing their anxiety and strengthening their trust in the medical team.

NURTURING EQUITY MINDED HEALTHCARE EXERCISE

As you break into small groups for reflection, consider these five thought-provoking questions designed to encourage respectful dialogue among nurses and healthcare providers who may hold differing views and values regarding the LGBTQIA+ community.

Our goal is to foster empathy, self-awareness, and professional growth within the context of patient-centered care.

Take a moment to reflect on and answer the following questions in the space provided. If you desire, you can then discuss your answers with the group.

1. How do your personal beliefs and values influence the way you provide care to LGBTQIA+ patients, and how do you ensure that these beliefs do not compromise the quality, equity, and dignity of the care you deliver?

2. When faced with a patient whose identity or life experience challenges your worldview, how do you navigate your biases to maintain a therapeutic, nonjudgmental, and compassionate relationship?

3. Can you reflect on a time when a patient's identity or background made you uncomfortable? How did you handle the situation, and what did you learn about yourself as a healthcare provider?

4. What does it mean to provide culturally competent and trauma-informed care in a diverse healthcare environment, especially when caring for individuals from the LGBTQIA+ community?

5. How do you reconcile your personal moral or religious convictions with the ethical obligation to respect patient autonomy, confidentiality, and the right to receive unbiased, affirming healthcare?

ADDITIONAL RESOURCES:

GLMA: Health Professionals Advancing LGBTQ Equality - www.glma.org

Family Equality - www.familyequality.org

The Trevor Project (Crisis Support and Education) - https://www.thetrevorproject.org

Section IV

Jordyn M. Jenkins

PROVIDING CARE WITH HEART

OVERVIEW OF SECTION IV

WHAT YOU WILL LEARN (AND DO) IN THIS SECTION:

Chapter 21: Empathy: A Tool to Mitigate Implicit Bias: In a world where racism often seeks to dehumanize and divide, empathy is a radical force for unity and justice. It compels us to see each other fully, act with compassion, and stand together against oppression. Empathy alone will not solve racism, but it is a powerful starting point. By connecting hearts and minds, it fuels the drive for systemic change, turning awareness into action and solidarity into justice.

Chapter 22: Empathy for Multi-Disciplinary Team Members: A Healing Presence:
Empathy is the cornerstone of effective care, offering patients and their families a deep sense of being seen, heard, and valued during some of the most challenging moments of their lives. If you are a healthcare professional, chances are you work as part of a multi-disciplinary team to support patients through these extreme life events. This chapter explores what empathy at the bedside looks like for these teams, breaking it down into actionable practices, emotional awareness, and spiritual insight.

Chapter 23: Cultural Humility: In this chapter you will explore the value of embracing different cultures, values, and experiences. You will also interact with an algorithm for caring for marginalized families who have a history of trauma-based care.

Chapter 24: Commit to S.E.A.L: Learn various techniques that support respectful, maternal, care- based support.

Chapter 25: Fitted for Equity Lens: Examine your own biases and microaggressions. You will try on an equity lens to aid in your care.

Chapter 26: Delivering Bad News with R.E.S.P.E.C.T: Discover the art of delivering bad news with empathy, dignity and R.E.S.P.E.C.T.

Chapter 27: Supporting Partners in Traumatic Deliveries: Learn about the various traumatic events partners are often exposed to, and how to provide patient family-centered care that ensures partners are considered and compassionately cared for.

Chapter 28: Perinatal and Neonatal Loss: Maternal and infant mortality are sobering realities that impact families across the globe, but they occur at alarmingly disproportionate rates among historically marginalized Black and Brown communities. These disparities highlight the urgent need for compassionate, culturally sensitive, and equity-minded care for families navigating the grief of perinatal loss.

Chapter 29: Medical and Emotional Debriefings: Processing Traumatic Events and Self-Care: Maternal health nurses work in a highly demanding and emotionally charged environment, where they are responsible for managing a wide spectrum of complex and often unpredictable events. This chapter explores ways of processing these events and finding adequate self-care for long-term health and resiliency.

INTRODUCTION: EMPATHY AND EQUITY IN PROVIDING CARE WITH HEART

If you work as a provider or clinician in maternal health, chances are you work in a highly demanding and emotionally charged environment. Providers and nurses in these settings are responsible for managing a wide spectrum of complex and often unpredictable events. This section aims to employ the power of empathy in supporting both healthcare providers and their patients, creating a healing presence in the midst of difficult situations.

For nurses and other healthcare professionals, empathy is not merely a soft skill; it is an integral part of clinical practice that enhances patient outcomes and fosters trust. Empathy in healthcare means understanding the patient's experience and responding with genuine care, all while balancing the demands of a high-pressure, fast-paced environment.

Empathy is also much more than a professional skill—it is a moral and relational cornerstone that builds trust, enhances patient outcomes, and humanizes the practice of medicine. At the bedside, empathy allows patients to feel understood and valued, even in moments of uncertainty or vulnerability. In this section, we will discuss the role and skills of empathy, including in situations of delivering bad news or supporting partners through distressing situations. We will embrace the skills of cultural humility and reflect on the importance of debriefings. By connecting hearts and minds, we can fuel the drive for systemic change, turning awareness into action and solidarity into justice.

CHAPTER TWENTY-ONE
Empathy, Part 1: A Tool to Mitigate Implicit Bias

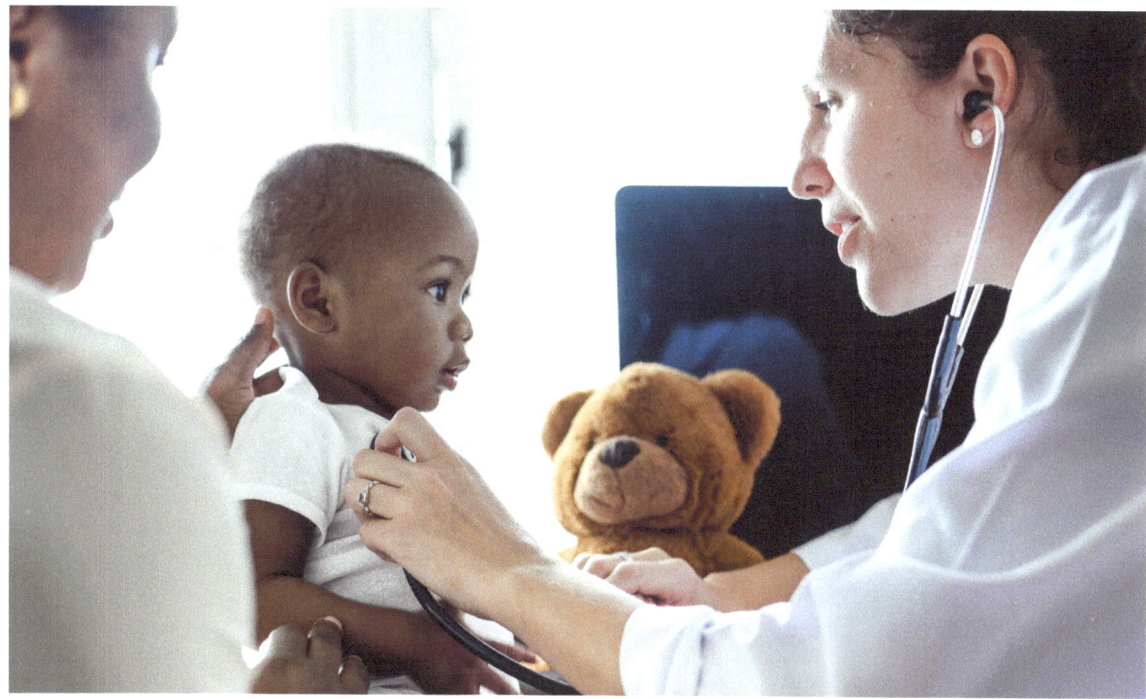

In a world where racism often seeks to dehumanize and divide, empathy is a radical force for unity and justice. It compels us to see each other fully, act with compassion, and stand together against oppression.

Empathy alone will not solve racism, but it is a powerful starting point. By connecting hearts and minds, it fuels the drive for systemic change, turning awareness into action and solidarity into justice.

As you engage with this chapter, consider how empathy can deepen your commitment to anti-racism and inspire you to help build a world where equity and inclusion are not ideals, but realities.

The Heart of Empathy in Healthcare

For nurses and other healthcare professionals, empathy is not merely a soft skill; it is an integral part of clinical practice that enhances patient outcomes and fosters trust. **Empathy in healthcare means understanding the patient's experience and responding with genuine**

care, all while balancing the demands of a high-pressure, fast-paced environment.

Empathy is also much more than a professional skill—it is a moral and relational cornerstone that builds trust, enhances patient outcomes, and humanizes the practice of medicine. At the bedside, empathy allows patients to feel understood and valued, even in moments of uncertainty or vulnerability. While chaplains and nurses may complement a patient's care, doctors and clinicians often serve as the primary point of connection, making their capacity for empathy vital.

Empathy enables doctors, clinicians, and other providers to strengthen the doctor-patient relationship, increase patient compliance with treatment plans by fostering trust, and address not just physical symptoms but the emotional and psychological impacts of illness. Research shows that empathy is linked to improved clinical outcomes, patient satisfaction, and even fewer malpractice claims. This chapter explores how doctors and clinicians can embody empathy at the bedside, balancing the art of compassionate care with the demands of modern medicine.

Empathy as a Healing Force

At its core, empathy is not just about responding to pain but about fostering trust and empowering patients to participate in their care. It humanizes the healthcare experience, reminding patients that they are more than their diagnosis. Empathy also strengthens the bond between the nurse, patient, and family, creating a sense of partnership in the healing process.

Here are some helpful ways to practice the soft skills of empathy in your workplace:

Connecting with Patients: Start each interaction by addressing the patient by name and making eye contact (if culturally appropriate). Use a warm tone of voice, even during routine procedures. Acknowledge their fears or discomfort by saying words like, "I know this might be overwhelming, but I'm here to help you through it." Minimize distractions by silencing devices and focusing entirely on the patient. This demonstrates that their time and concerns matter.

Active Listening: Listen without interrupting, even during short conversations, to understand both verbal and nonverbal cues. Encourage patients to share their concerns by asking open-ended questions like, "How are you feeling about what's happening today?" Go beyond symptoms to understand how the patient feels about their condition. Statements like, "I hear you're worried about what this diagnosis means for your family," validate their emotional experience.

Validating and Adapting to Emotions: Acknowledge and normalize their feelings. For example: "It's understandable to feel anxious about this procedure; many people feel the same way." Avoid dismissing concerns with overly clinical or technical language and adjust your approach based on the patient's emotional state. For example, offer reassurance to someone anxious about a procedure or a calm presence for someone in distress. Be mindful of their individual values and preferences, ensuring their dignity is upheld at all times.

Compassionate Communication: Use plain, clear language when explaining medical procedures or conditions, and check for understanding. Offer hope, even in difficult situations, by focusing on what can be done rather than what cannot.

Nonverbal Empathy: Be mindful of your facial expressions, posture, and body language, as these can convey empathy or detachment. Maintain an open posture and relaxed demeanor. Use appropriate physical gestures, such as a reassuring nod or a compassionate hand on the shoulder (if appropriate).

Empathy is a clinical skill: it can be cultivated and practiced. As a provider, you can enhance your empathy by regularly reflecting on patient interactions to identify areas where empathy was effectively demonstrated or could be improved, asking patients and colleagues for input on communication style and bedside manner, and participating in workshops or training focused on emotional intelligence, communication skills, and empathy in healthcare.

In the end, empathy benefits not only patients but also clinicians themselves. Studies show that practicing empathy reduces burnout and enhances job satisfaction by reinforcing the deeper meaning and purpose of medical practice. By focusing on the human connection, doctors are reminded that their role extends beyond curing disease to caring for the whole person.

Why Empathy Matters in Addressing Racism

Racism is not just a personal prejudice—it is a structural system that perpetuates inequities in health, education, housing, and countless other aspects of life. Empathy serves as the emotional and cognitive lens through which we can understand oppression, build solidarity, and catalyze action.

Empathy helps us step into the shoes of those impacted by racism, allowing us to grasp the depth and nuance of their struggles. By connecting with the experiences of marginalized people, empathy fosters genuine relationships across racial lines, rooted in trust and mutual respect. Empathy motivates us to confront bias, challenge oppressive systems, and advocate for justice.

For individuals and communities who have endured centuries of systemic racism, the lack of empathy has often exacerbated harm. Being unseen, unheard, or dismissed intensifies the pain of oppression. Empathy, when practiced authentically, counters these injustices by centering marginalized voices and acknowledging pain, all while retaining the affirmation of their humanity. Empathy begins with listening—without interruption, defensiveness, or judgment—to the stories and truths of those who have been silenced or ignored. It requires us to recognize the trauma inflicted by racism and validate the emotions that accompany it, from anger and grief to resilience and hope. At its core, empathy affirms that every person—regardless of race or ethnicity—is deserving of dignity, respect, and equity.

Empathy in Action: From Awareness to Anti-Racism

While empathy is essential, it must be more than a feeling; it must lead to action. Anti-racism is the practice of actively identifying and opposing racism in all its forms, and empathy is the catalyst for this work.

Empathy is not always easy. Bias, discomfort, and fear can inhibit our ability to connect with others across racial lines. Overcoming these barriers requires intentional effort to **confront biases,** recognizing and challenging stereotypes and assumptions you may hold. It requires that we **sit with discomfort,** as growth often comes from uncomfortable conversations and reflections. And it requires us to **practice humility,** as we approach discussions about race with a willingness to listen, learn, and admit when we are wrong.

Our **S.L.A.C.K.** Tool ensures that we move from awareness to anti-racism in our empathy practice:

Self-Reflection: Examine your own biases and privilege. Ask, "How have I benefited from systems that disadvantage others, and how can I use my position to promote change?"

Learning: Learn about the histories and struggles of marginalized communities. Seek out perspectives from people of color, not to burden them with teaching, but to amplify their voices and lived experiences.

Advocating: Support policies and initiatives that promote racial equity. Speak out against microaggressions, discrimination, and systemic injustice in your personal and professional spheres.

Cultivating Inclusive Spaces: Foster environments where people of all races feel valued and safe. Challenge exclusionary practices and champion diversity.

Kindness: In healthcare, kindness is not just a virtue—it is a vital skill that bridges gaps and fosters trust. In an equity-centered setting, kindness means approaching every patient with dignity, respect, and compassion, recognizing their unique experiences and challenges. Kindness allows clinicians to connect on a human level, ensuring patients feel valued, heard, and understood.

Challenges in Empathy

There are many challenges to providing appropriate empathy to patients. One of these is time constraints: healthcare providers often juggle multiple patients and competing priorities. Practicing empathy within these limits requires quick yet meaningful interactions, such as pausing for a moment to listen or offering a kind word during care tasks. Quick, meaningful connections can be made by focusing on quality over quantity during patient interactions.

Another common barrier is emotional burnout. Healthcare providers witness suffering, provide end-of-life care, and navigate emotionally charged situations that can take a toll. Practicing self-care, seeking peer support, and taking mental health breaks are essential for sustaining empathy. Organizations should prioritize clinician well-being to sustain empathetic care.

The last common empathy barrier is balancing professional boundaries. Empathy involves emotional connection without over-identification with a patient's pain. Striking this balance helps nurses, clinicians and providers remain effective and compassionate.

Communicating with Compassion

When **delivering difficult news,** it is helpful to use clear, simple language, avoiding jargon. For example: "I wish I had better news to share, but I want to be honest about the challenges ahead." Pause to allow the patient to process information. Be ready to answer questions and address emotional reactions with patience. Balance honesty with hope, focusing on what can still be done to support the patient.

When **explaining treatment plans,** involve the patient in decision-making as much as possible, respecting their values and preferences. Reassure them that their voice matters in shaping their care plan.

Some **Empathetic Questions you can use with patients:**

- "How are you coping with all of this?"
- "What can I do to help make this easier for you?"
- "Is there anything you'd like me to know about what's most important to you?"

Sometimes, empathy at the bedside requires no words at all. A physician's calm and attentive presence during a patient's most vulnerable moments can speak volumes. Sitting beside a patient, holding their hand, or simply being there during a difficult procedure conveys care and solidarity.

For more tools on delivering bad (or potentially bad) news to patients and their families, see the Tool Index in the Appendix.

Empathy as a Revolutionary Act

In a world where racism often seeks to dehumanize and divide, empathy is a radical force for unity and justice. It compels us to see each other fully, act with compassion, and stand together against oppression.

Empathy alone will not solve racism, but it is a powerful starting point. By connecting hearts and minds, it fuels the drive for systemic change, turning awareness into action and solidarity into justice. As you engage with this chapter, consider how empathy can deepen your commitment to anti-racism and inspire you to help build a world where equity and inclusion are not ideals, but realities.

Empathy at the bedside transforms the clinical encounter into a sacred exchange of trust, understanding, and care. For doctors and clinicians, it is a daily opportunity to embody the healing mission of medicine—not just to treat, but to comfort; not just to diagnose, but to affirm the dignity of each patient.

Through empathy, clinicians honor the humanity of their patients and themselves, forging a bond that fosters healing even in the face of uncertainty.

CASE STUDY

Jane Ramierez is the Spanish-speaking mother of prematurely born triplets who are currently in the NICU. One week after the birth, you learn her partner has just lost their job. Jane begins to be more absent from the hospital as she tries to juggle working part-time along with carrying for their triplets. As a healthcare provider, you sometimes witness frustrating miscommunications or emotional outbursts, and you wonder how to respond.

NURTURING EQUITY MINDED HEALTHCARE EXERCISE

Break into groups of 2-3 and discuss the following questions together:

1. What does active empathy look like in your role as a healthcare provider?
2. What are three concrete ways you could demonstrate empathy in your interactions with Jane and her partner?
3. What barriers or challenges might you face?
4. Where might systemic racism be complicating Jane's story, and how can you access empathy to address this?
5. How do you know if your attempts to communicate empathy are successful?

CHAPTER TWENTY-TWO
Empathy at the Bedside, Part 2: A Healthcare Provider's Sacred Presence

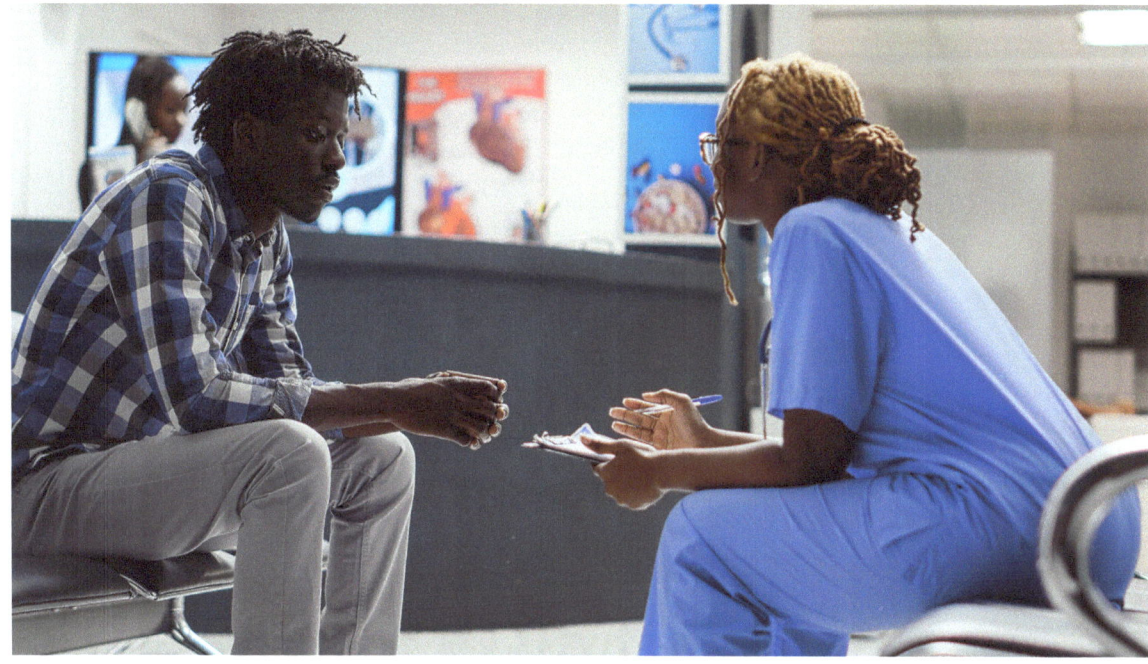

As we discussed in the preview chapter, empathy is the cornerstone of effective care, offering patients and their families not just spiritual support but a deep sense of being seen, heard, and valued during some of the most challenging moments of their lives. If you are a healthcare professional, chances are you work closely with a team involving chaplains, social workers, and other providers to support patients through these extreme life events. This chapter explores what empathy at the bedside looks like for members of these teams, breaking it down into actionable practices, emotional awareness, and spiritual insight.

The Heart of Empathy

Empathy involves understanding and entering into another's emotional and spiritual experience without judgment or distraction. For a provider, this means becoming fully present, creating a sacred space where individuals feel safe to express their fears, hopes, and struggles. It requires listening with the heart, discerning unspoken needs, and responding with compassion rooted in genuine care.

Preparing for Presence: A Chaplain's Role

Before stepping into a patient's room, a chaplain must prepare spiritually and emotionally to be fully present. This preparation includes:

1. Centering Prayer or Reflection: Taking a moment for grounding through prayer, meditation, or deep breathing to focus their heart and mind on service.
2. Intentionality: Entering the room with the goal to serve, not to fix. Empathy is not about solving problems but about accompanying others on their journey.
3. Cultural and Spiritual Sensitivity: Being mindful of diverse beliefs, values, and practices, ensuring that the encounter honors the patient's identity.

Chaplains work to practice empathy in their daily interactions with patients and create a safe space for them. This may including greeting the patient or family with warmth and respect, using open body language and maintaining an approachable demeanor, and allowing silence to hold space for their feelings; resisting the urge to fill it with words. They may reflect back what the patient is expressing to ensure understanding, e.g., "It sounds like you're feeling overwhelmed by the uncertainty," with the goal of avoiding interrupting, rushing, or offering unsolicited advice. They will then help the patient name the emotions they observe, such as fear, grief, or even relief, to validate their experience, and offer gentle encouragement for them to share more if they feel comfortable.

For chaplains, empathy is a sacred calling, reflecting God's unconditional love. By embodying Christ-like compassion, chaplains bring light to the bedside, offering hope in darkness. As the Apostle Paul wrote, "Rejoice with those who rejoice; mourn with those who mourn" (Romans 12:15). This mutual sharing of joy and sorrow creates a profound connection that can uplift and transform.

Empathy at the bedside is about being a witness to the sacredness of another's journey. It's about showing up fully, not with answers but with love. A chaplain's empathetic presence reminds patients and families that they are not alone and that God is with them, even in their pain. As chaplains, we are not called to have all the answers but to embody grace and understanding. When we meet others with empathy, we create a space where healing—spiritual, emotional, or otherwise—can truly begin.

Chaplains must navigate challenges just the same as any healthcare professional, such as compassion fatigue, boundaries, and the balancing of complex emotions. It is important to see these as part of the patient's processing, and maintain the balance between empathy and over-identification with the patient's pain. Just like for any other healthcare professional, support and self-care are essential to avoiding burnout.

Synergy of Chaplain and Nurse Roles

Chaplains and nurses often work in tandem, addressing the spiritual, emotional, and physical aspects of care. Empathy bridges their roles, allowing them to provide comprehensive support.

Empathy is the cornerstone of effective bedside care, shared between chaplains and nurses as they support patients and their families through the most vulnerable moments of life. While chaplains often focus on spiritual and emotional needs, nurses provide holistic care that encompasses the physical, emotional, and psychological dimensions of a patient's experience. Together, their empathetic presence creates a healing environment rooted in compassion and respect.

For example:

- A nurse might identify a patient struggling with fear or isolation and invite the chaplain for spiritual support.
- A chaplain, sensing a patient's unspoken concerns about their treatment, might collaborate with the nurse to address those worries.
- Both roles emphasize active listening and presence, reinforcing the patient's sense of being valued and cared for.

Practical Tools for Empathy

Whether you are a chaplain, a healthcare provider, or work in another role to support patients during their most difficult days, the following **S.E.T.** tool may be helpful as you think through what it means to be an empathetic presence.

Start with Emotional Assessment Questions:

- "What has been the hardest part of this for you?"
- "How are you managing to get through this moment?"

Empathetic Spirituality Reflections:

- Share scripture, prayers, or blessings tailored to their situation, always with permission.
- Acknowledge God's presence in their suffering and affirm their value and dignity.

The Ministry of Presence:

When words fail, your quiet presence can be deeply comforting. Sitting with someone in silence communicates solidarity and care.

The Role of Empathy in Social Work: Addressing Disparities in NICU and Maternal Health for Marginalized Communities

Social workers can be one of the forgotten disciplines that work alongside healthcare teams. Empathy is also a cornerstone of effective social work, especially when serving marginalized communities disproportionately impacted by disparities in maternal health and neonatal intensive care units (NICU). These disparities—rooted in systemic inequities, racism, and socioeconomic barriers—often lead to poorer outcomes for families of color, particularly Black mothers and infants. Social workers in these settings must approach their work with a deep sense of empathy, enabling them to understand, validate, and advocate for the unique challenges these families face.

Empathy allows social workers to connect with families on a human level, fostering trust and a sense of partnership. This is particularly critical in maternal health and NICU settings, where families often experience overwhelming stress, fear, and uncertainty. Empathy helps social workers acknowledge the systemic inequities that impact access to quality care, such as implicit bias, financial barriers, and inadequate support systems. By listening to families' stories, social workers can better comprehend the cultural, emotional, and physical burdens they carry.

Many families from marginalized communities may have a history of mistrust in healthcare systems due to past mistreatment or systemic racism. Demonstrating empathy helps build rapport, showing families they are seen, heard, and valued as equal partners in their care. Parents in the NICU and maternal health patients also often face feelings of fear, guilt, or helplessness. Empathy allows social workers to validate these emotions, providing comfort and reassurance during a vulnerable time.

Empathy in Action: Practical Applications in Social Work

All social workers must engage in active listening, allowing families to express their concerns and needs without judgment. Cultural humility is essential, ensuring the social worker respects and incorporates families' cultural beliefs, traditions, and preferences into care plans. Often, empathy drives social workers to advocate for systemic change, addressing disparities such as limited access to prenatal care, implicit bias in clinical decision-making, and inadequate NICU resources. Social workers can push for policies that ensure equitable treatment, such as culturally competent care training for staff or increased support for community-based maternal health programs.

Empathy also helps social workers anticipate the needs of families, connecting them to mental health services, financial aid, housing assistance, or lactation support. For many families, the NICU or maternal health challenges are traumatic. Social workers use empathy to recognize signs of trauma and provide interventions that prioritize healing and resilience.

Addressing Systemic Disparities with Empathy

Empathy alone cannot eliminate disparities, but it serves as a catalyst for identifying and addressing systemic barriers. The **C.P.R.** tool gives you a beginning:

Combating Implicit Bias: Empathy equips social workers to recognize and challenge biases that may impact care decisions, advocating for fair treatment of all families.

Promoting Health Literacy: Marginalized families often face barriers to understanding medical information due to language differences or limited education. Empathy ensures that social workers communicate clearly and compassionately, empowering families to make informed decisions.

Represent by Advocating for Diversity: Empathy highlights the importance of representation in healthcare teams. Social workers can advocate for hiring diverse staff who better reflect and understand the communities they serve.

Empathy often enhances the effectiveness of social work interventions, leading to improved trust and collaboration, reduced stress and anxiety, and better health outcomes. Families are more likely to engage with care plans when they feel understood and respected. Empathy provides emotional relief, helping families navigate the challenges of NICU stays or maternal health complications. And advocacy and support fueled by empathy can mitigate disparities, improving the overall care experience for marginalized communities.

In the face of persistent disparities in maternal health and NICU care, empathy is a powerful tool for social workers committed to equity and justice. It enables them to connect deeply with families, address their unique needs, and advocate for systemic change. By embracing empathy, social workers can create a healthcare environment where every family—regardless of race, income, or background—receives the dignity, respect, and support they deserve.

It's Not Just for Social Workers: Avoiding the Disproportionate Involvement of Child Welfare Services like DCFS (Department of Children and Family Services) in the Lives of Mothers of Color

All too often, resources can be weaponized against the most vulnerable, often unintentionally. When discussing multidisciplinary teamwork, it's important to remember that we all share a responsibility to make every effort to de-escalate situations with empathy, rather than cause further harm. Avoiding the disproportionate involvement of child welfare services like DCFS (Department of Children and Family Services) in the lives of mothers of color requires a systemic approach grounded in equity, cultural humility, and trauma-informed care. Here is a roadmap to creating a more equitable approach:

Understand the Context of Disproportionality and Historic Inequities

Communities of color, particularly Black, Indigenous, and Latina mothers, have historically faced surveillance, punishment, and systemic racism in healthcare, social services, and child welfare systems. For example, poverty is often misinterpreted as neglect, leading to unwarranted referrals. Professionals must reflect on and challenge their own biases that influence decision-making, often resulting in overreporting in marginalized communities.

Build Relationships Rooted in Trust

Mothers of color may be reluctant to engage with services due to mistrust stemming from past experiences. Establishing trust requires listening, validating, and avoiding assumptions. Understand the cultural practices, traditions, and norms that shape parenting styles in order to provide culturally appropriate support. Misinterpreting cultural differences as neglect can lead to unnecessary interventions.

Strengthen Community-Based Support

Instead of relying on punitive systems like DCFS, connect families to local organizations, mutual aid groups, and culturally aligned support networks. Peer-led programs allow mothers to receive guidance from others with lived experience, reducing the likelihood of misunderstandings and punitive actions.

Improve Training and Education for Mandated Reporters

Train mandated reporters to understand the difference between trauma-induced challenges and genuine cases of abuse or neglect. Emphasize that poverty-related issues, such as food insecurity or inadequate housing, do not constitute neglect and should not automatically trigger a DCFS referral. Equip professionals with tools to assess situations through a culturally sensitive lens to avoid racial or cultural bias.

Focus on Preventative Interventions

Ensure families have access to the resources they need to thrive, such as housing assistance, food programs, mental health support, and affordable childcare. Address underlying challenges holistically, including mental health care, substance use treatment, and parenting support, without immediately involving DCFS. Push for policy changes that prioritize prevention over punishment and ensure equitable allocation of resources to underserved communities.

Reassess Reporting Protocols

Encourage collaborative reviews before filing reports, especially in ambiguous cases, to ensure a fair and objective assessment. Require consultations with culturally competent colleagues or community advocates to provide additional perspectives or secondary opinions before making a referral. Establish systems where families and communities can report misuse of DCFS involvement or advocate for fair treatment through anonymous and transparent feedback systems.

Advocate for Systemic Change

Advocate for policies that separate economic hardship from allegations of neglect and prioritize providing aid rather than punishment. Call for data tracking and public accountability regarding the racial and demographic breakdown of DCFS referrals to identify and address patterns of inequity. Engage in ongoing efforts to dismantle systemic racism within institutions, including healthcare, education, and social services.

Encourage Open Dialogue

Mothers of color should know their rights when interacting with DCFS, including how to challenge decisions and seek advocacy. Collaborate with families, community leaders, and activists to create policies and practices that reflect the lived experiences of those most affected by DCFS involvement.

Avoiding disproportionate DCFS involvement with mothers of color requires addressing the systemic biases and structural inequities that perpetuate this issue. By shifting from punitive approaches to supportive, culturally responsive, and preventative interventions, we can build a system that uplifts and empowers families rather than punishing them. This transformation demands accountability, equity, and collaboration across all levels of social services, healthcare, and child welfare.

The Opposite of Empathy: Resisting Power Dynamics and Avoiding Intimidation in Postpartum Care

The postpartum period is an incredibly vulnerable time for mothers, especially those navigating the challenges of trauma, systemic inequities, or marginalization. Social workers and healthcare providers play a critical role in providing support and ensuring positive outcomes during this time. However, power imbalances and misuse of authority can inadvertently (or intentionally) intimidate postpartum mothers, exacerbating their trauma.

Here are some ways you can watch for power imbalances for postpartum mothers in your workplace:

Identify Signs of Intimidation: Watch for verbal or nonverbal cues that a mother feels threatened, overwhelmed, or silenced. Common signs include withdrawal, reluctance to share information, or compliance driven by fear rather than understanding.

Understand Trauma Responses: Recognize that postpartum mothers may be navigating prior traumas (e.g., abuse, racism, medical trauma) that can influence their responses to authority figures. Learn to identify when a mother's behavior reflects a trauma response, such as heightened anxiety, defensiveness, or distrust. We will continue to discuss this in the following chapters.

Foster Emotional Safety: Use calming, affirming language to create a space where mothers feel respected and supported. Avoid punitive language or insinuations that could be perceived as threats.

Empower Rather than Criticize: Frame feedback as collaborative problem-solving rather than fault-finding. Highlight the mother's strengths and affirm her role as the expert in her own life and her child's needs. Focus on the mother's existing capabilities, resilience, and successes rather than deficits.

Engage in Shared Decision-Making: Treat mothers as equal partners in decisions affecting their postpartum care and parenting. Offer choices and explain the rationale for recommendations, ensuring mothers feel ownership over their care.

Use Empathy as a Bridge: Validate the mother's feelings and experiences without judgment. Listen actively, showing genuine interest and understanding of her perspective.

Invite Feedback: Create opportunities for mothers to provide input on their experience of care, highlighting areas where they felt supported or intimidated. Implement anonymous feedback mechanisms to allow honest sharing without fear of reprisal.

By embracing trauma-informed care, cultural humility, and anti-oppressive practices, social workers and healthcare professionals can resist harmful power dynamics, foster trust, and contribute to healing rather than trauma. Creating equitable, empowering postpartum care begins with education, accountability, and a commitment to justice and empathy.

CASE STUDY

As you think through the role of an interdisciplinary team in your healthcare setting, let's revisit the Case Study in the chapter before, about Jane Ramierez:

Jane Ramierez is the Spanish-speaking mother of prematurely born triplets who are currently in the NICU. One week after the birth, you learn her partner has just lost their job. Jane begins to be more absent from the hospital as she tries to juggle working part-time along with carrying for their triplets. As a healthcare provider, you sometimes witness frustrating miscommunications or emotional outbursts, and you wonder how to respond.

NURTURING EQUITY MINDED HEALTHCARE EXERCISE

Break into groups of 2-3 and discuss the following questions together:

1. What addition would the role of a chaplain bring to this scenario?
2. How could you see nurses, healthcare providers, and clinicians partnering with a social worker to best support Jane and her family?
3. What challenges do you foresee in this scenario?
4. How will you know if this empathetic support for Jane and her family is successful?

CHAPTER TWENTY-THREE
Cultural Humility & Empathy

Understanding Cultural Humility

When understanding cultural humility, it is important to first know how we define cultural humility. In their scientific article for the Journal of Counseling Psychology, titled <u>Cultural humility: measuring openness to culturally diverse clients</u>,[1] Hook, et. al. defines cultural humility as "having an interpersonal stance that is other-oriented rather than self-focused, characterized by respect and lack of superiority toward an individual's cultural background and experience." As we discussed in the Foundations of Section One, this means that cultural humility involves understanding what might be an important value in a different culture, and respecting that, rather than judging it.

---

1 Hook, Joshua N et al. "Cultural humility: measuring openness to culturally diverse clients." Journal of counseling psychology, National Library of Medicine, Vol. 60,3 (2013): 353-366. doi:10.1037/a0032595, <u>https://pubmed.ncbi.nlm.nih.gov/23647387/</u>.

For example, to a person of Chinese descent, eating food with chopsticks is the most common pattern, whereas, in the life of many Indian families, hand-eating is most common. Both of these traditions may seem unusual to a Westerner who is used to eating with a spoon or fork, but as always, different does not mean deficient. The ability to maintain an openness and acceptance to these important traditions and values is cultural humility.

A vital aspect of cultural humility includes focusing on self-humility, and approaching new cultures from a "learning" position, rather than from an "othering" position. In other words, cultural humility is the process and practice of replacing one's own assumptions and education about another culture and opening oneself up to being taught. There is an essential value to appreciating what others see and hear as they define their cultural expression of lineage and personal ethos. As we grow in respect and understanding for the cultural humility of others, we in turn grow in our own self humility.

Nurse Researchers on Cultural Humility

Recently, substantial attention has been given to the role that cultures play in the healthcare field. It is no secret that our world is becoming more diverse and multicultural. As a result, those in the healthcare field have been increasingly inspired to learn more about cultural differences and how they may impact health. In their article, Cultural humility: Essential foundation for clinical researchers,[2] authors Yeager and Bauer-Wu suggest that researching cultures through the cultural humility lens is vital and transformational for every nurse or provider who authentically wants to reverse the healthcare disparities in our country. This must be particularly true for Black America, which has the highest disparities across the board in maternal mortality and infant loss. Impressive work has been done by nurse and doctor researchers in hopes to mitigate these inequalities in healthcare.

These authors rightly acknowledge that, "Understanding and eliminating health disparities requires a close examination of our past work and future focus in health care research across settings. How we approach the many factors that contribute to health disparities and social inequities requires an examination of the environment, context, and culture of those experiencing these disparities."

---

2 Yeager, Katherine A, and Susan Bauer-Wu. "Cultural humility: essential foundation for clinical researchers." Applied nursing research, National Library of Medicine, Vol. 26,4 (2013): 251-6. doi:10.1016/j.apnr.2013.06.008 https://www.ncbi.nlm.nih.gov/pmc/articles/PMC3834043/.

NURTURING EQUITY MINDED GROUP EXERCISE

Break into groups of 2. Reflect and discuss about the first time you encountered interacting with a culture different from your own (i.e., school, neighbor, work).

1. What was unique about their culture?
2. What did you learn about their traditions?
3. What commonalities did you share?

Have you ever found yourself disliking someone based on their culture alone? After meeting and interacting with someone from this culture, please share how your opinions changed, or if they were reinforced.

Now we will move from the understanding of Cultural Humility to the advocacy of Cultural Empathy.

CULTURAL EMPATHY FOR BLACK FAMILIES

Cultural Empathy for Black Families

If we are serious about impacting healthcare disparities for Black people, then we need to focus on a practice that is currently lacking in healthcare: Cultural Empathy for Black Families (CEFBF). CEFBF is a new phrase, and proposed algorithm, that I, Dr. Candace Cole-Kelly, developed after the death of George Floyd and the worldwide pandemic.

Reeling from those events, the medical community was also becoming acutely aware of their part in racial disparity, and a new law, SBA 464 was created in response (see Chapter 32). This new legislation mandated for all hospitals to engage their staff in Diversity, Equity and Inclusion (DEI) trainings. After close examination, it was evident that this law was passed due to the disproportionate rates at which Black mothers and Black infants were dying.

Keeping this in mind, it became clear that we as healthcare providers must rise to this new challenge of reimagining how healthcare would look across the equitable landscape, using a specific empathy lens and algorithm for Black families. That is what inspired me to create CEFBF, a new algorithm that creates a specific workflow for Black patient populations in an effort to mitigate disparities in maternal mortality and infant loss in Black families. The current algorithms being used in healthcare up to this point have never taken in the specific contexts, histories, and cultural factors that affect Black families in healthcare - and we have lost far too many innocent lives because of it.

Benefits of CEFBF

When systematizing the Cultural Empathy For Black Families (CEFBF) algorithm in one's practices, healthcare providers are most likely to:

1. Improve their patient's overall experience.
2. Foster trust and mutual respect between themselves and their patients.
3. Improve the patient's emotional health.
4. Strengthen and affirm deeper connections with their Black patients by engaging in empathic communication.
5. Incorporate using the Double H.E.A.R.T. approach in all patient interactions (see chapter).
6. Be more knowledgeable about historical and traumatic backgrounds associated with the lived experiences, experimentations, and disparities.
7. Have sensitivity to implicit biases, discrimination, oppression and racism.
8. Be aware of psychosocial adjustments, and willing to support them.
9. Communicate their humanity and presence.
10. Contribute to a significant improvement in overall health outcomes by combining the use of all these systems and disciplines.

CULTURAL EMPATHY FOR BLACK FAMILIES ALGORITHM

ASSESSMENTS

- Clinical Conversation
- Patient Concerns
- Patient Care Priority
- When a Black patient has received bad care:
  - Escalate Service Recovery
  - Contact Nursing Managemnet

PATIENT APPOINTMENTS

- Discuss Plan of Care
- Diagnosis Referral and Consultation
- Shared Decision Making
- Patient Consent

REFERRALS

- Spiritual Care Consult
- Mental Health/Psychology Consult (Anxiety Driven Referral)
- Psychiatric Care
- Melanated Support Group
- Doula Consult
- Black Nurse
- Specialist Consultation
- Black Lactation Nurse
- Any Education and Resources

Algorithm Method (CEFBF)

Goals: To encourage understanding patients' emotions, feelings, and lived experiences in order to make more accurate diagnoses and treatment plans. Being active in verbal reassurance, interpreting nonverbal cues and asking questions in response to emotional cues.

Values: Connecting empathically and building trust.

- When doctors, nurses, specialists and other medical professionals attempt to connect empathetically with Black patients, they are engaged in building trust in the provider-patient relationship.

Shortcomings: Leaving biases out of patient care, resisting the urge to compartmentalize, and modeling care with empathy.

- It can be challenging for healthcare providers to leave their biases about Black people when caring for them as patients. Providers must slow their pace, and think critically, in order to engage in an empathic approach in clinical spaces with their Black patients and families.
- Another challenge includes resisting the urge to compartmentalize their feelings as providers, and to instead be open to care about their patients' feelings while also modeling respectful, and humanity-driven care with their hearts.

Strengths: Empathy, validation, understanding, taking in historical contexts, and affirming.

- The CEFBF algorithm encourages empathy to share the feelings of another person. It cultivates in one's practice the ability to recognize and validate a patient's concerns, apprehensions, anxieties, fears and pains without judgment.
- This algorithm also includes the ability to understand the epigenetic impact from cultural trauma embedded in a Black person's psychological and physiological health as it relates to historical exploitation and experimentation of Black bodies in healthcare. It allows for the affirmation and validation of these contexts as true, and the emotional reactions to this as valid.

NURTURING EQUITY MINDED GROUP EXERCISE #1

Janet is your new patient. She is a first time mother and a 38 year old Black Christian. She is visibly afraid and concerned about her first baby at her age. As a nurse/provider, what would be your plan to support this patient? List the patient priority care approach that you would take using the Cultural Empathy for Black Families Algorithm:

1. _____

2. _____

3. _____

4. _____

5. _____

6. _____

7. _____

NURTURING EQUITY MINDED GROUP EXERCISE #2

Form groups of 2 and consider the following scenario:

You have a Black postpartum patient who just delivered her third child. She has breastfed all of her children and plans to breastfeed her newborn beautiful daughter as well. Her White lactation nurse enters the room, and without even greeting her, says, "Oh you probably won't breastfeed, but I will leave the pamphlets on the counter just in case you change your mind," and walks out. Your patient buzzes you immediately and you find her deeply upset and hurt. She explains to you her unfortunate experience with the lactation nurse. What would be your initial response? Discuss in your groups.

Next, using the CEFBF algorithm, what would be your interventions? Discuss your steps and list any appropriate resources and referrals:

1. _____

2. _____

3. _____

4. _____

5. _____

Take a moment as we conclude Section 2 to reflect on all you have learned. What is one key takeaway you will retain from each chapter?

_____

_____

_____

_____

_____

_____

CHAPTER TWENTY-FOUR
Commit to S.E.A.L.

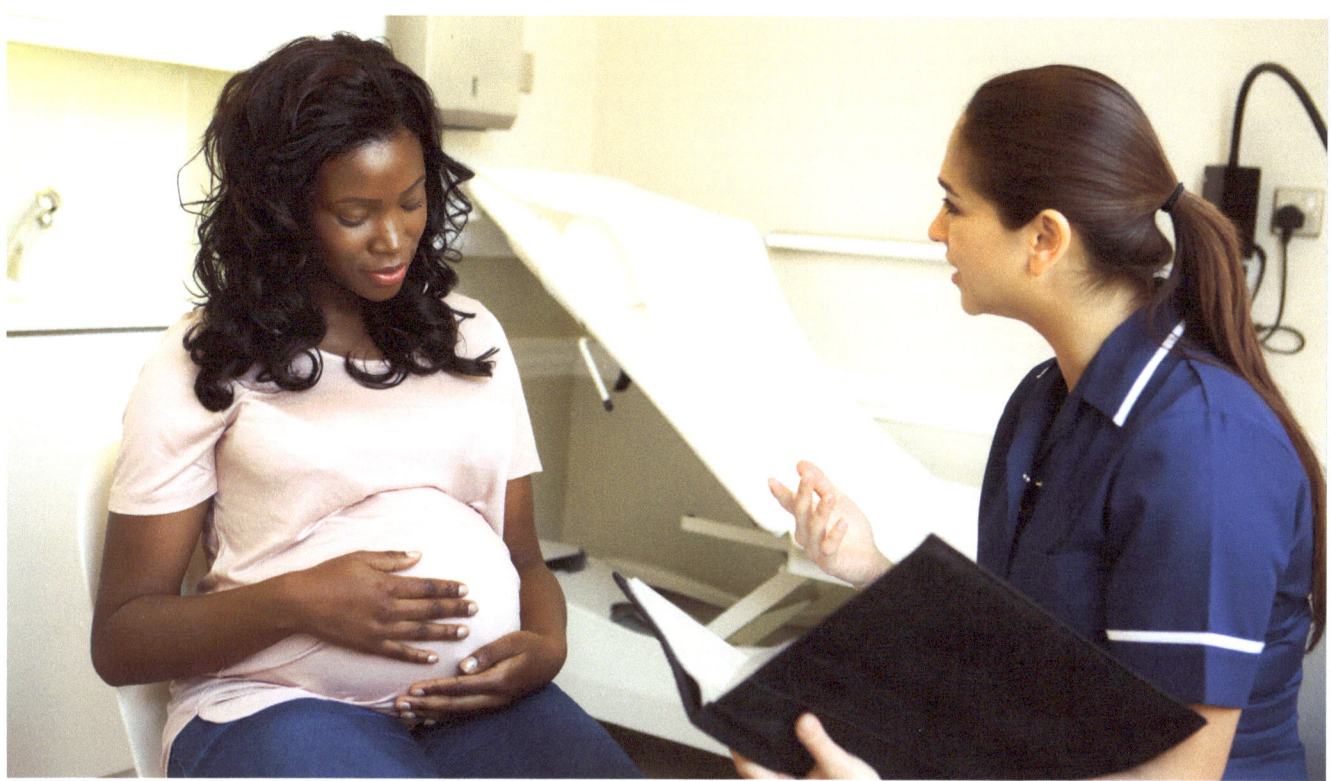

Introduction to Commit S.E.A.L.

Healthcare providers are called to provide care with dignity. And we can accomplish this with Commit to S.E.A.L. (Sit, Empathize, Advocate, Listen). The goal should be to bridge gaps in healthcare access, quality, and delivery through education, advocacy, and leadership development.

Every patient deserves respectful, compassionate, and culturally competent care—regardless of race, background, or socioeconomic status. Through evidence-based training, strategic partnerships, and a commitment to systemic change, Commit S.E.A.L. empowers healthcare professionals to provide inclusive, bias-free, and patient-centered care.

An important step in becoming a healthcare provider is that every clinician must take the Hippocratic Oath. One of the promises within that oath is: "First, do no harm."[1] I propose that

---

1 Though it has been contested that the exact phrase "do no harm" is not actually a part of the Hippocratic Oath, this author uses the phrase to represent the ideals physicians take to do good for their patient and to "abstain from whatever is deleterious and mischievous," as *is* written in the Hippocratic Oath, according to the Encyclopedia Britannica:
Britannica, The Editors of Encyclopaedia. "Hippocratic oath". *Encyclopedia Britannica,* 29 Apr. 2023, https://www.britannica.com/topic/Hippocratic-oath.

this oath should not just mean we avoid harm, but actively work to heal and do good. Just as healthcare providers take the Hippocratic Oath, we must also take the S.E.A.L. Oath.

Healthcare providers are called to commit to sit with their patients, taking the time to listen, understand, and acknowledge their unique experiencesMaternal health is more than just medical care—it is about ensuring every birthing person is seen, heard, and valued throughout their journey. Too often, marginalized communities experience disparities in maternal outcomes due to bias, systemic inequities, and a lack of culturally responsive care.

Seeing and Sitting with an Equity Lens

When we sit with a patient, we are not just meeting them at their eye-level physically, but psychosocially as well. So, when we truly commit to *seeing* a patient, this means seeing them with an equity lens. An equity lens is a process for recognizing underserved and marginalized individuals and groups, and creating protocols to help eliminate barriers.

Utilizing an equity lens while sitting with our patients means we commit to providing care, without judgment. We must see our patients as whole beings, the total person, and not just "the patient in room 5." We must see who they are in full: recognize their culture, background, spiritual traditions, and economic status, in order to provide the best care and resources possible. Our "compassionate heart" method (see Chapter 1) must come to the forefront.

The equity lens also encourages providers to ask themselves questions, such as: What might I NOT be seeing here? What am I missing? What am I really hearing? Is there underlying fear in my patient's words or expression? Are there questions they are hesitant to ask? What can I do to place their, and their support system's, hearts at ease? How can I assure they are experiencing a compassionate me? Am I being present, patient, and the best care provider I can be?

When empathizing with a patient, remember the acronym **H.E.A.R.T**:

Hear her

Empathize with her

Advocate for her

Respect her

Trust her voice

Diversity is not deficient, it's just different. Our opportunity is to celebrate this diversity with every patient.

Commit to Advocate

The tenants of advocacy in healthcare include, but are not limited to, addressing health inequities, influencing policies and philosophies, creating system changes, empowering patients with access to care, and mobilizing resources to mitigate healthcare disparities - one patient at a time.

Primary concepts in health advocacy are guided by social determinants of health and health inequities.

Our patients are often in vulnerable positions as their health is at risk, and they may not always understand the medical terms.

We, as clinicians, are the best advocates for their care, education and safety. Remember, you are sometimes the only difference between a patient feeling invisible, or feeling seen.

Listening with An Equity Understanding

When we listen with an equity understanding, we are sure to increase patient satisfaction, and trust in us as providers. The benefits to *active* listening, with an equity mindset, include:

1. Avoiding misunderstandings. When we <u>restate</u> what we hear our patients say, we confirm that we do really understand what they are trying to communicate, and they feel heard.

2. Building trust. Listening with empathy and understanding is the catalyst to building trust in your patient. They will feel safe to open up and say more, and know that what they say will be taken to heart.

3. Avoiding conflicts. As providers become more attuned to their patients' concerns, patients will not feel as though they're being dismissed.

The Association of Women's Health Obstetrics and Neonatal Nurses' (AWHONN) "Back to Basics" approach suggests care providers should "listen to hear, not to respond."[2] This approach, of hearing with an equity understanding, aids in holding space for patients in quiet moments. Let silence speak for itself.

AWHONN suggests that there are two types of silence that demonstrate our listening skills: invitational and compassionate. Invitational silence allows the patient some time to reflect on the events that are happening, and gives them the space to respond. Compassionate silence acknowledges an impromptu silence that has developed during conversation. This can occur when the clinician and patient are feeling emotions in tandem with each other, and sitting in silence with it. Or, when the clinician is pausing to empathize with the patient, and show compassion for them.

A Lived Experience:
The Gift of An Advocate By Francesca Douglass-Franco

During the birth of my second daughter, I experienced many traumas that I am thankful to have survived. I believe the

---

[2] AWHONN. "Back to Basics - Be Present for Your Patient.". *AWHONN,* Association of Women's Health, Obstetric, and Neonatal Nurses, 2019. www.awhonn.org/wp-content/uploads/2020/07/Back-to-Basics-Be-Present-8.5x11.pdf.

only reason I did is because of the care and compassion of the nurses that treated me, and the thoughtful training they must have received, especially in active listening. Looking back, meeting the nurse that accompanied me during the later hours of my labor felt like a miracle.

When I mentioned to her that we were going to do a VBAC (vaginal birth after Cesarean), my nurse very adamantly suggested that I opt for the epidural, even though my husband and I had been toying with the idea of a romanticized natural birth. She said I could always change my mind if I didn't want it, but if I needed life-saving surgery for any reason, it would be too late to get it without being prepped for the epidural. Our nurse explained this to us with great compassion, based on her own personal experience of unexpectedly needing to give birth to her second child without being able to get an epidural. Little did she know, at the time, just how profoundly her advice would impact the course of the night.

The actual birthing experience was magical, beautiful and everything we hoped it would be - especially following the experience of a very unemotional C-section 6 years prior. My daughter, Kallista, was perfect, and after pushing for only about an hour, I was holding her in my arms. We called our parents and our best friends in Germany and were basking in the warmth of our expanding family.

Before long, however, the night took a turn for the worse as the doctor and nurses started worrying that I was losing too much blood. They handed Kallista to my husband and the next thing I knew I was looking up to see 7+ people surrounding me.

They began performing life saving measures (including a blood transfusion, gauze, and a bakri balloon) that were all so incredibly painful, I would have passed out if I had never received the epidural. In fact, everyone was surprised I didn't pass out anyway. The doctor even mentioned that in her 7 years at that hospital, mine was only the second case she'd seen where the mother remained conscious.

Eventually I had a uterine embolization when none of the above interventions worked. But even through the haze of pain, I remember just being so grateful to have made it. I can recall laying in the hospital bed, breastfeeding my baby (both to bond and to help my uterus contract), and imagining that my bleeding completely stopped.

A few hours later, I started experiencing extreme pain - it felt like I was going into labor all over again. After the third time calling for the nurse, I remember apologizing before telling her I thought I needed to get the bakri balloon removed. She firmly held my arm and told me that even though textbooks will say to leave it for 12 hours, everyone's body is different, and no one knows our bodies better than us. It made all the difference in the world that this nurse believed me, believed my pain. She repeatedly called for a doctor, who found that I was indeed over-ready for the removal.

Had my nurse not believed me, not advocated for me, not been so insistent, I am not sure what would have happened.

It was already devastatingly painful at 4 hours post insertion, and even more so when it was finally removed 2 hours later. I can't imagine the level of pain I would have had to endure if no one had listened to me, and I shudder to think about what might have happened if they had waited too long.

So many factors contributed to surviving this traumatic post-partum experience, but none more important than the compassion, humility, and advocacy of my nurses. They fully saw me, and empathized with me as an individual. They not only advocated for me, but with their compassion, they empowered me to advocate for myself during a time of extreme vulnerability. They actively listened to my concerns and saw me as a human soul, rather than a chart. And their humanity saved my life.

CASE STUDY

Though we sit in the seats of authority and power as clinicians, may we never allow these positions to deaden our self-awareness by not reading our patients' emotional, physical and psychological health appropriately. As an example, Chaplain Green, a Black woman, walked into the room of a young Black couple and introduced herself, taking a seat near the bedside. The Chaplain could tell they were grateful to see someone who looked like them. She heard them sigh and saw the ease in their postures. Then the shifting of emotions emerged as her full term patient's eyes filled with tears. She immediately saw anxiety. After explaining her role in the unit, she began her clinical conversation and assessment. Their conversation went like this:

Question (Chaplain): What is your greatest concern at this time?

Answer (Patient): I have informed my nurse that I've been having severe chest pains and she seems to not be taking me seriously. I can feel something is not quite right. I want my baby to live beyond the delivery and that I live to enjoy my baby as well. (She said this with tears slowly flowing from her eyes).

Restate (Chaplain): I'm so sorry you've been experiencing severe chest pains. That has to be scary. I also hear that your greatest concern is the safety of both your life and your baby's life.

Answer (Patient): Yes, that's correct. Please pray for those two concerns. (Looking at daddy, he adds:) I want to take my family home. We have waited for this dream moment for so long, and do not want it to end in tragedy.

Reframe (Chaplain): You and mommy have planned, hoped and dreamed for this amazing experience of having your first baby. I hear how important your family is to you. I would be honored to pray with you, and for you, and your entire medical team. After our time of prayer, I will escalate your concerns with your medical team. I believe you are in lots of pain, and I will advocate for you to get the proper care you deserve.

Answer (Patient and husband): Thank you Chaplain Green. We appreciate your support and spirit.

Chaplain Green left her patient's room and spoke with the bedside nurse who in turn called the doctor. The doctor just happened to be entering the hospital and came immediately to the patient's room.

After examination, the doctor called the patient's cardiologist and was able to secure the appropriate intervention for the patient. The patient had a successful delivery, and her husband was overjoyed to take home his healthy wife and beautiful new baby boy.

At a post visit with her cardiologist, she was informed that had they not contacted him, things may have turned out different. They thanked Chaplain Green for taking the time to sit with them, and for her empathy, active listening, and advocacy.

NURTURING EQUITY MINDED GROUP EXERCISE

Assignment - Reflecting on the case study from the previous page, describe how Chaplain Green fulfilled each protocol listed below:

- I will commit to See & Sit:

  _____

- I will commit to Empathize:

  _____

- I will commit to Advocate:

  _____

- I will commit to Listen:

  _____

How did Chaplain Green's commitment to S.E.A.L. affect her patient's care and well-being? What may have happened had she not followed through with her commitment? Discuss in your small groups.

CHAPTER TWENTY-FIVE
Fitted For Equity Lens

Equity Lens

An equity lens is a process for analyzing, or diagnosing, and implementing policies on underserved and marginalized individuals, and groups, for the purposes of eliminating barriers.

The purpose of an equity lens is to aid one in providing dignified, respectful, and equitable care as an organization, unit, provider, or nurse as you make decisions.

The equity lens also introduces a set of questions into the decision that helps the decision makers focus on equity in both their processes and outcomes.

The business administrative team of Ontario, known as AMAPCEO, offers that "The Equity

Lens is a tool to help us analyze our actions and processes to ensure they support equity and inclusion. It is like a pair of glasses. It helps you see things from a new perspective and helps us to be more effective in our everyday work by getting a clearer focus and a more complete view of equity and inclusion."[1]

We need this type of lens in healthcare at all times with every patient to ensure patients are feeling included in their care plan and in shared decision making.

PREPARING TO SEE AND CARE FOR YOUR PATIENTS

Reflection Statement

"I treat all my patients the same."

What are the risks that we run with this belief in healthcare?

---

[1] "Equity Lens: Moving From Commitment to Action." *AMAPCEO*, 16 June 2021, https://amapceo.on.ca/equitylens#whatistheequitylens.

LET'S EXPLORE THESE IMPORTANT TERMS FOR NEW EQUITY LENS - **M.E.D.I.C.A.T.E.**

Microaggressions: A term used for commonplace daily verbal, behavioral, or environmental slights, whether intentional or unintentional, that communicate hostile, derogatory, or negative attitudes toward stigmatized or culturally marginalized groups. The term was coined to describe insults and dismissals from non-Black Americans on Blacks and other marginalized groups.

Equity: Equity ensures that individuals are provided the resources they need to have access to the same opportunities as the general population. Equity represents impartiality, i.e. the distribution is made in such a way to even opportunities for all people. Conversely equality indicates uniformity, i.e. where everything is evenly distributed among people.

Disparity: Disparity is a kind of "non-equality." The word is often used to describe a social or economic condition that's considered unfairly unequal: a racial disparity in hiring, a health disparity between the rich and the poor, an income disparity between men and women, and so on.

Implicit Bias: Comprise of negative attitudes or stereotypes towards most anything, including people. Most importantly, our biases can impact real world behavior. So if we want to promote a genuine impact of merit, we probably want to check whether we have biases before we make judgments.

Cultural Sensitivity: Serving others with empathy, kindness and respect. Cultural sensitivity includes taking the time to understand and respect everyone's unique needs and backgrounds through a whole person approach to healthcare and employment. Recognizes different does not mean deficient.

Advocate: A person who publicly supports or recommends a particular cause or policy. A person who pleads for another's cause or idea. A person who supports others to make their voices heard or ideally for them to speak for themselves.

Treatment: Fair treatment is quintessential when it comes to best practices and providing equitable service. Unfair treatment can cause risk factors.

Explicit Bias: Explicit bias is a conscious bias that you are aware of and you act on it. For example, you don't like working with Black people and so you choose to work with White people every time. This usually shows up when human beings are afraid of, or do not value and respect, others.

NURTURING EQUITY MINDED GROUP EXERCISE

Re-consider the case of new patient, Bridgette Taylor, found in Chapter 5 (Self-Actualization):

You have a new bi-racial patient, Bridgette Taylor. She is currently in the third trimester of pregnancy with her fourth child. You are concerned that she has not been in to get check-ups prior to this appointment, and you have internally deemed Bridgette as "irresponsible" as a result. Shortly after this, you discover that she is unhoused and having difficulty keeping up with providing basic needs like food and security for her and her family.

Discuss the following questions:

1. Upon this re-read, did you notice any biases (implicit or explicit) arising in you towards Bridgette before you knew her whole story? Did you make any unfair assumptions? If so, name them.
2. What would providing care with an equity lens look like in this case, and how might it change your approach with this patient?
3. Go through each term in the acronym "M.E.D.I.C.A.T.E" and discuss how each one might apply in this case.

CHAPTER TWENTY-SIX
Delivering Bad News with R.E.S.P.E.C.T.
DR. CANDACE COLE-KELLY AND CAROLE PIERCE, RN

How To Break Bad News

In this chapter we will address a very hard topic that every clinician at some point in their careers will, unfortunately, have to face: breaking bad news. This task is an important one to master, as it will set the trajectory of your patients' outlook on their prognosis/life and self.

In his book, How to Break Bad News,[1] Dr. Robert Buckman asserts, "most of us in clinical practice have not been taught very much (if anything) about the technique of breaking bad news. Furthermore, the psychologists and social scientists who carry out research in the subject and have the most data do not have to perform this task in daily practice. As a result, breaking bad news is something of an orphan."

---

1 Buckman, Robert, and Yvonne Kason. *How To Break Bad News: A Guide for Health Care Professionals*. University of Toronto Press, 1992, p4. *JSTOR*, http://www.jstor.org/stable/10.3138/j.ctt1h1hrxp.

For this reason, we join Dr. Buckman in finding extended compassionate and professional ways to break bad news to our patients and their families.

The 7 step R.E.S.P.E.C.T. tool outlined in this chapter will provide you with precise methodical ways to provide compassionate, dignified and thoughtful approaches to the difficult task of breaking bad news.

7 STEP PROTOCOL FOR BREAKING BAD NEWS

(Based on Dr. Candace Cole-Kelly's Protocol R.E.S.P.E.C.T.)

Too often during the rush of the day clinicians enters a patient's room and in record time, spew out devastating and unpleasant news and then rush back out the door to see the next patient. This can leave patients feeling uncared for. These experiences can be avoided if we simply stop and integrate a dignifying way to break bad news to our patients.

- **R**: Right Environment (Creating a respectful sacred space)
- **E**: Explore Effective Pathways to Communicate
- **S**: Seek to Understand Your Patient
- **P**: Presence (Be present, be compassionate and be tolerant)
- **E**: Empathize (Respond empathically by validating patient's feelings)
- **C**: Clinical Care Plan (Summarize the plan of care and medical information)
- **T**: Truth and Transparency

Descriptions of R.E.S.P.E.C.T.

- **R**: Right Environment (Creating a respectful sacred space)

    To create an encouraging environment:

    A. Make sure it is noise-free (all devices should be silenced).

    B. Make sure there are enough chairs placed in the room in a circular style so that everyone is connected on the same level (this creates intimacy and a collaborative environment resulting in a level playing field to enhance communication).

    C. Make sure you are able to hear one another.

- **E**: Explore Effective Pathways to Communicate

    A. Before meeting with your patient, be sure to review patient's chart, information and diagnosis.

    B. When meeting with them, gently let them know that bad news is forthcoming. For example, "I regret I have some bad news for you. We could not find any heart tones right now, I need to find a better machine or get ultrasound to better evaluate your baby."

    C. Ensure all sub-specialists are present (as appropriate).

- **S**: Seek to Understand Your Patient

    A. Establish this will be a reciprocal conversation by asking, "How are you feeling at this moment?"

    B. Be sensitive to asking patient if additional support (persons) are needed prior to starting the clinical discussion.

    C. Ask: What is your understanding of your current condition?

    D. Use prompters such as "what do you understand from what you have been told?" This will help you gather what the patient has been told and their interpretation of their health status.

    E. Assess for the patient's emotional/psychological well-being at this time as certain information can be overwhelming and even traumatizing. This will prompt you to secure all the resources needed for your patient (psychology, spiritual care, etc.)

- **P**: Presence (Be present, be compassionate and be tolerant)

    A. Be present to your patient and the conversation at hand.

    B. Try to stay focused on the now rather than thinking of your next patient.

    C. Be compassionate (bring your compassion)

    D. Be tolerant

- **E**: Empathize (Respond empathically by validating patient's feelings)

    A. Prepare yourself and your staff for a wide range of emotions to follow patient hearing this bad news. Reactions could range from loud outburst, panic, tears, denial, shock, numbness, anger, freedom, fainting, etc.

    B. Honor your patient by providing emotional space with appropriate pause. When they do speak, be attentive and use active listening by reframing their communication with you.

    C. Validate and acknowledge your patient's heartbreak by offering compassionate phrases such as "I know this is difficult and painful to hear." "I'm so sorry." "I can see you are in a lot of pain." "I am deeply sad that you are experiencing this loss."

    D. Invite dialogue when appropriate. For example: "Can you share a little bit of what you are feeling at this time?" "As I pause here, can you say in your own words what you understand is happening with your care?" Make sure to define all medical terms in real time as you explain the information and make sure patient understands by inviting them to summarize.

- **C:** Clinical Care Plan (Summarize the plan of care and medical information)

    A. Summarize your plan of care moving forward including: tests, exams, referrals and/or treatments.

    B. Make sure patient has all the information they might need including: phone numbers, addresses, contact persons or subsequent medical caregivers in the event something happens before the next planned visit.

    C. Before patient leaves, make sure all psycho-social needs are assessed and you feel that your patient is safe to go home. Discuss any resources that may be helpful to your patient such as: social work, lactation specialist, child life, religious or spiritual support.

    D. Document your medical plain in patient's EMR.

- **T:** Truth and Transparency

    A. Be mindful not to trivialize their trauma and to speak truthfully at all times.

    B. Be forward thinking and empathetic in your offerings avoiding false hope.

    C. Examples of helpful words to offer might include: "I won't say to you time will heal all wounds, but I can say what you do with the time, can heal all wounds." "When you are ready, support interventions can make a difference." "It's okay to exclude anyone who is not safe for you, and to advocate for safe spaces, safe places and safe persons."

P.A.U.S.E
(A SELF-CARE TOOL FOR CLINICIANS)

The acronym P.A.U.S.E. is a helpful tool for any provider that is about to deliver bad news. Before entering the interaction, P.A.U.S.E. can be utilized to help through what can be a painful and difficult conversation between both bearer, and recipient, of bad news.

- **P:** Pause. Still yourself before meeting with your patient. Take a few deep breathing exercises to ground yourself.
- **A:** Acknowledge. Name how difficult this news can be for your patient to hear and name how you feel delivering it. It's okay to feel however you are feeling.
- **U:** Understand. Understand your patient's culture, intersectionality, and vulnerability.
- **S:** Silence. Silence your cell phone during the consult to give yourself fully to your patient and the conversation.
- **E:** Empathy. Prepare yourself to step into your patient's shoes as a respectful, compassionate provider/nurse.

CASE STUDY – IVF

Split into groups of 3 and roleplay the following scenario as nurse, doctor, and patient. Keep the below information in mind for each "role":

Patient - You are a 40 year-old professional woman who recently married a doctor, and are pregnant with your first child. It has taken 3 attempts to finally become pregnant through in vitro fertilization, and both you and your husband were ecstatic with the news of successful pregnancy, after being told you had only a few healthy eggs remaining. You are currently in your sixth month, and this is possibly your only opportunity for pregnancy.

Nurse Clinician - You are currently on duty and are tasked to examine this mother to see how her baby is doing. After several minutes, you cannot find heart tones. How do you handle the next steps? What will your tone sound like when speaking to the patient? What will your facial and non-verbal cues look like?

Doctor - You were called in to take an extra shift and are not familiar with this patient and what she has gone through. She began spotting earlier in the day and is now in the hospital. After testing, no heart tone could be heard in the baby girl. You must tell her the child is deceased. (Be sure to use the 7-Step protocol).

For the doctor and nurse, please complete your P.A.U.S.E. Protocol before seeing your patient and implement your R.E.S.P.E.C.T. Protocol during your visit. Use the next page to plan your visit. For learning engagement, come together after the role play exercise, and discuss the strengths and weaknesses you observed. Discuss any opportunities for growth.

NURTURING MINDED EQUITY GROUP EXERCISE

Use the case study from previous page to practice how you would implement R.E.S.P.E.C.T. Protocol.

1. **R**_____
   _____

2. **E**_____
   _____

3. **S**_____
   _____

4. **P**_____
   _____

5. **E**_____
   _____

6. **C**_____
   _____

7. **T**_____
   _____

CHAPTER TWENTY-SEVEN
Supporting Partners in Traumatic Deliveries

Identifying Best Practices for Fathers or Partners in Moments of Stress

During moments of extreme difficulty, such as emergent codes (Emergent C-Section, Code Crimson, Fetal Demise, Maternal Mortality), the support systems around the patient must be taken into consideration as well. Addressing patient partners with compassion and equality is crucial.

Establish a compassionate standard of practice and protocol by:
1. Being mindful of all partners and their emotional responses to these codes.
2. Contacting Spiritual Care and Psychosocial resources to support partners during codes.
3. Assigning someone from the medical team/nursing management to meet and confer with partners immediately, and privately, to educate on the medical event.

Caring For Partners: A.T.T.E.N.D. Protocol

Supporting our patients in a family-centered manner of care, includes supporting their partners as well - especially during moments of increased trauma. This means special attention must be made to **A.T.T.E.N.D.** to fathers and partners at these times. While doing so, it is important to keep in mind some key values for providing support:

Acknowledgement: Acknowledge them, and their fears, right away.

Truth: Tell them the truth about the scenario.

Treatment: Treat them with dignity, and as a vital part of their partner's health.

Educate: Inform them of current happenings and educate them with any appropriate projections.

Normalize: Normalize their feelings, frustration, fears, and anger.

Dignify: Help them feel dignified in their experience.

CASE STUDY NO. 1 - Emergent C-Section

Linda, the Labor and Delivery Unit Chaplain, arrived at the room to find several medical team members preparing mom for an emergent C-section. Everyone was moving quickly to prepare her to go to the OR.

Linda looked for the nearest family member, and the father was visibly shaken, his eyes saying it all. She followed the team. Dad was being escorted to get dressed and instructed to stay in the room adjacent to the OR. Linda followed him into the waiting room and introduced herself, "Hi Mr. Lee, my name is Linda and I am the Labor and Delivery Unit Chaplain. Part of my job includes supporting patients and their family members. How are you doing at this time with all that's going on?"

The Conversation

Dad: (His eyes spoke before he did). I'm okay, I think. This is a lot.

Chaplain: Childbirth can be very frightening. (She names it!)

Dad: Yes, we had planned on having a vaginal birth and were looking forward to a normal delivery. I don't understand what went wrong. (He adjusts his chair)

Chaplain: It can be so hard to understand when things suddenly turn, after you have done all you can do to create a perfect birth experience (*Linda practices Acknowledgment*)

Dad: Yes. We did all the right things during her entire pregnancy. (He says this in a faint voice)

Chaplain: I am so sorry things did not work out according to your birth plan. I can understand how you can be so upset after all your careful planning. (*Linda Dignifies and Normalizes dad's reaction*)

Dad: I just want her and the baby to be fine now. I understand C-sections can be very dangerous. I mean they have risk, right?

Chaplain: Sounds like you have done some homework about C-sections. Yes, all surgeries have risks. She is in good hands and their priority is to care for her and your baby. *(Linda Educates and informs Dad with the Truth about what is happening)*

Dad: We knew what we wanted and did not want, and a C-section was definitely not what we wanted. Oh God, help us.

Chaplain: I hear this C-section is providing concern, Mr. Lee. May I ask if you have a religious tradition?

Dad: Hmm, what? (He raises his head up and looks at her).

Chaplain: Do you have a religious or spiritual tradition? Catholic, Christian, Jewish…

Dad: Oh, I am Christian and she is Catholic. We both believe in God.

Chaplain: May I pray with you for your wife and baby?

Dad: Yes, I definitely would like that.

After they pray for his wife and baby, the nurse rushes through the door and says, "We need you to come now." (*The nurse Treats Dad with dignity and respect, and as an important part of his wife's care*)

Dad: Thank you Chaplain, I appreciate your presence and support.

CASE STUDY: Circle Back

A few hours later, Linda made a point to visit mom and dad in the postpartum unit.

Upon entrance into the room, both mom and dad were bonding with their new son, Vincent, whom dad was holding.

Chaplain: Congratulations on your beautiful son!

Dad: Thank you Chaplain! Jennifer, this is the Chaplain I was telling you about.

Jennifer: My husband told me you were a calming effect and compassionate supporter.

Chaplain: Well thank you. How are you doing?

Jennifer: Thank God, I am doing much better. Meet my son, Vincent.

Chaplain: He looks just like his father.

Jennifer: I know! You would think that after all I went through, he would have at least favored me with some resemblance. (We all laughed)

Chaplain: Would you like a family blessing?

Jennifer: I would love for you to pray and bless our family. We are Christians and we know Jesus, along with our amazing medical team, are the reasons that we are here today.

Linda provided the pastoral blessing for the family.

NURTURING EQUITY MINDED GROUP EXERCISE

Reflecting on the previous case study, break into your small groups and discuss the following:

1. How might this scenario have been different if there was no support from the Spiritual Care Department?
2. How might dad's temperament have been without the calming presence of the unit's Staff Chaplain?
3. What difference did the Chaplain make in their spiritual life?
4. How did the nursing staff work as a team to implement the A.T.T.E.N.D. protocol?
5. Consider the next Case Study on the following pages (Case Study No.2 - Maternal Distress and Infant Loss). In your teams, identify the ways the medical team did/did not successfully implement the A.T.T.E.N.D. protocol with the father.
6. What additional best practices would you recommend in patient-family centered care? Discuss in your groups.

CASE STUDY NO. 2 - Maternal Distress & Infant Loss

Kevin Smith was pacing the waiting room when the Chaplain exited the elevator.

Chaplain: Hi Mr. Smith, my name is Chaplain Diane. I serve our patients and their families in our Birth Care Center. My role is to provide emotional and spiritual support. I want to first extend my deepest condolences for the loss of your son.

Kevin: Thank you. I just want to see my wife. They just took her to ICU and placed me in this room and I need to be by her side.

Chaplain: I can't imagine how being away from her at a time like this must feel like.

Kevin: Yeh, they told me they would come and get me, but I have not heard from anyone in about 15 minutes and I'm not doing okay with that.

Chaplain: I understand you need to know what's going on with your wife.

Kevin: Yes, I have heard the disparity rates with Black mothers and Black infants, I've already lost my baby, now I don't know what the hell is going on with my wife.

Chaplain: Mr. Smith, let me confer with the team and see if we can bring you back immediately.

Kevin: I'm going to go with you.

Chaplain Diane approached the wife's room and was able to speak with the provider (Dr. Theos) about dad's need to be by his wife's side if at all possible. Mr. Smith was right behind her.

Dr. Theos: Mr. Smith, we are doing all we can to sustain your wife and make sure she is fine.

Kevin: I need to see her and be with her, can I do that?

Dr. Theos: It would be preferred if you waited in the waiting room.

Kevin: If it was your wife, who you promised to be with through thick and thin, to protect, to love through everything, and never leave - would you insist on being with her, or would you be okay just waiting alone in another room?

Dr. Theos (dropping his head): I would want to be with her, but protocols are protocols. (The doctor walks out).

Kevin (visibly upset): This is a critical situation and no husband should be relegated to a room all by himself to wait and see if his wife is going to live or die and not be present with her in those moments. I apologize but I'm going in.

Chaplain (Gently places her hand on his shoulder): Mr. Smith, you are right. You should be able to be with your wife. Let me speak with the team once more. I will be right back.

The Chaplain returned to inform Mr. Smith that he could join his wife in her room, as long as he was sure not to disrupt any of the medical team in their proceedings.

Kevin: Chaplain, thank you for your help and support. And thank you for advocating for me so that I can be with my wife at this critical time.

CHAPTER TWENTY-EIGHT
Perinatal and Neonatal Loss

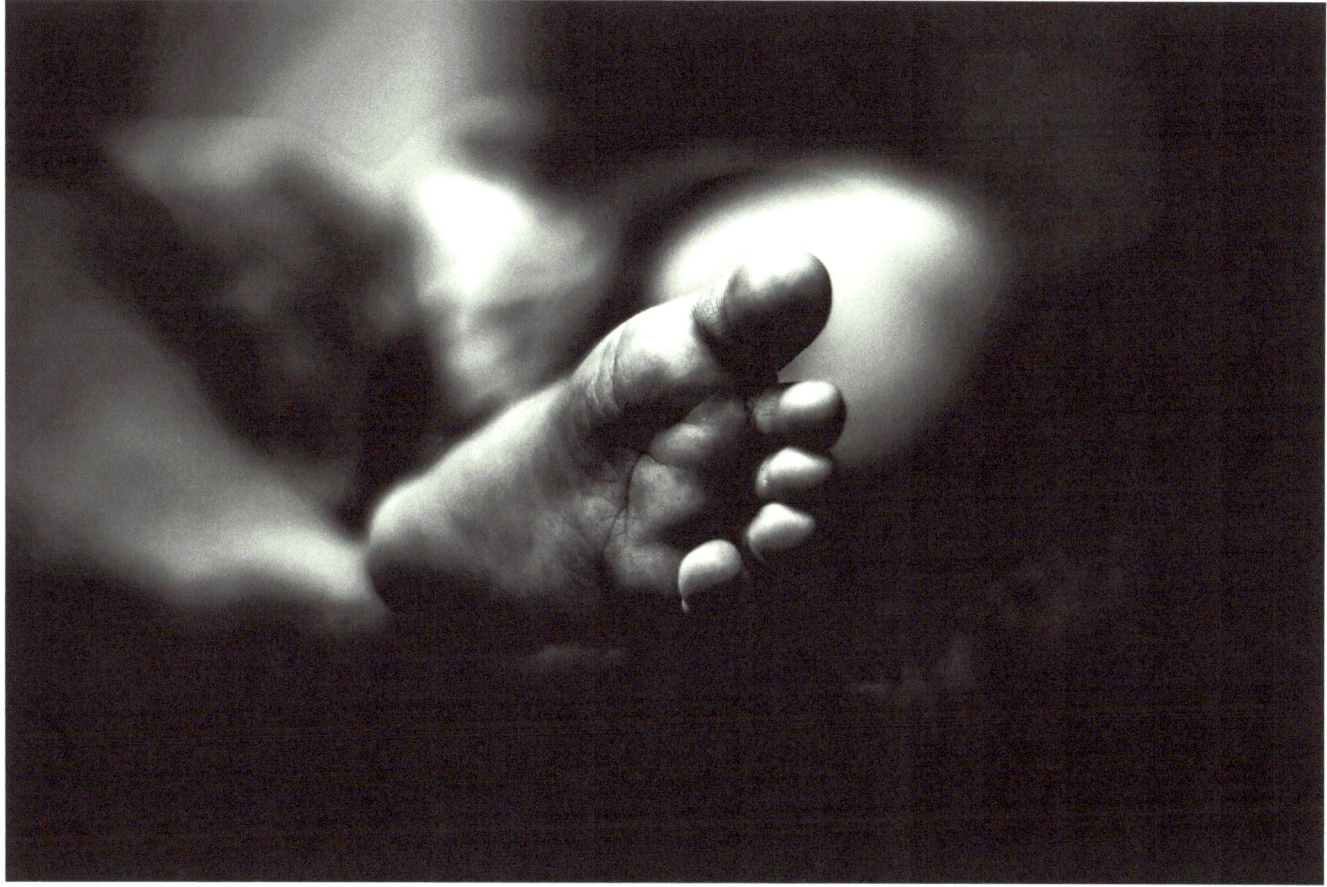

Maternal and infant mortality are sobering realities that impact families across the globe, but they occur at alarmingly disproportionate rates among historically marginalized Black and Brown communities. These disparities highlight the urgent need for compassionate, culturally sensitive, and equity-minded care for families navigating the grief of perinatal loss.

As I am a **Train the Trainer Educator** in Resolve Through Sharing (RTS) Perinatal Loss Education, I have had the privilege of teaching numerous healthcare providers how to offer compassionate presence and care to families suffering these unimaginable losses. This unique approach to care is an art, fueled by compassion, presence, and empathy. It emphasizes not only the medical aspects of care but also the emotional and human connection that is essential for healing.

In light of the alarming data in the United States showing Black babies die at a disproportionately high rate, our responsibility as healthcare providers goes beyond addressing individual cases; it requires a commitment to delivering care with equity and empathy. Every interaction with a grieving family must reflect an understanding of the systemic inequities that have contributed to these disparities and a determination to provide culturally competent and dignified support.

Through the RTS Perinatal Loss Education program, we strive to ensure that every healthcare provider understands the profound impact of their presence and actions. By fostering compassion and prioritizing equity, we can transform the care of families experiencing loss into a source of hope and healing for communities that have been disproportionately affected by these tragedies.

In this chapter, you will explore **10 essential competencies** for serving families who have experienced a perinatal loss. These competencies are foundational for providing care that is compassionate, equitable, and sensitive to the unique needs of grieving families.

Each competency is designed to equip healthcare providers, birth workers, and support teams with the skills and knowledge necessary to create a supportive and healing environment. These include fostering emotional connection, addressing cultural and systemic inequities, and embodying the principles of presence, empathy, and active listening.

By mastering these competencies, you will be better prepared to offer meaningful care that respects the dignity of every family, honors their grief journey, and acknowledges the profound loss they have endured. These skills are not only critical in addressing the immediate needs of families but also in advancing a culture of care that prioritizes equity and empathy for all.

Let us delve into these 10 competencies and learn how to transform moments of heartbreak into opportunities for healing and support.

Classifications of Perinatal Loss

Perinatal loss encompasses a wide range of experiences that vary by timing, cause, and circumstance. Below is a list of possible classifications to help frame the complexities of perinatal loss:

The Four Types of Perinatal Loss

Understanding the classifications of perinatal loss is essential for providing compassionate and effective care. Below are the four most common types of perinatal loss, along with their definitions and statistical context:

1. **Miscarriage**
   - **Definition:** Loss of pregnancy before 20 weeks of gestation.
   - **Statistics:** Up to **25% of confirmed pregnancies** result in miscarriage.
   - **Context:** Miscarriage is the most common form of pregnancy loss, often occurring due to chromosomal abnormalities, hormonal imbalances, or maternal health conditions.

2. **Stillbirth**
   - **Definition:** Death of a fetus at or after 20 weeks of gestation, resulting in no signs of life (e.g., no Apgar scores) at birth.
   - **Statistics:** Approximately **1 in 100 births** over 20 weeks gestation will result in stillbirth.
   - **Context:** Causes of stillbirth include placental issues, infections, maternal conditions such as hypertension or diabetes, and umbilical cord complications.

3. **Neonatal Death**
   - **Definition:** Death of a live-born infant within the first **28 days of life.**
   - **Statistics:** Neonatal deaths account for the majority of infant deaths globally, with causes including prematurity, infections, birth asphyxia, or congenital abnormalities.
   - **Context:** Effective neonatal care and timely interventions can help reduce the risks of neonatal death in vulnerable populations.

4. **Fetal Death**
   - **Definition:** Death of a fetus prior to complete expulsion or extraction from the mother, regardless of the duration of pregnancy. The death is indicated by the absence of signs of life such as breathing, heartbeat, umbilical cord pulsation, or voluntary muscle movement.
   - **Context:** Fetal death includes both early and late losses that occur prior to delivery and may overlap with other classifications, such as miscarriage and stillbirth.

Perinatal Mortality Context

The term **perinatal loss** encompasses deaths occurring from conception through the first 28 days of life, including miscarriages, stillbirths, and neonatal deaths. The disparities in perinatal outcomes, particularly among historically marginalized communities, highlight the importance of equity-focused care to improve survival rates and support grieving families.

What you can do to help

You can be the greatest gift to grieving parents. Holding a hand, touching a shoulder, giving a hug says, "I'm here. I care." By letting parents talk about their pain, you can help them come to grips with it.

What does grief look like?

STAGES OF GRIEF AND STEPS IN GRIEVING

Grief is a natural response to loss, and while it is deeply personal, many people experience common stages as they process their emotions. Developed by psychiatrist Elisabeth Kübler-Ross, the **five stages of grief** offer a framework for understanding the grieving process. These stages do not necessarily occur in a linear sequence, and individuals may revisit or skip stages altogether. Below is a description of each stage:

1. **Denial**
   - **Description:** This initial stage serves as a defense mechanism to shield individuals from the immediate shock and overwhelming reality of loss. In this phase, individuals may struggle to accept the situation, often feeling numb or in disbelief.
   - **Common Thoughts:** "This can't be happening," or "There must be some mistake."

2. **Anger**
   - **Description:** As the reality of the loss sets in, feelings of anger or frustration may emerge. This anger can be directed at oneself, others, the deceased, or even a higher power. It often stems from a sense of helplessness or perceived unfairness.
   - **Common Thoughts:** "Why did this happen?" or "It's not fair."

3. **Bargaining**
   - **Description:** In this stage, individuals often attempt to regain a sense of control by making deals or promises, either with themselves, others, or a higher power, in the hope of reversing or lessening the loss.
   - **Common Thoughts:** "If I had done things differently, this wouldn't have happened," or "If I do this, can things go back to the way they were?"

4. **Depression**
   - **Description:** This stage is marked by deep sadness as the individual confronts the full weight of the loss. Feelings of emptiness, withdrawal, and hopelessness are common, as the reality of the situation feels inescapable.
   - **Common Thoughts:** "What's the point of moving forward?" or "I'll never feel okay again."

5. **Acceptance**
   - **Description:** The final stage is characterized by a gradual coming to terms with the loss. Acceptance does not mean forgetting or diminishing the importance of the loss, but rather finding a way to live with it and adjust to a new reality.
   - **Common Thoughts:** "This is my reality, and I can find a way to move forward."

Additional Perspectives on Grieving

While Kübler-Ross's model provides a helpful structure, grief is not a one-size-fits-all experience. Many people may experience emotions outside of these stages, such as guilt, confusion, or relief. Cultural, religious, and personal beliefs can also shape the grieving process.

Ultimately, grief is a unique journey for every individual, and understanding these stages can provide valuable insight into the complex emotions that accompany loss. Support, empathy, and patience are critical in helping oneself and others navigate this journey.

Steps of Grief and Grieving

Grieving is a process that unfolds in steps, guiding individuals through the emotional journey of processing loss. These steps, while not universal or linear, provide a framework for understanding how people adapt to life after a significant loss. The steps include emotional, cognitive, and behavioral responses that help individuals cope and eventually find a sense of healing.

Step 1: Acknowledgment of the Loss

Description: The grieving process begins with recognizing and accepting that a loss has occurred. This step often includes moments of shock, disbelief, or numbness as the reality of the situation begins to sink in.

Key Focus: Allow yourself time to process and accept the initial impact of the loss.

Step 2: Experiencing the Pain of Grief

Description: This step involves fully feeling the emotions associated with loss, such as sadness, anger, guilt, or loneliness. It is an essential part of grieving that helps individuals begin to process their feelings.

Key Focus: Embrace and express emotions without judgment, whether through talking, writing, or crying.

Step 3: Adjusting to Life Without the Loss

Description: As the acute pain of grief subsides, individuals start adapting to a new reality without the person, relationship, or situation they have lost. This involves developing new routines, roles, and ways of functioning.

Key Focus: Focus on rebuilding a sense of stability while honoring the loss.

Step 4: Navigating Triggers and Reminders

Description: Certain experiences, dates, or objects may evoke strong memories of the loss. This step involves learning to cope with these reminders while continuing to process feelings.

Key Focus: Develop strategies to handle grief triggers, such as mindfulness or seeking support from loved ones.

Step 5: Finding Meaning and Growth

Description: Over time, individuals may begin to reflect on the significance of their loss and explore ways to find meaning or purpose in their experience. This could involve honoring the memory of a loved one or using the experience to help others.

Key Focus: Look for ways to integrate the loss into your life story positively.

Step 6: Rebuilding and Moving Forward

Description: The final step involves reinvesting in life and re-engaging with the world, while still carrying the memory of the loss. This does not mean "getting over" the loss but finding a way to live alongside it.

Key Focus: Cultivate hope and pursue activities, relationships, or goals that bring joy and fulfillment.

Individual Variations

It's important to remember that grief is a highly personal journey. These steps may occur in different orders, repeat, or overlap. Cultural and personal values, the nature of the loss, and available support systems all influence how someone progresses through the grieving process.

Support for Grieving

Recognizing these steps can help individuals and caregivers navigate grief with greater understanding and compassion and empathy. Whether through professional counseling, support groups, or personal reflection, finding resources to support each step is vital for healing.

The Resolve Through Sharing (RTS) program was founded by **R.N. and Perinatal Loss Advocate Susan H. Soderberg** in the early 1980s. Her groundbreaking work emerged from a deep compassion for grieving families and a commitment to improving the care provided to those experiencing perinatal loss.

As a nurse, Susan Soderberg observed a profound gap in the healthcare system's approach to addressing the emotional needs of families grieving the loss of an infant. At the time, there was little recognition of the lasting psychological and emotional impact of perinatal death. Motivated by the absence of compassionate, structured support for grieving families, she sought to create a program that emphasized empathy, education, and empowerment for both families and healthcare providers.

Under Susan's leadership, RTS became a pioneering model for bereavement care, offering healthcare professionals comprehensive training in compassionate presence and evidence-based practices for supporting families during their most vulnerable moments. Her work emphasized the importance of acknowledging grief, fostering communication, and creating personalized rituals to honor the lives of lost infants.

The program she established continues to influence healthcare systems worldwide, empowering providers to deliver equitable and empathetic care and ensuring that no family endures the pain of perinatal loss alone or unsupported.

WORDS TO SAY AND NOT SAY:

Don't say:

- You're young; you can have others. (Parents have to mourn this child before they can have another. One child does not replace another.
- You have an angel in heaven. He/She's in a better place. This happened for the best. God knows what is best for you.
- Better for this to happen now, before you knew him/her (Though well-meant, these kinds of statements do not resonate well. The parents are in pain-they do not feel peace or relief to have lost their precious child.
- Now accept it and move on.
- Don't be sad. Don't cry. (Avoid telling them how to feel; acknowledge the way they are already feeling.) By saying, "I know you are sad." "I am too."
- If you need anything, call me. (The bereaved rarely reach out. State a specific time that you'll check in ad then do so.

Do say:

- **"I'm so sorry for your loss. I can't imagine how hard this must be for you."**
- This expresses sympathy without assuming or minimizing her grief.
- **"Please know that I'm here for you, and you don't have to go through this alone."**
- Offering support and reassurance that she is not alone in her grief can be comforting.
- **"It's okay to feel however you're feeling right now. There's no right or wrong way to grieve."**
- Validating her emotions and reminding her that there is no timeline for grief helps her feel understood.
- **"Your baby will always be a part of your heart and your life, and you'll always have the love you shared."**
- Acknowledging the bond she had with her child can provide a sense of connection, even in grief.
- **"I'm here to listen, whether you want to talk, cry, or just sit in silence."**
- Offering a listening ear without pressuring her to speak can give her the space she needs to process her emotions.
- **"If there's anything you need, whether it's practical help or just a friend to be with you, I'm here."**
- Sometimes, offering specific forms of help (like running errands or providing meals) can alleviate some immediate stress.
- **"Your grief is valid, and it's okay to take your time to heal. Be kind to yourself."**
- Encouraging self-compassion and a gentle pace for recovery can help her feel less pressured to "move on."

It's important to avoid minimizing her loss with statements like "It was meant to be" or "You can try again," as these can inadvertently invalidate her pain. Instead, be present, empathetic, and ready to support her in whatever way she needs. Every mother's grief journey is unique, and simply showing up with care and sensitivity is the most meaningful way to offer comfort.

RESPONSES FROM FAMILY MEMBERS SUFFERING PERINATAL LOSS

Perinatal loss is a deeply emotional and life-altering event that affects each family member differently. Understanding these varied responses can provide better support for all individuals navigating through their grief.

Mothers

Mothers who experience perinatal loss often face the most visible and widely studied emotional impact, as they are physically and emotionally connected to the child. The grieving process for mothers is unique, and it often involves complex emotions that include guilt, self-blame, and a damaged sense of self-worth.

- **Emotional Experience:** Because the child was once physically a part of her, mothers may feel an overwhelming sense of loss not just of a baby but of their own identity as a mother. Many mothers question if they could have done something differently to prevent the loss, even when the cause is beyond their control.
- **Feelings of Rejection:** A mother may feel deeply hurt if her husband or partner does not grieve in the same way or is ready to "move on" before she is. This may be perceived as a personal rejection, as though her grief, or the memory of the child, is not as significant to him.
- **Need for Validation:** In these moments, mothers often require validation of their grief and emotional pain. Their mourning is often tied closely to the recognition of their baby's life, no matter how short, and their grief can feel invalidated if the support from others is insufficient.

Fathers

Fathers often have a different experience of perinatal loss, shaped by cultural gender norms that discourage emotional expression, especially when it comes to grief.

- **Emotional Expression:** Fathers often find it difficult to express their emotions due to social expectations that they should be "strong" and composed, not openly showing vulnerability or pain. This leads many fathers to bottle up their grief.
- **Protective Instinct:** Many fathers take on the role of protector for their partner, focusing on supporting their wife or partner during her grief. While this can provide a sense of purpose, it can also mean that their own grief goes unaddressed.
- **Isolation and Marginalization:** As society places more emphasis on maternal grief, fathers may feel marginalized and isolated in their experience. Despite the lack of social support, fathers can experience grief just as intensely—if not more so—than mothers, as they navigate the emotional aftermath without an outlet to express or process their feelings.
- **Need for Acknowledgment:** Fathers need acknowledgment of their grief and opportunities to express their emotions without judgment. Being able to grieve openly can significantly aid in their emotional healing.

Siblings: The Invisible Loss

For siblings, especially those who are young or were not yet able to fully understand the pregnancy, the loss of a baby can feel invisible and go largely unacknowledged.

- **Emotional Experience:** The grief of siblings can often be overlooked. Children may have many questions but receive little validation for their feelings. They may not understand why the baby is gone and may not have had the chance to bond with the child. In many cases, siblings are not allowed to see or meet the deceased baby, which can leave them feeling confused and disconnected from the grieving process.
- **Changing Practices:** In recent years, however, this dynamic has begun to shift. Hospitals now encourage or allow siblings to meet and say goodbye to the baby, which provides them with an opportunity to process the loss and be a part of the family's grieving.
- **Need for Communication:** Siblings often need clear, age-appropriate explanations about what has happened. They benefit from seeing their parents grieve and being included in the process in ways that allow them to express their own sadness or confusion.
- **Invisible Grief:** Despite this growing awareness, sibling grief is still often left out of conversations, and their emotional needs can remain unmet. It is important to recognize and validate the unique grief of siblings to avoid it being overlooked or dismissed.

Grandparents: Grieving Twice

Grandparents often experience a unique form of grief in the wake of perinatal loss. While they mourn the loss of their grandchild, they also grieve the pain of seeing their own children suffer. This dual experience of grief—mourning both the baby and their child's heartache—can be emotionally complex.

- **Grief for the Grandchild:** Grandparents feel the loss of the baby, though they may not have had the same attachment as the parents, they still grieve the loss of the life that never had the chance to develop. Their sadness stems from the loss of what could have been—the joy of watching their grandchild grow, and the future memories they would have created together.
- **Grief for Their Child:** In addition to mourning their grandchild, grandparents also grieve for their children, who are experiencing profound pain. This can be especially challenging for grandparents, as they may feel a deep sense of helplessness. Watching their child in sorrow, especially if they cannot "fix" the situation or alleviate the pain, can lead to feelings of frustration or sadness.
- **Helplessness and Protective Instinct:** Many grandparents struggle with feelings of helplessness. They may feel the urge to protect their children from further emotional harm, but at the same time, they may feel limited in what they can do to support them. This can lead to a sense of powerlessness, as they navigate their own grief while trying to be a source of support for their children.
- **Support Needs:** Grandparents often find it hard to express their grief in the same ways parents or siblings can. They may not feel as though society acknowledges their grief, as the focus is often on the parents. As a result, grandparents can become isolated in their mourning. It is important for family members to recognize and include grandparents in the grieving process, allowing them the space to grieve the loss of their grandchild and the sorrow of seeing their children suffer.
- **Need for Validation:** Just as parents and siblings need their grief to be acknowledged, so too do grandparents. Their role in the family may leave them feeling like their grief is secondary, but it is equally important to validate their pain. Providing emotional space for grandparents to express their sorrow can help them in their grieving process.

Grandparents often experience a unique form of grief—grieving for both the grandchild they lost and the pain their child is enduring. It's essential to recognize and support grandparents through this dual grieving process, offering them space to mourn and providing emotional support to help them navigate their loss. Their grief is just as valid and deserves acknowledgment within the family and community, as they too are an integral part of the healing journey.

Conclusion

Perinatal loss affects each family member in distinct ways, and these differences can cause tension if not understood or addressed. By recognizing the emotional responses of mothers, fathers, and siblings, caregivers and family members can provide a more compassionate, inclusive support system for all those affected. Grief does not follow a set path, and everyone in the family will mourn in their own way, but by acknowledging and honoring these different experiences, healing can begin for all.

CULTURAL ASPECTS RELATED TO ADAPTATION TO LOSS

When families experience perinatal loss, their responses to grief and healing are influenced not only by individual emotions but also by cultural values and traditions. The way grief is expressed, processed, and supported can differ widely across cultures. Understanding these cultural aspects is crucial for providing compassionate, culturally sensitive care and support to families navigating such profound loss. Here are several key cultural aspects related to adaptation to loss:

1. **Humility**
    - In many cultures, humility is a valued trait that can shape how grief is expressed and managed.
    - Cultural Influence: In some cultures, humility may involve accepting a loss with quiet dignity, not drawing attention to oneself or one's suffering. Families may internalize their grief, believing that mourning should be done in private.
    - Impact on Adaptation: The grieving family may not seek outward support or may refrain from sharing their feelings with others, choosing instead to rely on inner strength and community for solace. Health providers should be sensitive to these cultural nuances, offering support without pushing for overt expressions of grief.

2. **Authority**
    - The role of authority figures, such as parents, elders, or religious leaders, is critical in how loss is managed and understood within different cultural contexts.
    - Cultural Influence: In some cultures, the authority of elders or religious leaders may dictate the grieving process. These figures may provide guidance on how to process the loss and offer comfort through spiritual or communal rituals.
    - Impact on Adaptation: Families may turn to these figures for emotional support, advice, and decisions about burial or memorialization practices. Acknowledging the authority of these figures can be key to respecting the grieving family's wishes.

3. **Communication**
    - Communication practices, both verbal and non-verbal, can vary greatly across cultures when coping with loss.
    - Cultural Influence: Some cultures encourage open expression of grief through storytelling, chanting, or communal gatherings, while others may

value silence, restraint, or stoicism. The way family members talk about their grief, express emotions, and seek support can be shaped by cultural norms around communication.
- Impact on Adaptation: It's essential to be aware of cultural preferences regarding communication. Some families may require more time to process their grief before discussing it, while others may be more vocal and expressive. Understanding these cultural differences allows for more respectful and effective support.

4. **Doctor's Right**
    - In certain cultures, there is a high level of trust and deference given to medical professionals and authority figures, which can affect how families cope with loss.
    - Cultural Influence: In some cultures, families may place complete trust in the decisions and advice of doctors, even when those decisions involve difficult discussions about perinatal loss. The medical professional's opinion is often considered the final word, especially in contexts where respect for authority is strong.
    - Impact on Adaptation: Medical providers should be open to discussing and respecting cultural preferences for care. Sensitivity to alternative healing methods, alongside providing medically appropriate care, can help families feel respected and supported in their grief journey.

5. **Medical Standard of Care**
    - Cultural values around healthcare practices can influence how families understand and react to medical care during the perinatal period.
    - Cultural Influence: Some cultures may have strong preferences for traditional or holistic healing practices over conventional medical interventions. This can influence how families perceive the standard medical care provided by hospitals, including decisions about the handling of the loss, such as autopsies, postmortem care, and funeral arrangements.
    - Impact on Adaptation: Healthcare providers must be open to discussing and respecting cultural preferences for care. Sensitivity to alternative healing methods, alongside providing medically appropriate care, can help families feel respected and supported in their grief journey.

6. **Cultural Uniqueness**
    - Each culture has its own customs and rituals for mourning, and these practices can profoundly affect the grieving process.
    - Cultural Influence: Specific rituals, such as mourning periods, memorial services, food offerings, or visits from religious or spiritual leaders, can provide comfort and meaning in times of loss. These practices might also guide the family through the stages of grief, providing structure to their healing process.
    - Impact on Adaptation: Families may have specific expectations about how they should be allowed to grieve, and these expectations might differ from the practices common in the healthcare setting. For example, some cultures may expect an immediate and large family gathering after a loss, while others may want a more private ceremony. Understanding these practices is essential for offering support in a culturally appropriate manner.

7. **Spiritual Tradition**
    - Spirituality and religious beliefs are often central to how families understand life, death, and grief.

- Cultural Influence: Many cultures have spiritual or religious beliefs that provide comfort during times of loss, such as the belief in an afterlife, reincarnation, or that the deceased is in a better place. Rituals such as prayer, memorial services, or spiritual healing ceremonies play an important role in the grieving process.
- Impact on Adaptation: Families may seek spiritual guidance from their faith leaders, and the presence of prayer, rituals, or spiritual counseling may be an essential part of their mourning process. Healthcare providers should be respectful and open to including these traditions in the care plan and should collaborate with the family to support their spiritual needs in addition to their emotional and physical well-being.

8. **Humility in Healthcare Providers**
    - Doctors and nurses should walk in humility even though they hold positions of authority in healthcare settings.
    - Cultural Influence: While medical professionals are expected to provide expertise and guidance, it is essential to recognize that the patient and their family members know their bodies and what they desire when it comes to treatment and care. In cultures where patients have a strong sense of autonomy, families may expect to have their wishes acknowledged and respected.
    - Impact on Adaptation: Healthcare providers should listen actively to the family's concerns and preferences, offering medical advice while honoring the family's decisions. This humility in practice fosters a sense of trust and respect, allowing for a more collaborative approach to care during such a sensitive time.

Conclusion

Cultural aspects such as humility, authority, communication, and spiritual tradition play significant roles in how families adapt to perinatal loss. Being aware of and sensitive to these cultural values allows healthcare providers to offer care that is not only medically sound but also emotionally and culturally supportive. Recognizing the unique needs of each family member and the cultural context in which they grieve can make a profound difference in the healing process, fostering a compassionate, empathetic, and inclusive environment during one of the most difficult times in a family's life.

DISCUSS NURSING MANAGEMENT:

Etiology: How It Happened?

In some cases of intrauterine fetal death (IUFD), the exact cause may remain unknown despite extensive investigation. The loss could be due to a variety of factors, such as a thrombus (blood clot) or an umbilical cord issue, such as cord prolapse, cord entanglement, or cord accidents that interrupt the fetal blood flow. Other causes may include chromosomal abnormalities or structural issues with the baby that are undetectable during pregnancy. In many instances, there are no fetal tones or the heartbeat stops suddenly, and without clear explanation, the loss is simply deemed unexplained. While the cause may never be fully understood, it's important to recognize that the grief and impact on the family are real, regardless of the reason for the loss.

Diagnosis: IUFD, Fetal Demise, or Neonatal Death

Intrauterine fetal death (IUFD), fetal demise, or neonatal death can occur at various stages of pregnancy, with significant implications for the family and healthcare team. The diagnosis of IUFD is typically made when there is a sudden cessation of fetal movement or the absence of a fetal heartbeat, confirmed through ultrasound or Doppler examination. IUFD most commonly occurs after 20 weeks of gestation, but can also occur earlier, even as early as 16 weeks, though the incidence is less frequent.

Fetal demise can also happen closer to full term, sometimes as much as 36 weeks, although this is a less common scenario. In these cases, the fetus may pass away in utero due to a variety of factors such as cord accidents, placental insufficiency, infections, or other complications. Neonatal death refers to death occurring shortly after birth, within the first 28 days of life, and is often associated with severe prematurity, congenital anomalies, or complications during labor and delivery.

When IUFD or neonatal death occurs, the diagnosis is usually confirmed through clinical findings, such as the absence of fetal heart tones or abnormal findings on an ultrasound. Prompt diagnosis is crucial for facilitating appropriate management and providing care to the grieving family. The role of the healthcare team in this process is to provide accurate, compassionate information and support to the family as they process this devastating loss.

Nursing role in assisting the family to cope

As nurses, our primary role in assisting families experiencing the devastating loss of a fetus or neonate is to provide respectful, dignified care effectively

This includes creating a compassionate environment where the family feels heard, supported, and valued throughout the grieving process. Nurses should offer empathetic listening, allowing family members to express their emotions, ask questions, and process their feelings without judgment.

Supporting their grief involves acknowledging the intense and varied emotions they may experience, including sadness, anger, guilt, and confusion. Providing clear, honest, and sensitive communication about the situation and available options is essential. Nurses can offer guidance on making decisions, such as whether to see or hold the baby, and respect the family's cultural and personal preferences during the grieving process.

Furthermore, nurses must recognize that grief is a complex and individual experience. Some family members may wish to spend time with the deceased infant, and others may need space. It is important to validate the family's emotional needs, provide referrals for counseling or support groups, and ensure that the family has the resources to cope with the immediate and long-term effects of their loss. Ultimately, our role is to walk alongside the family with care, humility, and unwavering support during one of the most difficult times of their lives.

Caring for yourself after a loss:

Most hospitals have a wellness program, code lavender, emotional debriefing, tea for the soul, compassionate sensitivity.

CHAPTER TWENTY-NINE
Medical and Emotional Debriefings: Processing Traumatic Events and Self-Care

Maternal health nurses work in a highly demanding and emotionally charged environment, where they are responsible for managing a wide spectrum of complex and often unpredictable events. From assisting mothers through labor and delivery to providing critical postpartum care, these nurses navigate high-stress situations daily, often dealing with emergencies such as postpartum hemorrhage, emergent C-sections, and fetal distress. Their roles extend beyond medical tasks, requiring them to offer emotional support and reassurance to mothers and families during vulnerable moments. The stress intensifies when complications arise, such as when a newborn requires care in the Neonatal Intensive Care Unit (NICU). The responsibility of ensuring the health and safety of both mother and baby, coupled with the emotional weight of supporting families through difficult circumstances, can significantly heighten the stress levels of maternal health nurses.

Despite these challenges, maternal health nurses remain dedicated to providing respectful maternal care that emphasizes patient and family-centered approaches. They strive to create a supportive environment that honors the preferences and needs of mothers while ensuring optimal outcomes. This commitment to patient-centered care involves not only addressing the medical aspects of childbirth and postpartum recovery but also recognizing the emotional and psychological needs of mothers and their families. By offering compassionate care, clear communication, and advocacy, nurses work tirelessly to empower families, foster a sense of trust, and enhance the overall birthing experience, even in the face of complex and high-stress situations. Their role is crucial in navigating the delicate balance between clinical expertise and empathetic support, ultimately contributing to the well-being of mothers, babies, and families during one of the most critical times of their lives.

Sometimes, outcomes in maternal health care are not favorable, leading to traumatic experiences not only for patients and their families but also for the staff involved. Events such as fetal demise, maternal complications, or unexpected surgical interventions can leave a lasting emotional impact on nurses, who often form deep connections with their patients. These situations can be profoundly distressing for healthcare providers who strive for the best outcomes but must also cope with the realities of loss and trauma. Therefore, providing robust support systems for staff is critical in any hospital setting. Access to mental health resources, peer support, debriefing sessions, and creating a culture of open communication can help nurses process these difficult experiences, maintain their emotional well-being, and continue to deliver compassionate care.

We have listed some practical and helpful strategies specifically designed for nurses managing complex cases, traumatic maternal surgical procedures, fetal demise, neonatal deaths, maternal mortality, postpartum hemorrhage, and emergent C-sections. These approaches aim to address and process trauma, promote self-care, and build resilience among healthcare professionals in these highly emotional and challenging situations:

Debrief After High-Stress and Traumatic Events

Debriefings are important as they provide education and information that help clinicians understand the medical and emotional impact of the procedure. This is also a time to educate the clinician on the impact they may experience i.e., your sleep, eating habits, compassion fatigue, depression, mood swings, etc., Debriefings show care for your staff. These sessions allow nurses and the care team to express their emotions, discuss what happened, and identify improvement areas, helping mitigate the emotional impact of these intense experiences. Nurses will feel affirmed and their feelings validated.

Access to Mental Health and Trauma Support Services

Ensure availability of mental health professionals, such as psychologists or trauma counselors, for nurses who manage complex and traumatic maternal cases. Providing access to these services helps nurses process their experiences, especially after events such as fetal demise or maternal death. Some hospitals have a Spiritual Care Department and Chaplains may also be a helpful resource to have present at debriefing for extra support.

Peer Support Networks

Establishing a peer support program for nurses to connect with colleagues who understand the unique emotional challenges of complex maternal and neonatal cases, can be very resourceful. Peer support can offer emotional validation, practical advice, and a sense of community among those facing similar stresses.

Promote Mindfulness, Relaxation, and Grounding Techniques

Mindfulness practices such as meditation, deep breathing exercises, or grounding techniques before and after handling high-stress surgical procedures like emergent C-sections or postpartum hemorrhage can help manage stress, lower heart rate and help clear the mind.

Ongoing Education on Trauma-Informed Care

Understanding the effects of trauma on both patients and healthcare providers will help nurses better manage their emotional responses and deliver compassionate care during sensitive and distressing procedures. In addition, take a proactive approach in taking care of themselves after stressful events.

Designated Quiet Spaces for Reflection and Recovery

Dedicated quiet rooms or reflective spaces within the hospital are suitable for nurses to retreat after handling emotionally challenging events, such as maternal mortality, stillbirth, fetal demise, traumatic deliveries or neonatal death and can be therapeutic and healing. These areas can offer a brief respite for nurses to regroup, process, reflect, and journal the event.

Establish Healthy Boundaries and Self-Compassion

Cultivating emotional boundaries and practicing self-compassion helps the recovery process. Avoid internalizing negative outcomes or feeling personally responsible for traumatic events, such as fetal demise or postpartum hemorrhage, recognizing that not all outcomes are within your control.

Resilience and Coping Skills

Nurses should attend resilience training and stress management workshops as a self-care management.

Check your hospital policies for short-term mental health leave after particularly traumatic events, sentinel events, such as neonatal death or complex surgical procedures. Time away from the clinical environment can provide the necessary space to process difficult experiences and recover emotionally.

Foster a Culture of Open Communication and Non-Judgmental Feedback

Nurse Leaders should maintain an open and supportive work culture where nurses feel comfortable discussing their emotional responses to traumatic cases without fear of judgment. Encourage feedback loops that allow nurses to voice concerns, suggest improvements, and feel heard in their professional environment.

Nurse leaders should consistently acknowledge the emotional toll of traumatic cases, such as fetal demise or maternal death. Validation from supervisors help to normalize stressful feelings, reducing the stigma associated with emotional vulnerability in healthcare settings.

Encourage Self-Care and Rejuvenating Activities Outside of Work

Nurse leaders should self-care activities outside of work, such as exercise, hobbies, creative outlets, or spending quality time with family and friends. These activities can help nurses decompress and recharge, enabling them to return to work with renewed energy and resilience.

These strategies are specifically aimed at helping nurses cope with the intense emotional demands of handling complex and traumatic maternal and neonatal cases. By fostering a supportive environment and encouraging self-care, these approaches can help nurses process trauma, build resilience, maintain their well-being and secure work force retention.

Case Study: Nurse Sarah's Experience with Maternal Mortality

Background:

Sarah is a highly experienced labor and delivery nurse with over 10 years of practice in a busy urban hospital. She is known for her calm demeanor, clinical expertise, and compassionate care. Sarah has managed numerous high-risk pregnancies and complicated deliveries, consistently providing excellent care and emotional support to her patients and their families.

The Event:

One evening, Sarah was assigned to a patient, Jessica, a 32-year-old woman in her second pregnancy with no significant medical history, who was admitted in active labor. Initially, the labor progressed well, but complications arose when Jessica suddenly developed severe postpartum hemorrhage following delivery. Despite immediate interventions, including medications, blood transfusions, and an emergency surgical procedure, Jessica's condition rapidly deteriorated. The obstetric team, along with Sarah, worked tirelessly for over an hour, but despite their best efforts, Jessica passed away due to uncontrollable bleeding—a tragic and rare maternal mortality event.

Impact on Sarah:

Witnessing Jessica's death was deeply traumatic for Sarah. She felt overwhelmed by a mix of emotions: shock, grief, helplessness, and a lingering sense of guilt, questioning if anything more could have been done. The sound of alarms, the frantic efforts of the medical team, and the heart-wrenching moment of informing Jessica's family replayed in Sarah's mind long after her shift ended. She found it difficult to process the event, feeling both personally and professionally affected by the unexpected loss. Sleep became elusive, and Sarah started experiencing anxiety at work, particularly when faced with patients who exhibited even mild complications.

Debriefing:

Following the event, Sarah's hospital facilitated a debriefing session for all staff involved, allowing them to discuss the clinical aspects of the case and express their emotions in a supportive environment. Although helpful, Sarah found herself needing more individualized support. She began attending sessions with a trauma-informed therapist, who helped her process the emotional impact of the event through mindfulness and coping strategies. Sarah also engaged in peer support meetings with fellow nurses who had experienced similar sentinel events, finding solace in shared experiences.

Lessons Learned:

Sarah's experience highlighted the critical need for comprehensive support systems for healthcare professionals dealing with traumatic events like maternal mortality. Access to mental health resources, ongoing peer support, and the encouragement of self-care practices such as mindfulness were essential in Sarah's journey toward emotional healing. Her story underscores the importance of hospital environments that prioritize the well-being of their staff, recognizing that sentinel events affect not just the patients and families involved but also the dedicated professionals who strive to provide the best possible care under extraordinary circumstances.

NURTURING EQUITY MINDED HEALTHCARE EXERCISE

Break into small groups and discuss the following questions:

1. How did Sarah's experience with this sentinel event impact her emotional and mental well-being, and how might similar experiences affect you?

    - Explore how traumatic events in the healthcare setting can deeply affect healthcare professionals and discuss ways in which you have personally been impacted by similar situations.

2. What self-care strategies, such as mindfulness or peer support, do you currently use or would consider using to manage the stress and emotions related to traumatic events at work?

    - Share personal self-care practices and discuss additional techniques that could be beneficial in managing emotional responses to high-stress incidents.

3. How can healthcare professionals recognize signs of emotional burnout or trauma within themselves and their colleagues, and what steps can be taken when these signs are identified?

    - Discuss the warning signs of burnout or trauma, both in yourself and others, and brainstorm actionable steps for seeking support or providing assistance.

4. What role does debriefing and open communication play in helping nurses process traumatic events, and how can these practices be improved in your workplace?

    - Reflect on the effectiveness of debriefing sessions and other supportive communications following traumatic events. Consider ways to enhance these practices within your own healthcare setting.

5. What barriers might prevent nurses from seeking help or engaging in self-care after experiencing a traumatic event, and how can these barriers be addressed in your workplace?

    - Identify potential obstacles to self-care, such as stigma, lack of time, or insufficient support, and discuss strategies to create a more supportive and open environment that encourages self-care and seeking help.

Section V

WHERE DO WE GO FROM HERE?

OVERVIEW OF SECTION V

WHAT YOU WILL LEARN (AND DO) IN THIS SECTION:

Chapter 30: Modern Laws: The United States has often been seen as a leader in healthcare, but the alarming reality is that it has found itself on the wrong side of justice in healthcare disparities. This chapter focuses on modern laws both current and proposed in the State fo California.

Chapter 31: Team Building for Maternal and Infant Equity Groups: Discover different -isms that divide birth equity teams and learn many interpersonal skill sets that help build a strong equity team with mutual respect, dignity, and transparency.

Chapter 32: Racism Amid Nursing Staff: Uncover the racism historically steeped within the nursing profession, and develop ways to mitigate its presence through intentional practices.

Chapter 33: Creating Diversity in the Nursing Workforce: This chapter reveals the disparities amid the workforce which contributes and perpetuates the explicit biases in staff and management. You will learn ways in which your hospital can transform your service line to include equity, equality and diversity in your birthcare center.

Chapter 34: Anti-racism: Leaders Step It Up: Leadership, Step it Up! Come face-to-face with how upper management can be complicit in upholding inappropriate microaggressions, implicit biases and explicit biases if they do not address the rampant racism in their units. You will reflect on 3 action plans that work to eradicate racism and build healthy leadership.

Chapter 35: The Heart of Justice: Providers and clinicians will read the graduating address from the Dean of Harvard Medical School charging his students to advocate for marginalized populations and to remember to see all their patients as deserving of the best care they can provide.

Chapter 36: Closing Letter to All Healthcare Providers: Hear the heart of the author and her passionate impetus for presenting this work as you read her closing remarks and final hopes for her readers.

INTRODUCTION: CLOSING THE DISPARITY GAP FOR MARGINALIZED COMMUNITIES

As healthcare systems, we often adopt corporate practices from successful companies like Toyota to streamline efficiency, enhance product offerings, and drive bottom-line financial outcomes. Similarly, we seek to emulate various franchises' like the Ritz Carlton which are renowned for their customer service to attract patients to our service lines. And what do they receive? At these highly reputable establishments, constituents are accommodated royally from the reservation to check-out, with first-class rooms that are fully equipped, spacious, and beautifully decorated. Guests enjoy exceptional customer service, luxurious robes, extravagant jacuzzi tubs, comfortable beds, and timely room service, all crafted to create an unmatched experience.

However, despite these strategic efforts and enormous investment in adopting corporate branding and marketing, we have consistently failed to invest in addressing the deep-rooted disparities that have persisted for years in Black and Brown communities. We have overlooked the critical need to allocate resources to hire culturally sensitive and competent providers, clinicians and ancillary staff members who can deliver care with empathy and equity.

To close the significant gaps in health outcomes, especially for Black and Brown patients, it is imperative that we train all healthcare professionals new and tenure to provide optimal care rooted in understanding, respect, empathy and cultural competence. This is not just a moral obligation but a necessary step toward building a healthcare system that truly serves all individuals equitably.

So we must do more than adopting the right equity phrasing, updating our websites, integrating all the right language to promote our service lines, we must be integrous in fulfilling our vision and mission statements and healthcare philosophies.

Like the Ritz Carlton, best practices should be met by our patients from admission to discharge - We too should roll out the red carpet not only for our insured and privileged patients, but for those from marginalized communities—who have historically faced barriers to access—instead of receiving care that reflects their marginalized status, it should address them. Then and only then will we move the equitable needle in the right direction.

CHAPTER THIRTY
Modern Laws

Maternal Mortality Disparities in Healthcare

The United States has often been seen as a leader in healthcare, but the alarming reality is that it has found itself on the wrong side of justice in healthcare disparities.[1] And while these disparities are prevalent in general in the United States,[2] for the purposes of our work, we are concentrating on maternal mortality and infant loss in Black mothers and babies in the state of California.

State Legislative Approaches to Address Disparities in Maternal Mortality

According to the CDC, in their grant proposal for Preventing Maternal Deaths: Supporting Maternal Mortality Review Committees, "Considerable racial disparities exist, with Black women

---

1   Alhusen, Jeanne L., et al. "Racial Discrimination and Adverse Birth Outcomes: An Integrative Review." *Journal of Midwifery & Women's Health*, National Library of Medicine, Vol. 61, No. 6, Wiley, Oct. 2016, pp. 707–720. https://doi.org/10.1111/jmwh.12490.

2   MacDorman, Marian F et al. "Recent Increases in the U.S. Maternal Mortality Rate: Disentangling Trends From Measurement Issues." *Obstetrics and gynecology* Vol. 128, 3 (2016): 447-455. doi:10.1097/ AOG.0000000000001556. https://www.ncbi.nlm.nih.gov/pmc/articles/PMC5001799/.

almost four times more likely to die from pregnancy-related complications than White women. However, findings from Maternal Mortality Review Committees (MMRC) indicate that more than half of these deaths are preventable."[3]

In response to the information that Black mothers and babies are 3-4 times more likely to die during childbirth, new state legislation, entitled SBA 464 CA Dignity in Pregnancy and Childbirth Act[4] was created in 2019. This California law would mandates that hospitals provide diversity, equity, and inclusion training (DEI) in order to help mitigate the furtherance of these disparities. The legislation, CA Senate Bill 464, states, in part, "This bill would make legislative findings relating to implicit bias and racial disparities in maternal mortality rates... would require a hospital that provides perinatal care...to implement an evidence-based implicit bias program...for all health care providers involved in perinatal care of patients within those facilities...would require the health care provider to complete initial basic training through the program and a refresher course every 2 years thereafter, or on a more frequent basis if deemed necessary...would require the facility to provide a certificate of training completion upon request, to accept certificates of completion from other facilities, and to offer training to physicians not directly employed by the facility."

A Multidisciplinary Approach

The CDC's grant for Preventing Maternal Deaths: Supporting Maternal Mortality Review Committees3 also proposed the release of $43 million to provide for organizations that commit to helping prevent these unnecessary deaths. "This funding will support Maternal Mortality Review Committees [MMRCs] to identify and characterize maternal deaths with the goal of identifying prevention opportunities...This funding opportunity aims to better understand and prevent pregnancy-related deaths by supporting [MMRCs] to get the most detailed, complete data...to develop recommendations for prevention. This multidisciplinary approach encourages collaboration with clinical and non-clinical partnerships to improve quality of care and address social determinants of health to reduce health inequities. [MMRCs] systematically and comprehensively review deaths to develop recommended strategies for preventing future deaths."

As a result of government responses such as these, many hospitals around the state have begun to engage in training modules from Diversity Science and other programs on "Eliminating Inequities in Perinatal Care" to comply with this new legislation, and to begin to do their part in reversing these heartbreaking disparities. The work that we as birth equity advocates aim to accomplish goes directly in hand with these goals.

Further Proposed Laws to Address Maternal Disparities, Infant Mortality, and Equity

1. **Maternal Health Equity Accountability Act (MHEAA)**

    Summary: This law would mandate comprehensive data collection and public reporting on maternal health outcomes disaggregated by race, ethnicity, and socioeconomic status. It would also require hospitals to implement equity-based training and hire equity officers to oversee maternity wards.

    Key Provisions:
    - Mandatory implicit bias training for all healthcare professionals in maternal care.

---

3   Centers for Disease Control. "Preventing Maternal Deaths: Supporting Maternal Mortality Review Committees." *GRANTS.GOV*, Health and Human Services / USA.Gov, 5 Mar. 2019, www.grants.

4   Mitchell, S, et al. "SB-464 California Dignity in Pregnancy and Childbirth Act." *California Legislative Information*, 7 Oct. 2019, leginfo.legislature.ca.gov/faces/billTextClient.xhtml?bill_id=201920200SB464.

- Funding for community-based maternal health programs targeting marginalized populations.
- Annual public reporting of disparities in maternal outcomes to promote transparency.

Legislative Authors: U.S. Representative Lauren Underwood and U.S. Senator Cory Booker.

2. **The Respectful Maternal Care and Infant Equity Act (RMCIEA)**

    Summary: This law would establish a national framework for respectful maternal care, requiring healthcare facilities to adopt protocols that prioritize dignity, informed consent, and cultural sensitivity.

    Key Provisions:
    - Establishment of a federal task force on respectful maternal care.
    - Penalties for healthcare institutions found guilty of negligence or mistreatment related to racial bias.
    - Grants for maternal health advocates and doulas in underserved communities.

    Legislative Authors: U.S. Senator Elizabeth Warren and U.S. Representative Ayanna Pressley.

3. **The Weathering Mitigation Act (WMA)**

    Summary: This legislation would address the cumulative effects of chronic stress and systemic racism (the "weathering effect") on Black and Brown mothers. It would fund programs to provide holistic prenatal care, including mental health support, stress management training, and access to doulas and midwives.

    Key Provisions:
    - Universal mental health screenings for pregnant women of color.
    - Subsidized access to holistic maternal care providers.
    - Federal funding for research into the biological impacts of stress on maternal and infant health.

    Legislative Authors: U.S. Representative Barbara Lee and U.S. Senator Raphael Warnock.

4. **The Equity in Maternal Health Workforce Act (EMHWA)**

    Summary: This law would increase diversity in the maternal health workforce by providing scholarships, loan forgiveness, and mentorship programs for individuals from underrepresented communities entering maternal and infant care fields.

    Key Provisions:
    - Scholarships for students pursuing careers in obstetrics, midwifery, and lactation consulting.
    - Incentives for bilingual and culturally competent healthcare professionals.
    - Creation of mentorship programs for women of color entering the maternal health field.

    Legislative Authors: U.S. Senator Tammy Duckworth and U.S. Representative Pramila Jayapal.

5. **Social Determinants of Maternal and Infant Health Act (SDMIHA)**

    Summary: This law would integrate social determinants of health into maternal and infant care by providing funding for housing, nutrition, and transportation programs that directly support pregnant individuals and new mothers.

Key Provisions:

- Expansion of Medicaid to cover wraparound services for pregnant women.
- Grants for community organizations addressing housing and food insecurity for new mothers.
- Establishment of maternal health hubs in low-income and rural communities.

Legislative Authors: U.S. Representative Katie Porter and U.S. Senator Kamala Harris.

6. **The Maternal Mental Health and Wellness Act (MMHWA)**

    Summary: Focuses on addressing postpartum depression and anxiety in underserved populations through expanded access to mental health services.

    Key Provisions:

    - Mandatory postpartum mental health screenings for all mothers, with emphasis on Black and Brown communities.
    - Funding for maternal mental health hotlines staffed by culturally competent professionals.
    - Grants for organizations providing postpartum counseling services in underserved areas.

    Legislative Authors: U.S. Senator Kirsten Gillibrand and U.S. Representative Grace Meng.

    Year Enacted: 2026

7. **The Safe Birth Act (SBA)**

    Summary: Establishes national standards for birth care facilities to reduce maternal and infant mortality rates.

    Key Provisions:

    - Certification requirements for birthing centers to ensure they meet safety and equity standards.
    - Incentives for hospitals that achieve measurable reductions in maternal and infant mortality disparities.
    - Establishment of a federal hotline to report unsafe birthing practices.

    Legislative Authors: U.S. Representative Lucy McBath and U.S. Senator Tammy Baldwin.

    Year Enacted: 2027

8. **The Comprehensive Doula Access Act (CDAA)**

    Summary: Expands Medicaid and private insurance coverage for doula and midwifery services nationwide.

    Key Provisions:

    - Federally mandated reimbursement for doula services under Medicaid.
    - Funding for doula training programs in communities of color.
    - Incentives for hiring doulas in rural and underserved areas.

    Legislative Authors: U.S. Senator Alex Padilla and U.S. Representative Cori Bush.

    Year Enacted: 2025

9. **The Infant Equity and Early Development Act (IEEDA)**

    Summary: Provides funding and resources to improve neonatal outcomes for infants in marginalized communities.

    Key Provisions:
    - Nationwide access to early intervention programs for NICU graduates.
    - Free developmental screenings for infants in federally qualified health centers (FQHCs).
    - Subsidies for breastfeeding education and lactation support.

    Legislative Authors: U.S. Senator Patty Murray and U.S. Representative Ilhan Omar.

    Year Enacted: 2028

10. **The Maternal Justice Act (MJA)**

    Summary: Implements legal protections for pregnant individuals experiencing discrimination or neglect in healthcare settings.

    Key Provisions:
    - Protections against racial and gender discrimination in maternal healthcare.
    - Establishment of a federal Maternal Health Ombudsman Office to investigate complaints.
    - Penalties for healthcare providers found guilty of discriminatory practices.

    Legislative Authors: U.S. Senator Mazie Hirono and U.S. Representative Maxine Waters.

    Year Enacted: 2027

Timeline of Enactment

Maternal Health Equity Accountability Act (MHEAA) – 2024

Respectful Maternal Care and Infant Equity Act (RMCIEA) – 2024

Weathering Mitigation Act (WMA) – 2025

Equity in Maternal Health Workforce Act (EMHWA) – 2025

Social Determinants of Maternal and Infant Health Act (SDMIHA) – 2025

Maternal Mental Health and Wellness Act (MMHWA) – 2026

Safe Birth Act (SBA) – 2027

Comprehensive Doula Access Act (CDAA) – 2025

Infant Equity and Early Development Act (IEEDA) – 2028

Maternal Justice Act (MJA) – 2027

These laws collectively form a robust framework for addressing maternal and infant health disparities, ensuring equity, and fostering compassionate care for underserved populations and addressing trauma informed care.

NURTURING EQUITY MINDED GROUP EXERCISE

As a group, discuss your awareness and your perspective of the growing epidemic in the loss of Black mothers and babies.

Share your thoughts around the new CA legislation (SBA 464) and how this impacts the issues.

Describe ways that you as a healthcare provider would approach solving these disparities.

Discuss any policy changes and nursing/medical philosophies that may need to be implemented in your organization.

How can you ensure your intention and motivations for doing the DEI work is from the heart and not performative? How can we keep our focus on the goal of mitigating these racial disparities, and saving lives, rather than on simply fulfilling "requirements" for new legislation.

Still Resilient Redefining Maternal & Infant Health Incorporated
www.Stillresilient.org

OUR EDUCATION & TRAININGS INCLUDE:

- Implicit Bias Training
- Communication & Language Matters
- History of Obstetrics and Race based Care
- Trauma Informed Care
- Neonatal Intensive Care Disparities
- Breastfeeding Disparities
- Coaching Nurse Leadership
- Breaking Bad News
- Building A Unit Culture
- Perinatal & Neonatal Loss
- Respectful Hand-offs
- Patient Family Advocates
- Empathetic Doula Training
- Mental Health Services
- Deescalating Guidelines
- How to Honor Spirituality for Your Patients and Families

EQUITABLE EMPATHY TRAINING CLASSES

REQUEST ESTIMATE | ONLINE CLASSES | HYBRID CLASSES

REGISTER FOR YOUR CLASSES IN JUST 5-10 MINUTES

CALL US: 323-817-9925

GET 10% OFF ON YOUR FIRST EQUITY BUNDLE OF CLASSES
SOON COMING - CEUs AVAILABLE FOR PROVIDERs and NURSES

TRAUMA-INFORMED HIRING PROFESSIONAL

ASSESSMENT-BASED CERTIFICATE PROGRAM 2.0

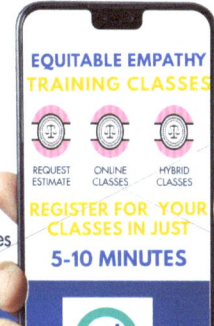

The Trauma-Informed Professional (TIP) 2.0 Assessment-Based Certificate Program equips neonatal clinicians with the tools, knowledge, and transformative insights to elevate care for babies, families, and themselves. With a blend of science, soul, and skills, TIP 2.0 goes beyond education—it's a path to professional and personal fulfillment.

Mary Coughlin, MS, NNP, NCC

APPLY NOW!
WWW.CARINGESSENTIALS.NET

SECTION V | CHAPTER THIRTY: Modern Laws

CHAPTER THIRTY-ONE
Team Building for Birth Equity Groups: A Response to SBA 464

BY REV. DR. CANDACE COLE-KELLY AND SHAWYA MOGHARABI

Team Building in a Multi-Disciplinary Team

In the year 2019, the state of California introduced into law Legislation SBA 464,[1] requiring healthcare organizations, agencies and clinics to implement diversity, equity and inclusion (DEI) training for all staff/healthcare providers. This was done in an effort to work towards the end of structural racism through awareness, education, and transformation.

Multidisciplinary teams throughout California began the work. Pilot programs were launched as grants, funding, and resources were poured into birth equity non-profit organizations.

---

1   Mitchell, S, et al. "SB-464 California Dignity in Pregnancy and Childbirth Act." *California Legislative Information*, 7 Oct. 2019, leginfo.legislature.ca.gov/faces/billTextClient.xhtml?bill_id=201920200SB464.

But, let's face it, there was one critical piece missing in the robust proposal to the DEI work we were required to do. That was, preparing multi-diverse and multi-disciplinary teams to first address their own potential implicit/explicit biases and microaggressions. To explore how they have either experienced or projected stereotypic caricatures on others. To explore comfort zones in working with Black people and understanding the historical data of racism. To engage team building exercises that included group sessions, games, one on one's, and teaching opportunities just for the strengthening of the group.

Because the truth of the matter is this - healthcare institutions have been suddenly tasked, without warning, to engage in this work of creating birth equity teams, partnerships and collaborations without any guiding education, models to follow, coaching or training. Many were simply thrust into this delicate work without the proper preparations to navigate such a large undertaking. Furthermore, due to the sensitive nature around subject matters concerning race and ethnicity, these discussions have often been met with tension and resistance, sometimes before the work could even get started, and without the tools necessary to work through it. Not only are so many new faces, backgrounds, cultures, experiences, and personalities, coming together at the table for maybe the first time, but they are now tasked with bridging any differences in order to work on a sometimes misunderstood, and therefore already divisive, subject matter that has previously been avoided or ignored altogether.

Many of us have never sat around a table with multi-racial, multi-disciplinary team members for 3-4 years to address structural racism in healthcare. It's a topic many do not want to talk about, or know how to talk about, for several reasons. There are legitimate questions that must be answered, i.e. Who can best lead this discussion and initiative? Who has the most experience and empathy in this area? How can we take a posture of learning around the table as we discuss this very sensitive topic? Who should be in the learner's chair and who should be in the leader's chair? How can learners and leaders both communicate the important takeaways after each meeting? Should tensions arise during these discussions (as they often do), who should be assigned to arbitrate any disagreements? How do we assign the best person for that position?

This work is critical and vitally important, but there will, undoubtedly, be times of division, tensions, fall outs, departures, misunderstandings, and hurt feelings. It is for this reason that those who choose to be part of the teams engaging in this work, must be willing to learn, seek to understand, and open to change.

Just as our self-work allows us to provide the best possible care for our patients (See Section I), so too will it allow us to be the best team-mate possible in these settings. Coming from a place of self-worth, of empathy, and of understanding, we can take a humble posture of learning that will help us navigate through this sensitive work.

Thinking through not only our own feelings and emotions, but also trying to imagine the psychological questions and layers each individual around the table might be struggling through, will help us all become better partners in this work.

Emotions can often, understandably, run high in this type of work, but it is our task as individuals, not to let our emotions supersede the overall vision and goal which is to see everyone through an equity lens of respect, dignity and honor.

There will be a wide range of varying experiences coming together from different ends of the spectrum. Some individuals will know what privilege looks like, and others will know what it looks like to be marginalized. Our undertaking will be to bridge these gaps, working to bring together these two diametric opposing realities to focus on the common goal. It takes empathy and heart to accomplish this.

We must flesh out and strengthen our relationships within our own group, or else run the risk of becoming a misunderstood and fragmented team. We each arrive at the table with our own insecurities, experiences, opinions, values, and wonderings.

Hearing One Another

This means everything said, discussed, and viewed is heard in a real, raw, authentic expression, that is not always entirely understood by others in the group. We have not yet learned about one another. We have not yet processed our personalities, or had learning sessions of "how I am and who I am, who you are and how you are?" Without this critical piece, before long, we can be tempted to abandon the entire goal for unprepared personality clashing. We must invest first in the team to see what the team is made up of and how to fortify its members and unify them for one collective goal, checking all egos at the boardroom door.

In her book Reality-Based Leadership,[2] Cy Wakeman states, "sooner or later, practically all of us receive negative feedback, whether it's in the form of poor results, a talking-to from the boss, or a colleague who cares enough to be honest. It can be hard to take, even when you know you deserve it or the bearer of the news is doing you a favor. So, what do you do when the voices of doubt are coming at you from outside?" This 'outside' can represent other team members, leadership, consulting partners, or coaches, that are fully invested in the success of your project and your collective efforts to steer you in the right direction.

5 Steps to Receiving Feedback

Wakeman further offers **five steps** to gleaning the maximum benefit from negative feedback. Bad feedback does not have the power to stall your career, but an unwillingness or inability

---

2 Wakeman, Cy. *Reality-Based Leadership: Ditch the Drama, Restore Sanity to the Workplace, and Turn Excuses into Results.* Jossey-Bass, 2010.

to absorb it and act on it does. She warns her readers, "don't avoid the teachers in your workplace. Treat them as valued coaches who show you what you need to work on. Your coach will not necessarily come to you with the attitude of a cheerleader."

In our collaborative work in birth equity it is essential that we strive to give and receive feedback in the most beneficial ways possible. To do this, here are 5 steps we can take, adapted from Wakeman's work:

1. Welcome the news with respect and gratitude, rather than defense.

2. Beware of your ego-centric side, and letting ego control your reaction. Maximize your learning and respond with openness and willingness.

3. If hearing feedback feels challenging, consider Cy Wakeman's suggestions for effective ways to receive feedback. Rather than personalizing, it can be helpful to react with one of these five responses instead:

    a. "Thank you for caring enough about me to give me that feedback."

    b. "I've noticed that about myself too, and it's something I'm working on."

    c. "Will you help me to improve?"

    d. "I am willing to see if I can find some truth in that."

    e. "I used to think that about myself, too, and here is what I did to change it."

For birth equity groups, you can adapt these personal approaches to your whole team's needs by pluralizing these 5 considerations. I.e. for response "a" consider: " Thank you for caring enough about **us** to offer that feedback."

If feedback is given in a perceived disrespectful or harsh manner, you may want to consider addressing it head on, so you can focus on the true intent behind the message, rather than the tone. For example: "I really respect you as an expert in this work, and admittedly, I am having a hard time receiving this feedback due to your delivery. Would you mind re-stating what you would like me/us to do in a more encouraging tone?"

4. Feedback is often given when we need to grow, or learn a lesson. When we try to ignore these lessons, we are only inviting them to return again, and again, until we are finally open to receiving the message we are being given. It is better to face these lessons head on, and learn to be accountable for the thoughts and actions that led to these results, rather than become a victim of circumstance.

5. Once you have become open and willing to learn and grow from negative feedback, be sure to stay focused on yourself, rather than resorting to pointing fingers or placing blame on others. When we remember that the only things we can affect are our own thoughts and actions, we take back our own agency and are more likely to view these experiences as positive ones where we are in control of our choices, growth, and progress.

While it is important to stay focused on yourself when receiving feedback, we must also remember not to let this make us egocentric in our work. Rather than only working from a place of "what can I receive" (i.e. approval, power, appreciation, and accolades), turning our attention to "what can I give" (i.e. how can I best help the goals of mitigating disparities in Black maternal mortality and infant loss, how can I best serve birth equity work with the team) will make us happier, more productive, less stressed, and overall more free to act without fear. When the motives behind our work are to gain things from others, we take away our own power, and put our confidence in the hands of someone else. Leading from a place of service, over ego, means we can be more confident, centered, and action-based - rather than critical, insecure, and prone to abandoning the work because we do not receive all the praise we might otherwise feel entitled to.

Aim For Common Ground

It can be a great challenge to keep your ego in check, especially when you feel you could make better decisions than your leaders. But this is when it becomes essential to put your ego aside, and lend your services to the common goal instead. So when a decision is made, or agreed upon, by others, make a concerted effort to immediately get on board with the idea, without hesitation.

If the decision is made without your input, or is one that you do not agree with, always aim for common ground instead of offering a knee-jerk reaction of criticism. Remember you are part of a team, and consensus is the best course of action when working for a common goal. Try asking yourself how you can be of support, rather than thinking of ways to discourage. How can you use your energy to be a champion, rather than wasting it on disagreement.

According to Wakeman, "Many bright and talented professionals derail themselves by editorializing, critiquing decisions, and even withholding their experience in order to prove a point. What begins as letting off a little steam or even chiming in with one's opinion can quickly turn into a habit that, over time, leads others to question your buy-in, alignment, and willingness to do whatever it takes to ensure success. Resistance squanders a great deal of energy that could be used to validate and contribute to the effort rather than attempting to block it or redirect it in a self-serving way."

Conflict Resolution Styles and Tools

According to experts Thomas, K.W., and R.H. Kilmann's conflict resolution work, they propose we all have something in common. The article Conflict Resolution Styles[3] suggests that "When conflict is the topic of discussion, most people don't realize that we all have a default that we tend to reset to when faced with pressure." Thomas and Kilmann's 5 styles of conflict management model can help you identify your style of conflict management.

Further, they suggest "Knowing these 5 styles can circumvent conflict…" This tool also provides personal growth, adaptability in leadership and self-awareness to each team member as they discover or revisit their conflict resolution style. As you read through the list, make a note of which style you identify with most.

The article further expresses two necessary aspects to these styles: "assertiveness and cooperativeness." They outline the 5 styles as follows:

1. **Accommodating**
   The accommodating style is unassertive and cooperative. A person adopting this style will play down the conflict and will rather focus on creating harmony among the other parties. Self-sacrifice is an essential part of this approach as it values relationships above achieving goals.

2. **Avoidance**
   This approach is when you are not geared toward your own or others' goals. The relationship is therefore not important either. Simply put, you avoid the issue in totality. The low cooperativeness and assertiveness become damaging when it becomes a long-term solution.

3. **Collaborating**
   This style brings win-win results as it draws from partnering to bring a joint solution. This approach requires input and buy-in from all parties to work toward a common goal that satisfies all involved and therefore puts relationships on a high importance level.

4. **Competing**
   This style assertively achieves goals and does not require any collaboration with the other parties involved.

5. **Compromising**
   This approach aims to find middle ground regarding goals. It requires an element of sacrifice from each party to reach a solution that appeases everyone.

CASE STUDY - Feedback

Review the Case Study from Chapter 4 (Self-Awareness) on the former Paralegal, Jennifer, that received feedback at a company retreat. The case study is re-explored below, with additional details:

Jennifer was a former Paralegal in Civil Litigation. During a company retreat, she was given candid feedback, as her colleagues decided this would be the best place to voice their concerns about her recent inactions and seeming lack of commitment and focus. Though she eventually used this feedback to discover that law was no longer her passion, and was inspired to leave the legal field to pursue nursing, it took some time for her to receive this feedback with the openness that would eventually get her there. The conversation, including her initial response, went as follows:

Jared (direct supervisor, starting the conversation after lunch): Jennifer, do you remember the feedback seminar we attended 1 year ago?

Jennifer: Of course, I do. You were in the hot-seat and we had a good time giving you negative and constructive feedback. We didn't think you would survive. In fact you might not have, if it wasn't a role play activity - I remember you got pretty heated!

(The group laughs in reflecting)

Jared: Well, I am happy to hear your vivid reflection of that event. You know that we care for you and appreciate our team.

Jennifer: Yes, and I likewise.

Jared: Well, that is why this is a little hard for me to bring up, but please keep in the forefront of your mind that we care for you and that is why we must have this conversation.

Jennifer: Oh boy, this sounds serious. Go ahead.

Jared: Jennifer, in the last 6 months, you have not been as engaged at work, and often seem to be in another world. I mean, your passion seems to be really absent. We have had to correct some really important misses.

Jennifer: (Defensively) Why are you attacking me? I work hard and I thought I expressed my appreciation to each of you for covering me for those few misses!

Karen (co-worker): Yes, you did Jennifer, and everyone agrees you are a hard worker. Yet, we are still seeing some areas of opportunity, and just want to support you. How can we best do so?

Jennifer (Beginning to cry): I'm not sure, but I have to be honest with you. The truth is that I think I have just lost my

---

3 Dannhausser, Danny, and Belinda van Rensburg. "Conflict Resolution Styles." *Knowledge2Motion*, 21 May 2019, k2mskills.com/conflict-resolution-styles/.

passion for the law. And it has been difficult to admit that even to myself. The cases have just been so stressful, and I find it hard to come to work at times. I thought I might still be able to fake it for a while, but I guess I was wrong. So thank you for bringing this to my attention. I appreciate your feedback, and it's spot on.

Jared: I'm so sorry you have been going through this alone. You could always talk with us. We are a team.

Jennifer: I know. I just didn't know if I was going through a phase that would pass or if this was it for me. Many of my family members are in the medical field, and I've started to wonder if that's where my passion actually lies. I've been thinking about changing careers actually.

Karen: Wow, now that's a big shift. Have you really thought about that?

Jennifer: Yes I have. And it feels like a weight off my shoulders just to admit that out loud! I'm so glad we are discussing this. Thank you for bringing your concerns to my attention, Jared. I know I was defensive at first, which is not what we learned in the "receiving negative or constructive feedback" seminar. It is much harder to remember in real-life practice! But I know this feedback was necessary - I put our firm and clients in jeopardy, and for this I am genuinely sorry.

Jared: Now you know what it's like to be in the hot seat!

(Everyone chuckles)

Jennifer: Yes, I do. Well, since it's out now - I've actually discussed with my husband what changing careers would mean for our household. I have even looked at a few schools while I was doing some exploration. I will make sure going forward to keep each of you in the loop. Thank you all for being so supportive.

Considering the case study above, discuss in small groups how Jennifer incorporated (or ignored) the 5 steps to receiving feedback. Continue discussing the following in your small groups.

After receiving her feedback, Jennifer was able to do the introspection needed, and felt encouraged enough, to pursue her real passion and switch careers. Re-imagining the case study above, what might have happened if Jennifer had been unable to receive this feedback with any sense of openness or gratitude? How might the results of this interaction have changed, if she had responded only with defensiveness and avoidance?

Building Trust

The case study above is an example of how constructive feedback can create empowering results. But it is important to note that in Jennifer's example, the team providing this feedback had already developed a strong foundation of trust within their team. These types of interactions are most successful when teams have established enough trust to create the safe environments needed to both deliver, and receive, feedback.

Consider the following quote from Heidi Zdrojeski's article, Building Trust in High Performing Distributed Teams,[4] "Trust is everything. It takes time to build and can be gone in an instant. It can also be the foundation on which to build even stronger connections if tested…Without it organizational cultures can move from thriving to toxic."

An imperative part of team-building includes finding ways to create strong bonds of trust. This will not only allow members to feel more comfortable voicing their concerns in the first place, but those receiving feedback will be more inclined to listen with open willingness. Teams should be sure to take the time needed to engage in exercises, voice specific needs, and develop the bonds needed to establish a strong foundation of trust.

Proposed Structure of Birth Equity Meetings

The following are suggestions for facilitating successful meetings in groups that are multi-disciplinary and multi-racial.

Create guidelines and communication formats in order to ensure an effective meeting. For example:

I. **R**espectful gathering and reflection
II. **E**ngage group to share one word or sentence from reflection
III. **S**hare overall focus of the meeting
IV. **P**resentation of report outs
V. **E**nter any new agenda items at this point
VI. **C**all for any clarifications needed after each report. This can include addressing any inappropriate or offensive communications.
VII. **T**akeaways for the day's meeting

Transforming Questions for Birth Equity Teams

Birth equity work is hard, and often presents unique challenges. But if you integrate your heart, and work from a place of humility, it becomes easier to push past any barriers. Remember that this is deserving work that you can be proud of, and thankful for, and that can ultimately change history.

---

4   Zdrojeski, Heidi. "Building Trust in High Performing Distributed Teams." *Coaching Right Now*, TopLine Communication, 12 Aug. 2020, www.coachingrightnow.com/blog/building-trust-in-high-performing-distributed-teams/.

Consider these questions for your birth equity team:

1. How vested are you, both in and out of birth equity meetings, to work on eradicating racism in healthcare?
2. Why is it important to you that Black mothers and Black infants achieve equity, survive and thrive?
3. What are the strengths you see in our birth equity team?
4. Describe any opportunities you see in the birth equity team and share how those opportunities could show up as strengths.
5. What have you observed as some opportunities in the birth equity team for growth?
6. What are the threats you see in the birth equity team, organizational system, coaches and advisers?
7. What has been a challenge for you personally, in doing the work of eliminating structural racism?
8. How do you receive constructive feedback well? How do you give constructive feedback?
9. How important is negative feedback?
10. Share your understanding of both implicit biases and explicit biases. Have you observed either in yourself or others?
11. How have you demonstrated amongst staff the importance of this work?
12. How has your organization informed the Black patient population of this project?

NURTURING EQUITY MINDED GROUP EXERCISE #1

Break into groups of 2 or 4 and brainstorm together creating an exercise that would build diverse racial bonds while educating one another about your cultures. Write your concept below:

_____

_____

_____

_____

_____

_____

_____

NURTURING EQUITY MINDED GROUP EXERCISE #2

As a group, pick some of the following trust-building questions to answer and work to begin laying the building blocks for open communication, active listening, mutual respect, and allyship. Remember to be open, nonjudgmental, and seek to understand. Continue asking each other questions either from this list, or questions of your own, during breaks, team meetings, etc. in order to continue building these important bonds.

1. If you had to eat one meal for the rest of your life, what would it be?
2. What is a family or cultural tradition that you cherish?
3. What is your greatest personal success?
4. What is one of your worst fears?
5. What would you like to be remembered or known for?
6. What's the most important lesson you've learned this year?
7. What's something that always makes you smile?
8. What are the toughest challenges you've had at work?
9. How do you like to receive feedback?
10. Where did you grow up? Where is home now?
11. What's the furthest away from home you've ever been?
12. What's one misunderstanding that happened on your team recently and how was it resolved?
13. What's the last film, TV show, or book you really enjoyed?
14. When was the last time you asked a teammate for help? What happened?
15. Who has helped make your job easier recently? What did they do?
16. What's one moment of success you experienced this week?
17. How do you feel about conflict? What conditions help you feel comfortable when engaging in conflict?
18. How/when does someone earn your trust?
19. What's one thing you would recommend to improve our workplace culture?
20. What's the best thing about working here?

CHAPTER THIRTY-TWO
Racism Amid Nursing Staff

Let's Start At Home

In the article written by Ron Southwick, entitled Nursing profession is 'steep in racism', he writes, "The majority of nurses from minority groups say they've personally experienced racism, either from peers or from managers. Nurses are demanding change."[1]

Racism in healthcare is a national crisis and ultimately creates a safety issue for patients and families. While Gallup poll surveys taken as recently as December 2022 show that nursing has ranked as the most trusted profession for the last two decades,[2] recent studies reveal a sad undercurrent.

---

1 Southwick, Ron. "Nursing Profession Is 'Steeped in Racism.'" *Chief Healthcare Executive,* OncLive, 21 Feb. 2022, www.chiefhealthcareexecutive.com/view/nursing-profession-is-steeped-in-racism-.

2 Brenan, Megan. "Nurses Retain Top Ethics Rating in U.S., but Below 2020 High." *Gallup.com*, Gallup, 24 Jan. 2023, news.gallup.com/poll/467804/nurses-retain-top-ethics-rating-below-2020-high.aspx.

Southwick's article shows that, according to the National Commission to Address Racism in Nursing, "Nearly half of 5,600 nurses surveyed said racism was widespread..." It further revealed that "A vast majority of Black, Latino and Asian American nurses said they have personally experienced racism in the workplace."[1]

To make matters worse, most who have filed complaints said they were not heard, and actions were not taken. In such a culture of vilifying the culprits and victimizing the vulnerable, it's only a matter of time before it spills into patient care as disparities continue to persist. Toxic environments that turn deaf ears to these very serious lived experiences is the reason racism continues to exist even in our "most trusted" profession.

It's in the Statistics

Sometimes the truth of a matter is so overwhelming that it shakes your very soul. The outcomes seem ethically impossible. It is hard to believe we are still facing this age-old struggle. President of the Nursing Association, Earnest J. Grant, and his colleagues express their deep disbelief and devastation at the results of the report by stating, "My colleagues and I braced ourselves for these findings. Still, we are disturbed, triggered, and unsettled by the glaring data and heartbroken by the personal accounts of nurses."[1]

The glaring data and disheartening accounts of experienced racism that Grant refers to, included the following[1]:

- Nearly 2 in 3 nurses (63%) said they have experienced an act of racism in the workplace, either from peers (66%) or a manager (60%).
- More than half (57%) said they challenged racist treatment in the workplace, but 64% said it made no difference.
- Almost all Black nurses surveyed (92%) said they have personally experienced racism at work, and 70% said it came from leaders, while 66% said it originated from peers.
- One nurse recalled being called "colored" by a nurse manager, the commission reported.
- "I have staff — both Black and White — who disrespect you; they make fun of you; I looked forward to retirement," one nurse said.
- "Even our Black patients have bought into believing that Black nurses are less than and cannot provide qualified care," another nurse told the commission.

These abuses are just some of the many ways in which day-to-day interactions can have a long-lasting effect.

Black Nurses Report Higher

According to the American Nurses Association,[3] the report found that due to these tolling experiences, more than 75% of Black nurses felt that they were "negatively impacted [in] their professional well-being" as a result. What's more, the survey found that not only do Black nurses experience acts of racism more frequently, but that they are also more likely to "confront acts of racism." The findings continued with the following statistics:

- Most Black nurses who responded (72%) say that there is a lot of racism in nursing compared to 29% of White nurse respondents.
- The majority (92%) of Black respondents have personally experienced racism in the workplace from their leaders (70%), peers (66%) and the patients in their care (68%).

Adrianna Nava, president of the National Association of Hispanic Nurses, and Commision Co-lead, expressed similar feelings of disbelief at these findings. She states, "The acts of exclusion, incivility, disrespect and denial of professional opportunities that our nurses have reported through this survey, especially our Black, Hispanic and Asian nurses, is unacceptable. Racism is a trauma that leaves a lasting impact on a person's mental, spiritual, and physical health as well as their overall quality of life."[3]

It would be naivety to not see the safety issues racism causes in the workforce. A nurse's mind should be free to focus only on providing excellent care to her patients, not contending with "friendly fire" amidst her peers. The health of our nation depends on the health and well-being of our nurses.

Weathering In The Workplace

The healthcare profession is often one of long hours, and grueling work. Black nurses and people of color signed up for these conditions when they chose to be a healthcare provider. What they did not sign up for, was to be subjected to daily demeaning, comparing, bullying and judgment - often by the very group of "teammates" they once hoped would be a source of support. This type of work environment can wear down even the most committed professionals, making them feel alone, hopeless, powerless, and even inferior. This is just one more instance of the multi-faceted weathering effect (see Chapter 17).

The ripples of these experiences can continue on well past the end of the work-day. Toney addresses this feeling, stating "You get to the point where you don't want to go in. Now you're home and you're still thinking about it. Healthcare is already difficult and challenging when you're dealing with seriously

---

3   McClendon, Shannon. "New Survey Data: Racism Within the Nursing Profession Is a Substantial Problem." *American Nurses Association*, ANA, ANCC, American Nurses Foundation, 25 Jan. 2022, www.nursingworld.org/news/news-releases/2021/new-survey-data-racism-in-nursing/.

ill people. To have to deal with all the other issues, racism and lack of opportunities, it makes you wonder if it's worth it."[1]

Due to these workplace stresses, exacerbated by the COVID-19 pandemic, and coupled with the added discriminatory experiences that follow nurses home, many hospitals have found it increasingly difficult to keep nurses on staff. Yet, even with the struggle to retain nurses, and the continued problem of understaffing, minority groups still seem to be overlooked for hospital positions. Diverse new nurses, ready to do the work, are still struggling to find jobs, as hospital leadership continues to underestimate non-White working professionals.

Committing to Change

Holding leadership accountable is an important step in addressing racism in the nursing profession, but it is not the only step needed in the road ahead. Instead, it is up to every nurse to commit to change, and then follow through with the work needed. For too long now, have many of the daily discriminatory offenses against people of color gone unacknowledged, ignored, dismissed, and swept under the rug. Organizations often *say* they want to do better, but fail to follow through with their actions. This must change. Commission Co-lead, Daniela Vargas, echoes these sentiments by explaining the situation as such, "'The next generation of BIPOC nurses deserve more than performative activism and empty words that continue to yield no progress toward structural changes within the nursing profession or racial equity. The breadth of the nursing profession through the Code of Ethics for Nurses holds all nurses accountable for calling out racism and replacing racist policies rooted in White supremacy with ethical and just policies that promote and implement accountability, equity, and justice for nurses and the communities that we serve.'"[3]

As a profession that is widely considered one of the most ethical and trusted in America, it is crucial and urgent that these racial injustices are seriously addressed. It is vital to the health of our nurses, their patients, and the greater society at large, that our hospital settings be safe, collaborative, and just environments for *all* staff, and *all* patients - with diversity, equity, and inclusion at the forefront.

Strategies for Change

Dr. Barbara Broome poses similar observations and conclusions in her article, Racism, Nursing, and Strategies for Change.[4] In this scholarly work, Dr. Broome states, "How is it that in 2021 we still can't seem to value individuals for their contributions, credentials, experience, outcomes, and recommendations rather than their physical appearance?" In concurrence with Dr. Toney's assertions, Dr. Broome raises our consciousness to the existence of racism in nursing and urges nursing leadership to rise to the occasion of eradicating these ills in our institutions by acknowledging the valuable presence of Black clinicians. She illustrates this further by discussing the harmful and persisting perceptions that "when a person of color is hired, it must be an example of quota hiring." Dr. Broome goes on to explain how this is especially frustrating and counterproductive because, "When individuals make this assumption, they often fail to assist, mentor, and support the person of color and instead ridicule her or his speech, pronunciations, and appearance, which contributes to a negative work environment."

As someone who experienced multiple instances of racism, microaggressions, and harmful perceptions throughout her own life and career, Broome is no stranger to the discriminations rampant in nursing institutions - from leadership directors down to nursing students - and provides priceless insights into the ways racism continues to exist in both nursing, and America, in general.

Ten Tips for Solutions

Nursing is a well-respected and widely trusted profession for good reason. And it is precisely because nursing is held in such high regard that it is so imperative these issues are addressed and worked on within the nursing profession. Broome provides ten tips for beginning this work (briefly paraphrased below), and concludes her work by adding "These are only suggestions; change comes from self-reflection and a willingness to view events from another person's perspective. Most of all, change comes from the heart."[4]

1. Recognize and acknowledge your own biases and prejudices.
2. Avoid making assumptions and respect others' privacy rather than jumping to negative conclusions.
3. Remember that all people are different individuals, and no one person of any group should be considered the "expert" based solely on their personal experiences.
4. Listen well - both to what is said, and what might be unspoken, but seen.
5. Be respectful, and remember that respect is a two-way street.
6. Embrace differences and diversity as beneficial.
7. Care well for others, and allow others to care for you.
8. Adhere to the nursing Code of Ethics.
9. Communicate thoughtfully by asking questions with respect, listening to and reflecting on different lived experiences, and seeking to understand.
10. Learn about and embrace other cultures, but be careful not to appropriate them.

---

4   Broome, Barbara. "Racism, Nursing, and Strategies for Change." *Journal of obstetric, gynecologic, and neonatal nursing.* National Library of Medicine. *JOGNN* vol. 50,5 (2021): 507-511. doi:10.1016/j.jogn.2021.07.008. https://pubmed.ncbi.nlm.nih.gov/34389286/.

NURTURING EQUITY MINDED GROUP EXERCISE

In groups of 2 or 4 discuss the following questions:

1. In your understanding, describe White privilege.
2. Can you describe historically how White privilege was established?
3. How do you understand the "angry Black woman" caricature?
4. What might she be angry about, in your estimation, if you think both in historical and present day context?
5. What do you think the perception is for a Black woman to be totally confident, having faith in her own abilities and communicating her views and perspectives strongly? How do you think she may be perceived by White colleagues?
6. Same question - what do you think the perception is for a White woman to be totally confident, having faith in her own abilities and communicating her views and perspectives strongly? How do you think she may be perceived by Black colleagues? How might she be perceived by other White colleagues?
7. As a White professional in management, how would you feel if your White boss retired and, in light of your organization working to diversify the workforce, her position was filled by a Black professional woman.
8. Take a moment to reflect on how you would honestly receive this new change. Speak from a place of authenticity, rather than what you think might be the "right thing to say." There has never been a Black director in the history of your organization. Are you on guard or are you celebrating?

CHAPTER THIRTY-THREE
Ethnic Diversity in the Nursing Workforce

Workforce Diversity Matters!

One look at the nursing workforce in our hospitals and clinics presents the compelling reality that diversity within our nursing staffs is sorely lacking. This is a truth not only easily recognized by both staff and patients alike, but one that affects the experiences of our patients as well.

When patients have a provider that looks like them, they not only feel more comfortable, but they also often receive better care as a result. For example, a study published by the Proceedings of the National Academy of Sciences (PNAS) found "that when Black newborns are cared for by Black physicians, the mortality penalty they suffer, as compared with White infants, is halved."[1] This means that the mortality rate of Black babies decreases significantly

---

1   Greenwood, Brad N., et al. "Physician–patient Racial Concordance and Disparities in Birthing Mortality for Newborns." *Proceedings of the National Academy of Sciences of the United States of America*, vol. 117, no. 35, National

simply by having a Black doctor. These findings of increased ease, and superior care, are not just significant, but often corroborated by anecdotal evidence as well.

For instance, my birth sister shared certain perceptions of her doctor's appointments and hospitalizations with me. She said, "I often enter my own private doctor's office, realizing that a Black staff/nurse provider may not be available. This creates a subtle and subliminal message in my consciousness. I find myself more guarded, and more inquisitive about their attitude towards me. Will this person have my best at heart? This is not necessarily a question that comes to mind when I have a care provider that is Black, like me. I would not have the immediate anxiety and suspicion I feel when they are White. I believe this is primarily due to my epigenetic make up and historical collective trauma. I am less stressed when my providers are of my same race/ethnicity." This is a clear indication of how diversity in the workforce can increase patient comfort.

Close Call…

Likewise, I myself had a harrowing experience with lack of diversity in the healthcare workforce as well. I will never forget my experience of having a partial hysterectomy. I was completing my last year in graduate school and my White female gynecologist informed me that she needed to remove my fibroid tumors before I had greater problems. I consented to the procedure, and after completion was discharged without further care.

A week later, I found myself hemorrhaging and having to be rushed into emergency surgery. Afterward, the gynecologist shared with me that, "it was a close call." She never expounded on what a "close call" was, nor did I ask, being deeply traumatized by all the blood and suddenness of everything.

Seeing the terror in my eyes, my doctor stated "this was not supposed to happen after the surgery. I'm very sorry, something went wrong. You should not have experienced that." This made me feel like she was negligent and maybe did not want to disclose the full truth to me. She never went into details with me, and I changed gynecologists as a result, searching for a Black female gynecologist instead.

Was this an example of the gynecologist experiencing discomfort with her Black patient? Or, was it my own subconscious discomfort with having a gynecologist of a different race? Or both? Either way, communication was lost, and as a result, I was left not only feeling uncomfortable, but that my life was at risk.

We must consider how the negligence that caused this "close call" (and could have resulted in a much bigger tragedy) might have been avoided with a more diverse staff.

Academy of Sciences, Sept. 2020, pp. 21194–200. https://doi.org/10.1073/pnas.1913405117.

5 Strategies for Increasing Diversity in Nursing

1. Working to improve equity in healthcare is of the utmost importance. In order to accomplish this, healthcare executives and management teams must make the hiring of a culturally diverse workforce a priority. This means creating specific plans for recruiting, and maintaining, diverse nursing staff.

2. Plans for recruiting diverse staff should be varied, adaptable, multi-layered, and include supports for maintaining new hires. Added efforts should be made for increasing diversity in leadership roles, as the goal should be increased inclusivity throughout every level of the organization's infrastructure.

3. Supports for maintaining diverse hires include encouraging professional development, advocating for mentorship, and providing employee resources that incorporate affinity-based support groups.

4. These dedications to increasing diversity in the overall workplace, and especially to encouraging advancement to leadership roles, will ensure continued diversity in staff through both future, and maintained, diverse hires. This will ultimately benefit everything in the organization from patient outcomes, to clinical care, to workplace culture.

5. All aspects of the healthcare profession can, and should, use these strategies to diversify their workforce in order to improve health equity, enhance family-centered care, and provide the best experience possible for both patients and staff.

In humble form, this approach provides a great opportunity for replication within other health care disciplines - including social work, pharmacy, spiritual care, nutrition, physical and occupational therapy, and beyond. In order to sustain progress for nursing, and all disciplines, continued investments in diverse talent and programmatic support are required.

NURTURING EQUITY MINDED GROUP EXERCISE

Describe your unit's current workforce in terms of diversity:

_____

_____

_____

_____

_____

_____

Where do you see room for improvement, or opportunities for increasing/maintaining diversity in staff?

_____

_____

_____

_____

_____

_____

CHAPTER THIRTY-FOUR
Anti-Racism: Leaders, Step It Up!

Actions Speak Louder Than Words

In this chapter, authors Samantha E. Erskine, Sheila Brassel, and Kathrina Robotham introduce us to two concepts (Allyship and Curiosity) that measure how leaders are authentically working toward mitigating racism in their respective work environments. The research data embodied in their work is compelling and does not allow for "well intentions by leaders only giving lip service." Let's begin with their provocative survey of women who have experienced racism in the workplace. It is worth citing at length their research findings,[1] "This survey of 2,734 women from marginalized racial and ethnic groups in Australia, Canada, South Africa, the United Kingdom, and the United States finds that 51% of respondents have experienced racism in their current workplace. For the many leaders around the globe who pledged to

---

1 Erskine, Samantha E., et al. "Exposé of Women's Workplace Experiences Challenges Antiracist Leaders to Step up (Report)" *Catalyst*, 1 Mar. 2023, www.catalyst.org/reports/antiracism-workplace-leadership.

fight racism following the 2020 murders of George Floyd, Breonna Taylor, and Ahmaud Arbery in the United States, this finding points to a large disconnect in what leaders say they want to do and the reality that racism is still pervasive in workplaces internationally. What's worse, the links between the multiple oppressions that women from marginalized racial and ethnic groups experience at work are often ignored and go unaddressed."

While the gesture to speak up and out against racism is notable, the slow coming inaction from leaders speaks louder to the lack of real intent.

Combating Racism

The researchers readily offer solutions for eradicating the presence of racism by suggesting leaders demonstrate allyship and curiosity in their management practice. The results of implementing these suggestions are guaranteed to impact the work environment by promoting diversity, and lessening the climate of silence. The authors argue **"**If you are a senior leader committed to fighting racism at work, you need to absorb these findings and adopt an intersectional approach to antiracist leadership. By taking action to interrupt intersectional forms of racial trauma, you can help advance equity in your workplace."[1]

The research team at Catalyst provides the following definitions for "allyship" and "curiosity"[2]:

- "Allyship means actively supporting people from marginalized groups. It's about using as much institutional, social, and/or cultural privilege or power as you have to advocate for people who face oppression. Allies amplify unheard voices, call out barriers and biases that can inhibit progress, and act as role models in their commitment to diversity, equity, and inclusion."

- "Curiosity is about proactively seeking out different points of view, listening to others, learning, and reflecting on what you've heard. People who are curious are open to new perspectives, welcome respectful exchanges of ideas, and channel their learning into action. They recognize that each of us is exposed to just a fraction of the world, and they value the insights that diversity and difference bring."

Key Findings

The authors share their key findings including marginalized racial and ethnic groups, based on skin tones, sexuality and how senior leaders can interrupt and decrease the climate of silence by stepping up. Examine the following key findings[1]:

- Half (51%) of women from marginalized racial and ethnic groups experience racism at work.
- Women with darker skin tones are more likely than women with lighter skin tones to experience racism at work.
- Trans women (67%) and queer women (63%) are more likely than cisgender heterosexual women (49%) to experience racism at work.
- When senior leaders display allyship and curiosity, they can decrease the climate of silence and boost the diversity climate in their organizations, which in turn decreases the likelihood that women from marginalized racial and ethnic groups will experience racism at work.
- Senior leaders need to step up: 49% of survey respondents say their senior leaders do not engage in allyship, and 43% say they do not engage in curiosity.

Stories From Marginalized Women

This report[1] is careful to be inclusive of all women that are marginalized in different ethnic groups based on their experiences, and to center their voices so as to be clear on the group they aim to benefit. Unfortunately, the majority of corporate leaders are predominantly White men. This means that initiatives originally meant to benefit marginalized populations often get derailed and end up benefiting the White men in charge. That is why centering marginalized voices is so crucial to this work, so they don't end up getting overlooked further. In an effort to do this, the authors highlight many stories of experienced racism from the marginalized women they interviewed, saying "In this report, we shine a light on stories and experiences of women from marginalized racial and ethnic groups so that leaders at all stages can better understand how these women experience racism and what they as leaders can do to combat it."

In this compelling research study, the pervasive discriminatory acts against marginalized groups have their day in court. The pages of this report are full of documented instances in which diverse employees experienced comments full of egregious caricatures and hideous insults that were made in their so-called professional environments. We are only able to share a few of these unacceptable references toward anti-Blackness in later sections, however we encourage you to look at the full report for a more detailed account. These wrong-doings cannot be ignored or swept under the carpet of denial, neither can the very real undertones of these comments that implied a large bias towards "Whiteness" as the clear preference from leaders in these environments.

"We found that the darker a woman's skin tone, the more likely she was to experience racism at work. These findings are likely due to rampant global anti-Blackness—a term that

---

2   Brassel, Sheila, et al. "Allyship and Curiosity Drive Inclusion for People of Color at Work (Report)." *Catalyst*, 22 Nov. 2022, www.catalyst.org/reports/allyship-curiosity-employees-of-color/.

describes more than just racism against Black people but also a disdain, disregard, and disgust for Black existence and the refusal to recognize Black humanity. Across the globe, features that are "stereotypically Black" (e.g., wide nose, Afro-textured hair) are devalued relative to features that are "stereotypically White." Stories from survey respondents illustrate how colorism as well as texturism play out at work. They also highlight how women from marginalized racial and ethnic groups experience what scholars have called intersectional invisibility—where intersecting marginalized identities render some aspects of women's identities invisible and other aspects of their identity hypervisible."

Call to Action 1 - Use Allyship and Curiosity to Prevent Experiences of Racism

These stories, findings, and new understandings, reveal that leaders who want to truly commit to antiracism in their organizations must address discrimination head on. And they must do so with mindfulness, intersectionality, integrity, and an understanding that just because racist acts might sometimes go unreported, it does not mean that they don't occur.

The authors propose three Call to Action Formulas[1] that senior leaders can engage and integrate in their practice as a demonstration of their efforts. Knowing about racism is one thing, but doing something about it, according to the authors, is imperative. They argue, "Senior leaders must recognize the reality that racism is pervasive at work and redouble efforts to lead organizational change that will address these all-too-common experiences." In doing so, they send a message to all leaders and staff members under their leadership that this is unacceptable and there is zero tolerance to this type of behavior. The authors also propose, "They can do so by demonstrating allyship and curiosity, which…can decrease the likelihood of experiencing racism at work."

When leaders take into consideration the powerful impact of both allyship and curiosity, the patterns which show senior leaders falling short will have a transformational difference from the status quo.

Call to Action 2 - Strengthen Organizational Climate

How does leadership come to terms with whether to address a particular issue related to racism, discrimination or microaggressions? Each leader is unique, with different journeys and backgrounds. To this extent, it is reasonable to say that all leaders bring their own experiences, values, ideologies and personalities into view with every decision and action, or lack thereof, affecting the type of workplace they lead and nurture.

When leaders choose to be pro-allyship and pro-curiosity, the benefits outweigh the risks. According to Catalyst data, the authors assert, "When senior leaders demonstrate allyship and curiosity, they are strengthening their organizational climate. More specifically, our analysis shows that allyship and curiosity help senior leaders modulate two organizational conditions: climate of silence and diversity climate." It is clear to see, in taking a proactive approach to focusing on a climate of diversity, rather than silence, the likelihood of experiencing racism at work declines. These results lift morale and empower all members of the organization for the better. Consider the following: "The data from this study tell us that an organizational climate of silence is related to an increased likelihood of experiencing racism at work. 67% of women from marginalized racial and ethnic groups who work in a climate of silence experience racism at work, compared to 46% of those who do not work in a climate of silence."

The answer to these interventions and changing statistics is for everyone to find their voice and speak out. Unfortunately, this can often come at great cost to the speaker as well. "When employees speak up in a climate of silence, they risk being excluded, shut down or ignored, passed over for promotions, and/or punished with a mountain of work. Catalyst research finds that climates of silence help enable discrimination. Climates of silence are harmful for employees as well as their organizations and are linked with increased turnover rates and decreased employee job satisfaction and well-being." The catch-22 here echoes the sentiment "you are damned if you do speak up, and you are damned if you don't." Based on the data, it appears that one can run the risk of sacrificing their job stability in order to use their voice to require respect, equity, equality and honor. Once again, the onus lies on the employers to see the connection between high turnover rates and the culture of silence they promote.

Name the Issues

It is crucial to give marginalized groups a voice, yet there is little chance for these diverse voices to be heard if there are minimal diverse employees to begin with. That is why it is so important to not just lift the climate of silence, but to promote and celebrate diversity as well. The authors in this study found that, "Diversity climates benefit all employees and are associated with less discrimination at work, increased job satisfaction, organizational commitment, engagement, and performance, and decreased employee withdrawal. Research also suggests that its associations with positive outcomes are particularly strong for those from marginalized racial and ethnic groups."

Furthermore, the authors suggest for leaders to eradicate climates of silence, and promote diversity climates by actively speaking out against racism, by having conversations that consider different perspectives, and by directly mentioning racist acts by name. "Naming issues directly can spur personal and organizational responsibility for addressing them. For example, instead of using less direct phrases such as 'unconscious bias,' specifically name issues such as racism, White supremacy, anti-Blackness, anti-Asian racism, anti-Latinx racism, and systemic gendered racism." This creates an inclusive environment, and establishes leaders as allies that value diversity.

Additionally, leaders should engage in collaborative decision-making that normalizes cooperation amongst diverse coworkers. Finally, the authors urge leaders to "critically evaluate your hiring and promotion practices for bias and implement safeguards to ensure employees are evaluated objectively. In addition, determine whether policies such as sick leave are interpreted and applied similarly for all employees. Fairness perceptions play an important role in experiences of racism."

Call to Action 3 - Create Accountability Programs

Words are not abstract forms that simply dissipate in the air and fade away, once voiced. Instead, they leave lasting impressions that can sting and linger. Words, especially demeaning and cruel ones, can be like knives that pierce and cut and can cause catastrophic damage to one's emotional psyche. The authors measure the range and impact of such wound-causing words, carefully stating, "The emotional weight of these episodes contributes to enduring racial trauma, a form of psychological injury, as well as the Emotional Tax that many women from marginalized racial and ethnic groups experience in predominantly White organizations."

The authors then support these claims further, by demonstrating the kinds of damaging words many marginalized women have experienced in their workplace with little to no consequence for the offenders. They state, "Racism is pervasive. When asked to describe their experiences, survey respondents reported a wide range of covert and overt forms of racism, including: Negative assumptions, Belittling insults, Disparaging remarks, Discriminatory actions, and Outright racial slurs." The authors continue on with a warning that, respectfully, the following quotations contain racially sensitive material that may be harmful or traumatizing to some readers, as well.

Stories About Leadership

"[I was] told Black is disgusting."

"A number of women said they were called a n***** and that no one addressed or interrupted this blatant form of racism: 'One time at work, I was called the n-word. They laughed at me, and made jokes with my name. Then I told the manager. She said she will get back to me when she is done talking to them about the situation, which she never did.'"

These examples are heartbreaking, toxic, and lasting. And yet they occur far too often with no repercussions for those responsible. In fact, not only are offenders not held accountable by their leaders, but what's worse is the leaders themselves are often also at fault for the same disappointing behaviors. "Indeed, nearly a quarter (25%) of women from marginalized racial and ethnic groups believe that senior leaders in their organization would discriminate against an employee based on ethnicity, race, or culture." Here are some examples of such instances:

- "My manager chose to give my White colleague credit for a project that I have worked hard for. He did not apologize or try to resolve the issue. Instead, he continued giving her praise for the work that I have done."
- "I was mocked at a social event. A senior manager deliberately kept calling me by the other Black person's name, implying that he could not tell us apart."
- "A young White [man] was said to be more skilled to take the position I was fit for, only for me to end up having to train him. I am Black and female. The dichotomies and bias in the workplace are horrible."
- "I applied for a senior position and there were two contenders, myself and a White lady. I was more experienced and had worked with the company much longer. I did not get the job and when I inquired, I was told that they based their decision on what looks good for the company and that their Black Business Enterprise (BBE) requirements were well fulfilled."

Accountability in the Workplace

If senior leaders truly want to be antiracist allies, they need to hold any and all employees that go against this work fully accountable for their actions. Accountability is what can really begin to alter employee behaviors. This can mean disciplining (including firing) staff if they engage in racist behaviors, as well as motivating through rewards (such as bonuses) staff to be as inclusive as possible. Additionally, the authors encourage antiracist leaders to speak out, even when it may feel uncomfortable. They urge leaders, "It's time to center the intersectional forms of racial harm experienced by women in your workplace over White comfort so women from marginalized racial and ethnic groups in your workplace are no longer forced to endure racial trauma."

Speaking out, and dismantling a climate of silence, is critical as an antiracist leader. But these words must be then followed through with concrete actions for antiracist work to be truly effective. This means that seniors are encouraged to hold themselves accountable as well. The authors suggest for leadership to "create systems to gather feedback to measure if there is a gap between what leaders say about wanting to create inclusive workplaces and what women from marginalized racial and ethnic groups actually experience at work." Only once leadership can admit that racism is an urgent problem and that it will be condemned and deemed unacceptable in their organization, can real accountability begin to take shape. Leaders can assist in creating accountability programs that hold all staff accountable by tracking any behaviors that don't align with company standards on inclusivity, and that would allow for quick and clear consequences to follow, as needed.

The burden of breaking these cycles of racism, trauma, and toxicity on marginalized groups in the workplace rests with senior leaders. It is up to superiors to change the climate for their staff, to create an environment where marginalized women (and not just their White colleagues) can thrive in their workplace, free from the distress of racial harm.

NURTURING EQUITY MINDED GROUP EXERCISE

1. Consider your own workplace and the leadership team you work under. Do you believe your leaders show allyship and curiosity in their management styles? Explain your answer.

   _____

   _____

   _____

2. Have you personally experienced (or witnessed) any racist, demeaning, or inappropriate remarks or behaviors among colleagues? If so, describe the interaction below:

   _____

   _____

   _____

3. In the situation you described above, what were the repercussions? Did leadership get involved? What were the consequences, if any? Did anyone speak out after witnessing the event, or is there a climate of silence?

   _____

   _____

   _____

4. Take a moment to reflect on your work environment. How can leadership improve their commitment to anti-racism?

   _____

   _____

   _____

   _____

   _____

CHAPTER THIRTY-FIVE
The Heart of Justice

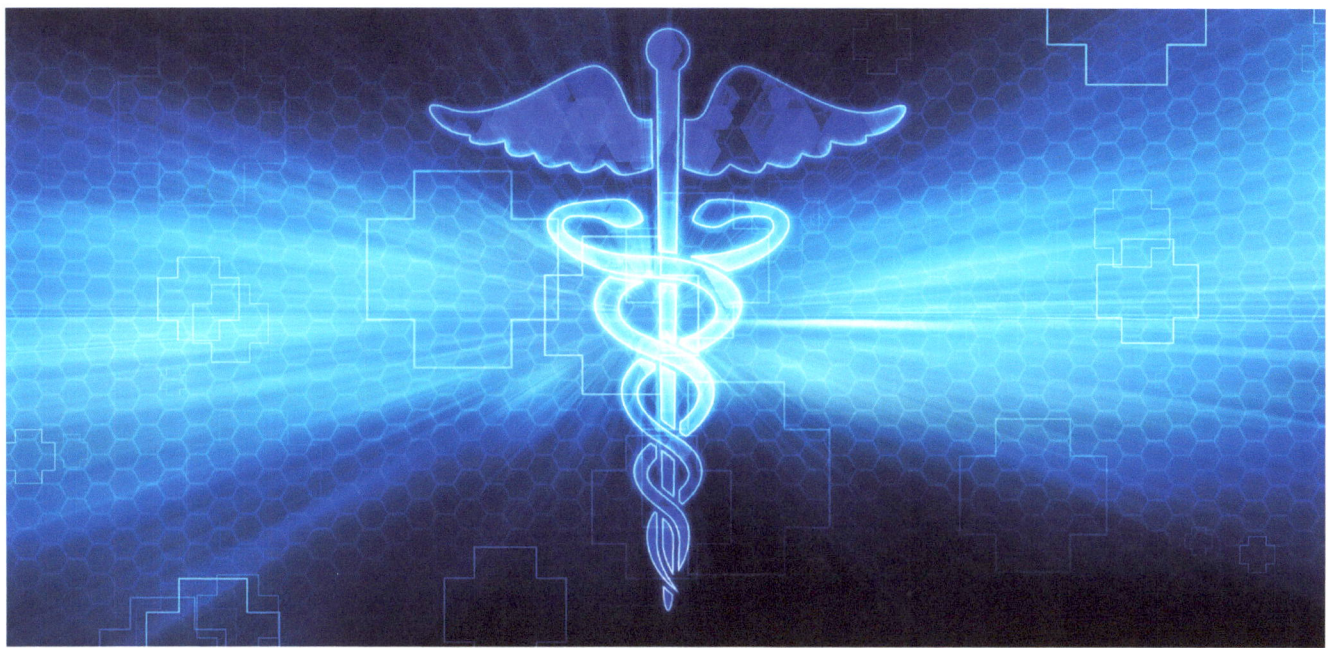

Speech of the Century - The Heart of Justice

I hope this book has armed you with new knowledge and practices for the fight ahead. Often, when we are given the gift of new knowledge it can be difficult to discern how to integrate this new information in our daily lives. So where do we go from here? The best answer I can provide would be to follow the advice and pleas urged by Dean George Q. Daley in the speech he delivered to the Harvard Medical Class of 2018, entitled "The Heart of Justice."[1]

After hearing his speech, I was deeply moved, challenged and changed as a result of his charge to this graduating class. It spoke to my ethics, character and practice. It challenged me to keep the good will intentions I began this journey with and to never lose sight of the human life in front of me. Further, it challenged me to care for every patient that I am privileged enough to sit with, and listen to, with heart and compassion. To see every patient, feel every patient, and see them as the amazing human beings they are, worthy of the best care available. I work every day to lead my care with this charge in mind. May this charge always inform your practice, choices and legacy, as well.

---

1   Daley, George Q. *2018 Class Day Address: HMS Dean George Q Daley. YouTube*, Harvard Medical School, 25 May 2018, www.youtube.com/watch?v=FVuv4lCWN4k.

A full version of Dean Daley's Speech can be found on YouTube,[1] or written on the following pages, as transcribed by Harvard Medical School[2]:

Good afternoon! I am thrilled to witness this gathering today of family, friends, mentors. We are here to celebrate you, the Class of 2018. I will address my words directly to our exceptional HMS graduates. Today is the last day I stand in front of you as your dean, and the first day I stand with you as your fellow physician. That makes me incredibly proud. And enormously hopeful as well.

Throughout your careers as physicians, you will treat thousands of patients with conditions both common and rare. You will relieve suffering for many. Despite your earnest efforts, some will die. Some of you will make life-saving discoveries. You will develop new medicines for illnesses presently incurable. You will train the next generation of physicians, direct research labs, launch companies. You will employ your gifts to make others healthier and to make the world a more hospitable and healthier place.

Today you and your family are pondering the exciting opportunities you have rightfully earned as a graduate of Harvard Medical School. But I encourage you also to ponder this uncomfortable truth: American health care offers the triumphs of modern medicine to many, yet leaves millions wanting for even basic health care. Recent news reported that 19 million Americans lack insurance coverage, and a significant but unknown number lack any access to meaningful health care. This is appalling.

Consider this: What if you become a brilliant cardiac surgeon, and you have to turn away an immigrant family whose cyanotic newborn infant has a surgically treatable heart malformation but no legal status and no insurance coverage? Dr. Atul Gawande, one of our most eloquent faculty members, recently asked in a most compelling article in The New Yorker: "Is health care a right?"

What do you think? Is health care one of the inalienable human rights asserted in the Declaration of Independence, one of those rights granted by our creator, a right our government is charged to protect? Is health care a means by which a just government ensures that its citizens enjoy "life, liberty, and the pursuit of happiness?" Or has health care in the U.S. become a privilege, accessible only to those with the resources to afford it?

As a practicing physician, you will confront this question with disturbing regularity. This will no longer be a Pathways classroom discussion meant to provoke analysis and debate. This issue of health care as an inalienable right will acquire flesh-and-blood dimensions; it will have a name, an age, a medical record number and a medical history that will include pain and disability.

At first, these encounters will rattle you to the core. But gradually—I warn you—you'll be at risk of becoming desensitized. My advice to you—Don't. You will be at risk of becoming comfortably numb to injustices you see in your practice, in health care, around the world. My advice to you—Don't. You will be tempted to rationalize away inconvenient truths and reach for the safety blanket of moral relativism. My advice to you—Don't.

Health disparities, income inequality, bigotry, racism, discrimination, xenophobia; you will encounter these on your hospital rounds, in the operating room, in your labs and in your community. These are maladies that ail modern society and modern medicine. Today, I implore you as physicians to seek to cure these ills; as surgeons, to excise them. Treating these ills requires no less urgency than pneumonia or cancer.

As you go forth into the world, I urge you to remember the core values of Harvard Medical School. These core values embody our reason for being—as clinicians, as scientists, as citizens. Serving humanity, conducting oneself with integrity and accountability, striving for excellence through lifelong learning and growth, embracing and championing diversity, practicing inclusiveness, not elitism—these are but a few of the core values that we have worked to instill in you at Harvard Medical School.

I urge you….Remain vigilant about biases you encounter. Remain vigilant about biases that impede your patients' access to care, biases that taint their outcomes.

I urge you….Respect and seek counsel from those who are different from you. Just as diversity propels biologic evolution, so it enriches us as clinicians, as scientists, as people.

I urge you….Resist becoming numb to injustice. Pay heed to painful feelings. Confront inconvenient truths.

Today I urge you: Yes, use your talents to discover new treatments for Alzheimer's, for diabetes, for cancer. Today I also urge you: Use your formidable medical skills to diagnose and treat the darker pathologies, those insidious behaviors that drive a wedge between races, ethnicities and religions. These are ailments every bit as worthy of your incisive medical attention. Today I urge you to diagnose and to treat them.

Martin Luther King Jr. once said, "of all the forms of inequality, injustice in health care is the most shocking and inhumane." His words ring true today, more than half a century later. The inequalities he spoke of are often subtle, at times less obvious than they were then, yet they surround us, and are insidious.

Perhaps one or more of you will pursue research that unravels the origins of the virulent pathologies that lead to health care inequalities. And it is my fervent hope that what you find will light the path to cure. Quixotically naïve? Perhaps. But remember, achieving equality in health care is at the heart of fairness and social justice. In my mind—and I hope in yours—it is an inalienable human right.

---

2 Daley, George Q. "Heart of Justice." *Harvard Medical School*, The President and Fellows of Harvard College, 24 May 2018, hms.harvard.edu/news/heart-justice.

As our newest Harvard Medical School physicians, as you advance our mission to alleviate human suffering, remember: this is the next frontier. This is the mission I call upon you—members of the HMS Class of 2018—to pursue.

Congratulations! I applaud each and every one of you on this great achievement in your life.

Adapted from a speech given by HMS Dean George Q. Daley on Class Day, May 24, 2018.[2]

CHAPTER THIRTY-SIX
Closing Letter to All Healthcare Providers: A Plea from the Author's Heart

As we come to a close of our reflections on equity in healthcare, it is my sincere hope that you feel more prepared, and nurtured, to do the hard work ahead of us in laying the foundations for compassionate and equitable healthcare for all. Thank you for entering this very important and life changing profession.

While working on this book, every chapter evoked deep thoughts, contemplation and even tears when I considered the medical field and medical professionals that provide care to patients while in their most vulnerable state. Black mothers' vulnerability comes with an inherent trust, as fragile as it may be, and a desperate inner cry which whispers, "please help me, do not harm me or my baby."

If I can have your ear, and your heart, for the next few pages, I would like to make a humble plea to your legacy. You have a golden opportunity to leave a legacy of ethics, respect, dignity and honor. 'One patient at a time' summons your human, and very empathetic, heart to show up *first*, and your academic, skillful medical training *second*. This order will guarantee that you see and hear every patient you care for.

I encourage you to reflect on the next pages, summarizing some of the main takeaways I hope you have gathered throughout this book. Determine which parts stood out most to you. Which was most transformational to you and your practice? Which will you consider most important for implementing in your continued care?

Some Main Takeaways

Remember,
- It's impossible to be a successful health care provider without practicing compassion.
- Seek guidance from your Higher Power. Be willing to give the best effort, but trust God to influence the outcome.
- Focus on the core foundations in your life to guide you in well-doing.
- Be self aware to allow for growth from your mistakes. Recognize your personality type and realize that no personality type is better than another but focus on your strengths and weaknesses and allow them to work for you in your accomplishments.
- Practice self-compassion over self-esteem. It is weightless in comparison to self-compassion.
- Build and maintain a mental toolkit that allows you to be resilient. At the completion of each day be sure that you've used the tools necessary to build

resilience while leaving no residual trauma or stress in your thought frame. With the start of each new day, be reminded that you have sufficient tools to build resilience for the new day.

- Study the section on Identifying Personal Loss and Grief (Chapter 10), allowing yourself to be led on processing your grief via practicing rituals, sitting with the pain, allowing sufficient time for grief, realizing there is no right or wrong way to grieve, and etc.
- Set and keep boundaries. Recognize that in setting them you are reflecting self love for yourself and self respect for others.
- Take an oath in the workplace of compassionate care for each and every person who is placed in your path for care, regardless of differences in ethnicity, race, gender, economics, sexual orientation, religion, and anything that can cause a mental separation from fair medical treatment.
- Very importantly, seeing your patient is respectful, sitting with your patient is honorable, empathy communicates your heart to your patient, advocating for their best care is being responsible, and being a good listener can actually save lives.
- Commit to advocate against healthcare disparities for Black mothers and Black infants.
- You can create a productive future if you resist the practices from the destructive past in obstetric care.

Why We Serve

As you ponder over some of these takeaways, I encourage you to look at the reasons you first chose this profession. You may have come into the medical field to care extravagantly for patients. For some of you, it was because you wanted to help mothers achieve a perfect birthing experience, against all odds. Others of you because you simply love delivering babies and seeing life enter the realm of this world. Others, still, because you wanted to do your best to help families accomplish their dream of having children and completing the cycle of life. And others are maybe attracted to all the perks of being a physician and the benefits they bring. Some may even have entered this field simply because it was the family expectation - as all the men or women are doctors or nurses in their family. The list goes on and on. But the most important reason to enter a field where life and death consequences are in your hands, should be to preserve life and bring the best outcomes for all patients.

How do you accomplish what you set out to do in your Hippocratic Oath to do no harm and to bring wholeness?

Every successful healthcare professional needs strong ethical boundaries, peer to peer accountability and empathy for every patient, every time, no matter their race, ethnicity, sexual orientation, gender or spiritual values.

I hope you have felt encouraged to reflect on your own desires and goals as a provider, and have gained some tools to help you be the best practitioner possible, moving forward. The work starts with ourselves - who are we as providers, and who we want to be. Learning the tools that allows us to better care for our own selves first, also allows us to better care for our patients. Tools such as self-awareness, self-compassion, self-esteem, boundaries, and resilience, not only provide the strong foundations needed for becoming the best care providers we can be, but the best humans we can be as well.

Walking the Path of Equity

Once we understand ourselves and how to nurture ourselves a little better, we can begin to examine the various ways in which we can better nurture our patients. This includes learning more about the history of both our patients, and healthcare, overall. When we learn about some of the atrocities that were committed towards Black people "in the name of science," and combine that with the understanding of epigenetics and the respect for different cultures, we put ourselves on the right path and begin to walk towards equity and justice.

Our work continues with how we use these new understandings to better treat, care for, and empathize with our patients. When we put ourselves in their shoes, treat them with the dignity they deserve, learn to S.E.A.L. our patient care, and approach all of our work with great H.E.A.R.T., we not only lean towards equity, but ultimately save lives. Even in times of unfortunate outcomes, may our care be experienced with R.E.S.P.E.C.T. as we share difficult news.

Beginning The Work Anew

Giving our patients a voice in making decisions for their own care, advocating for their well-being, and treating them with the dignity they deserve can help to mitigate some of the tragic statistics we see of disproportionate mortality in Black patients. The disparities we see in healthcare today can, and must, be rectified, and I hope you have begun to see the ways that this is possible by changing our attitudes toward patient care.

Our journey with this book may be coming to a close, but our work towards establishing true equity in healthcare is only just beginning. This is an opportunity for clinicians everywhere to become more engaged with their patients as individuals and participate in their birth experience by honoring and increasing the visibility of the patient's needs, desires, and concerns regarding their respective childbirth. Why? Because the gap in birth outcomes for Black women compared to all other races/ethnicities is unacceptable and must be closed. It is essential that we recognize and understand historical implications of obstetric abuse/racism and its consequences.

We must develop significant actions to mitigate the impact of obstetric abuse/racism on the victims (trauma-informed care) and ensure the associated behaviors and practices are forever eliminated.

I hope this guide can continue to nurture you along the way.

With compassion,

REV. DR. CANDACE COLE-KELLY

Post Workbook
Birth Equity Survey

POST SURVEY QUESTIONNAIRE:

1. What did you learn about preventable deaths in Black birthing persons?

   _____

   _____

2. Describe the danger of implicit biases and microaggressions in the healthcare system for patients and staff?

   _____

   _____

3. Name any character traits that you discovered need to change if you wish to be an equity healthcare provider.

   _____

   _____

4. What is your resulting conviction about a Black mother's pain tolerance in light of previous claims that suggested Black people and slaves had a higher pain tolerance?

   _____

   _____

5. How would you suggest healthcare systems close the disparity gap between Black birthing persons and their white counterparts?

   _____

   _____

6. After reading this workbook, have you discovered any evidence of systemic racism showing up in your own healthcare context? If so, how?

   _____

   _____

   _____

7. When you consider segregated birthing clinics, how would you suggest healthcare systems change their practice to provide respectful care and equity to all birthing persons, especially in marginalized communities?

_____

_____

_____

_____

8. What are your suggestions for increasing dignified care and support to traumatized partners and dads? This includes during stressful moments such as when their partners are undergoing C-sections, Emergent C-sections, or post-hemorrhage events?

_____

_____

_____

_____

9. How would you eradicate racism in healthcare if it was in your power to do so?

_____

_____

_____

_____

_____

_____

_____

_____

10. What messages are we sending when the management hierarchies in our hospitals, birthcare centers, and clinics lack Black leadership?

___

11. How does legislation contribute to healthcare disparities?

___

12. After reading this workbook, what is one goal you will commit to for your everyday practice that will improve your care as an equitable provider?

___

13. Reflect on a time when you felt a strong emotion while completing this workbook. It could be shock, sadness, shame, acceptance, hope, compassion, etc.

    a. Name the emotion and what brought it on. _____

    b. Now write about how you can use that emotional reaction as a catalyst for change in your practice and/or life.

    _____

    _____

    _____

    _____

    _____

14. What was your biggest takeaway from this workbook? What is something you learned here that you are looking forward to sharing with others?

    _____

    _____

    _____

15. List any equity topic(s) you would have appreciated being included in this workbook that was not covered?

    _____

    _____

    _____

Tools for Healthcare Providers: Quick Reference Guide

CHAPTER 1: PERSONAL DEVELOPMENT

H.E.A.R.T.
1. Hearing and validating our patient's concerns through active listening.
2. Empathizing with their lived experiences.
3. Advocating for our patients' needs and exploring appropriate resources.
4. Respecting our patients with dignity and honor no matter race and ethnicity.
5. Transformational care is care that builds trust, changing both patient and provider. You know you are doing a good work with others when you begin to change yourself.

CHAPTER 2: THE GIFT OF SURRENDER

Below is a Surrender Tool - **R.R.S.S.A.** (pronounced "ARSA") Let's make it personal by using "I" statements.

1. Recognizing the Signs: I usually notice it is time to surrender when I start feeling consistently stressed, anxious, or frustrated about a situation. If I am putting in a lot of effort without seeing any positive change, it is a clear sign that I need to step back.
2. Reflection and Acceptance: I take time to reflect on what is happening and accept that there are aspects I cannot control. This acceptance does not mean defeat, but rather acknowledging the reality of the situation. I have to accept everyone is not motivated to advocate for equity, empathy and dignity in healthcare and they have every right to that..
3. Seeking Perspective: Talking with trusted friends, mentors, or my small group helps me gain perspective. They can offer insights and support that make it easier to see the situation more clearly and decide what I need to let go of.
4. Setting Boundaries: Part of surrendering is setting boundaries to protect my well-being. This might mean limiting my involvement or emotional investment in a situation that I can't change.
5. Attachments to Let Go: This is the most challenging part. Letting go means releasing my attachment to a specific outcome and trusting that things will work out as they are meant to. It often involves a lot of internal work, such as mindfulness practices, prayer, or meditation, to help me find peace.

CHAPTER 3: IMPORTANT FOUNDATIONS FOR SELF ACTUALIZATION

S.H.O.W.
1. Sensitivity
2. Honoring
3. Offering
4. Weakness

CHAPTER 6: WORKPLACE BOUNDARIES

DEI PAUSE TOOL

P: Patient safety first.

A: Assess your patient's need for advocacy

U: Unit protocol (call Equity Team)

S: Seek to understand the scenario

E: Empathy approach in your responses

CHAPTER 11: WET NURSING AND BREASTFEEDING DISPARITIES

B.E.N.E.F.I.T.S. of Breastfeeding

Some patients may be hesitant to breastfeed. Below is a helpful acronym to remember when speaking to patients about the B.E.N.E.F.I.T.S. of breastfeeding:

B - Baby. Remind your patient that the motive behind encouraging breastfeeding is simply about thinking of what is best for the baby.

E - Education. Help provide your patient with the resources necessary for them to understand the research behind the importance of breastfeeding.

N - Nourishing Value. The richest resources for your baby can be found within your own amazing body. Breastmilk, and especially colostrum, can be an invaluable source of nourishment to your baby.

E - Empathy. Remember to use an empathic lens when discussing breastfeeding with patients. Not everybody has the same background or understanding when it comes to breastfeeding, and it is important not to judge any differing views, but to approach them with compassion and empathy.

F - Foundation. Breast Milk provides an important foundation to a baby's immune system. It can help prevent diseases and allergies, while supplying many other healthcare benefits.

I - Inclusion. It is important to approach all mothers with the same information. It is not up to us to determine who is more likely to use the information, we simply do our best to provide it to all mothers.

T - Talk about it. Be a willing and engaging advocate for breastfeeding by continuing to talk about it with patients - especially Black mothers, due to the disparity rates. Make sure to provide them with all the information and resources.

S - Safety. Breastfeeding is a safe and natural way to provide optimum nutrition and immunity for your baby.

CHAPTER 16: FAMILY-CENTERED CARE IN THE NICU

We have outlined the following tool to help you understand some of the potential barriers that a **FAMILY** may be struggling with:

Fear of their child dying and surviving the NICU

Access to empathetic and equitable care while in the NICU

Money - the many unexpected costs of managing NICU visits, i.e. parking, gas, public transportation, taking time off from work, food, getting childcare, and parenting additional children

Infections from illnesses pose a frightening and traumatic barrier that results in isolating parents from their child.

Language is a huge barrier as parents navigate the NICU culture in all of its complexities, including understanding what is happening, why things are happening, and the foreign language they hear daily.

Yearning to provide the appropriate care for their child despite the learning curve of caring for a child with special medical needs, sometimes as a single parent.

As providers, we must pay attention to the needs of both of our patients, rather than just the infant, and respond to both with **CARE**:

Compassion for parents who struggle with comparing themselves to the NICU team of nurses, gently bringing parents alongside the nursing team to empower and affirm. Being a compassionate nurse that identifies this fear present in a parent can be a gift that helps validate the parent's ability and capacity to care for their child.

Addressing any barriers to care for their babies that parents are facing with kindness and a sense of belonging.

Respecting parent's values, cultures, and beliefs as a way of supporting diversity and inclusion.

Equitable care for all parents, especially traditionally or historically marginalized parents who may need extra attention and resources for their baby.

CHAPTER 19: LANGUAGE AND COMMUNICATION

Recommendations for Clinicians: Communicating with Care To mitigate the effects of anchoring bias, clinicians should be mindful of the language they use when discussing neurodevelopmental outcomes with parents. Here are some recommendations:

Use Neutral Language: Avoid terms that might create a strong emotional response or set rigid expectations. Instead, use language that is descriptive but neutral, allowing room for a range of possible outcomes.

Provide Context: Ensure that parents understand the broader context of any prognosis. Explain that neurodevelopmental outcomes can vary widely and that early predictions are not always definitive.

Encourage Questions: Invite parents to ask questions and express their concerns. This helps ensure they have a clear understanding and can process the information more fully. Follow-Up

Communication: Recognize that initial conversations may set an anchor, but ongoing communication can help adjust and refine parents' understanding as their baby develops.

By carefully selecting words and being aware of the potential for anchoring bias, clinicians can provide information that supports parents in making well informed, balanced decisions about their premature baby's care.

CHAPTER 21: EMPATHY, PART 1: A TOOL TOOL TO MITIGATE IMPLICIT BIAS

Our **S.L.A.C.K.** Tool ensures that we move from awareness to anti-racism in our empathy practice:

Self-Reflection: Examine your own biases and privilege. Ask, "How have I benefited from systems that disadvantage others, and how can I use my position to promote change?"

Learning: Learn about the histories and struggles of marginalized communities. Seek out perspectives from people of color, not to burden them with teaching, but to amplify their voices and lived experiences.

Advocating: Support policies and initiatives that promote racial equity. Speak out against microaggressions, discrimination, and systemic injustice in your personal and professional spheres.

Cultivating Inclusive Spaces: Foster environments where people of all races feel valued and safe. Challenge exclusionary practices and champion diversity.

Kindness: In healthcare, kindness is not just a virtue—it is a vital skill that bridges gaps and fosters trust. In an equity-centered setting, kindness means approaching every patient with dignity, respect, and compassion, recognizing their unique experiences and challenges. Kindness allows clinicians to connect on a human level, ensuring patients feel valued, heard, and understood.

CHAPTER 22: EMPATHY AT THE BEDSIDE, PART 2: A CHAPLAIN'S SACRED PRESENCE

Practical Tools for Empathy

Whether you are a chaplain, a healthcare provider, or work in another role to support patients during their most difficult days, the following **S.E.T.** tool may be helpful as you think through what it means to be an empathetic presence.

Start with Emotional Assessment Questions:

- "What has been the hardest part of this for you?"
- "How are you managing to get through this moment?"
- "Is there anything you'd like me to pray for or bring to God on your behalf?"

Empathetic Spirituality Reflections:

- Share scripture, prayers, or blessings tailored to their situation, always with permission.

- Acknowledge God's presence in their suffering and affirm their value and dignity.

The Ministry of Presence:

- When words fail, your quiet presence can be deeply comforting. Sitting with someone in silence communicates solidarity and care.

Addressing Systemic Disparities with Empathy

Empathy alone cannot eliminate disparities, but it serves as a catalyst for identifying and addressing systemic barriers. The **C.P.R.** tool gives you a beginning:

Combating Implicit Bias: Empathy equips social workers to recognize and challenge biases that may impact care decisions, advocating for fair treatment of all families.

Promoting Health Literacy: Marginalized families often face barriers to understanding medical information due to language differences or limited education. Empathy ensures that social workers communicate clearly and compassionately, empowering families to make informed decisions.

Represent by Advocating for Diversity: Empathy highlights the importance of representation in healthcare teams. Social workers can advocate for hiring diverse staff who better reflect and understand the communities they serve.

CHAPTER 23: CULTURAL HUMILITY & EMPATHY

CULTURAL EMPATHY FOR BLACK FAMILIES ALGORITHM

ASSESSMENTS
- Clinical Conversation
- Patient Concerns
- Patient Care Priority
- When a Black patient has received bad care:
  - Escalate Service Recovery
  - Contact Nursing Managemnent

PATIENT APPOINTMENTS
- Discuss Plan of Care
- Diagnosis Referral and Consultation
- Shared Decision Making
- Patient Consent

REFERRALS
- Spiritual Care Consult
- Mental Health/Psychology Consult (Anxiety Driven Referral)
- Psychiatric Care
- Melanated Support Group
- Doula Consult
- Black Nurse
- Specialist Consultation
- Black Lactation Nurse
- Any Education and Resources

CHAPTER 24: COMMIT TO S.E.A.L.:

Commit to S.E.A.L. Your Patient Care

    Commit To See and Sit (with an Equity Lens)

    Commit To Empathize (with an Equity Heart)

    Commit To Advocate (with an Equity Perspective)

    Commit To Listen (with an Equity Understanding)

CHAPTER 25: FITTED FOR EQUITY LENS:

M.E.D.I.C.A.T.E.

Microaggressions: A term used for commonplace daily verbal, behavioral, or environmental slights, whether intentional or unintentional, that communicate hostile, derogatory, or negative attitudes toward stigmatized or culturally marginalized groups. The term was coined to describe insults and dismissals from non-Black Americans on Blacks and other marginalized groups.

Equity: Equity ensures that individuals are provided the resources they need to have access to the same opportunities as the general population. Equity represents impartiality, i.e. the distribution is made in such a way to even opportunities for all people. Conversely equality indicates uniformity, i.e. where everything is evenly distributed among people.

Disparity: Disparity is a kind of "non-equality." The word is often used to describe a social or economic condition that's considered unfairly unequal: a racial disparity in hiring, a health disparity between the rich and the poor, an income disparity between men and women, and so on.

Implicit Bias: Comprise of negative attitudes or stereotypes towards most anything, including people. Most importantly, our biases can impact real world behavior. So if we want to promote a genuine impact of merit, we probably want to check whether we have biases before we make judgments.

Cultural Sensitivity: Serving others with empathy, kindness and respect. Cultural sensitivity includes taking the time to understand and respect everyone's unique needs and backgrounds through a whole person approach to healthcare and employment. Recognizes different does not mean deficient.

Advocate: A person who publicly supports or recommends a particular cause or policy. A person who pleads for another's cause or idea. A person who supports others to make their voices heard or ideally for them to speak for themselves.

Treatment: Fair treatment is quintessential when it comes to best practices and providing equitable service. Unfair treatment can cause risk factors.

Explicit Bias: Explicit bias is a conscious bias that you are aware of and you act on it. For example, you don't like working with Black people and so you choose to work with White people every time. This usually shows up when human beings are afraid of, or do not value and respect, others.

CHAPTER 26: DELIVERING BAD NEWS WITH R.E.S.P.E.C.T:

Discover the art of delivering bad news with empathy, dignity and **R.E.S.P.E.C.T.**

R: Right Environment (Creating a respectful sacred space) To create an encouraging environment:

- Make sure it is noise-free (all devices should be silenced).
- Make sure there are enough chairs placed in the room in a circular style so that everyone is connected on the same level (this creates intimacy and
- a collaborative environment resulting in a level playing field to enhance communication).
- Make sure you are able to hear one another.

E: Explore Effective Pathways to Communicate

- Before meeting with your patient, be sure to review the patient's chart, information and diagnosis.
- When meeting with them, gently let them know that bad news is forthcoming. For example, "I regret I have some bad news for you. We could not find any heart tones right now, I need to find a better machine or get an ultrasound to better evaluate your baby."
- Ensure all sub-specialists are present (as appropriate).

S: Seek to Understand Your Patient

- Establish this will be a reciprocal conversation by asking, "How are you
- feeling at this moment?"
- Be sensitive to asking the patient if additional support (persons) are needed prior to starting the clinical discussion.
- Ask: What is your understanding of your current condition?
- Use prompters such as "what do you understand from what you have been told?" This will help you gather what the patient has been told and their interpretation of their health status.
- Assess for the patient's emotional/psychological well-being at this time, as certain information can be overwhelming and even traumatizing. This will prompt you to secure all the resources needed for your patient (psychology, spiritual care, etc.)

P: Presence (Be present, be compassionate and be tolerant)

- Be present to your patient and the conversation at hand.
- Try to stay focused on the now rather than thinking of your next patient.
- Be compassionate (bring your compassion)
- Be tolerant

E: Empathize (Respond empathically by validating patient's feelings)

- Prepare yourself and your staff for a wide range of emotions to follow the patient hearing this bad news. Reactions could range from loud outburst, panic, tears, denial, shock, numbness, anger, freedom, fainting, etc.
- Honor your patient by providing emotional space with appropriate pause. When they do speak, be attentive and use active listening by reframing their communication with you.
- Validate and acknowledge your patient's heartbreak by offering compassionate phrases such as "I know this is difficult and painful to hear." "I'm so sorry." "I can see you are in a lot of pain." "I am deeply sad that you are experiencing this loss."

- Invite dialogue when appropriate. For example: "Can you share a little bit of what you are feeling at this time?" "As I pause here, can you say in your own words what you understand is happening with your care?" Make sure to define all medical terms in real time as you explain the information and make sure the patient understands by inviting them to summarize.

C: Clinical Care Plan (Summarize the plan of care and medical information)

- Summarize your plan of care moving forward including: tests, exams, referrals and/or treatments.
- Make sure the patient has all the information they might need including: phone numbers, addresses, contact persons or subsequent medical caregivers in the event something happens before the next planned visit.
- Before the patient leaves, make sure all psycho-social needs are assessed and you feel that your patient is safe to go home. Discuss any resources that may be helpful to your patient such as: social work, lactation specialist, child life, religious or spiritual support.
- Document your medical plain in the patient's EMR.

T: Truth and Transparency

- Be mindful not to trivialize their trauma and to speak truthfully at all times.
- Be forward thinking and empathetic in your offerings avoiding false hope.
- Examples of helpful words to offer might include: "I won't say to you time will heal all wounds, but I can say what you do with the time, can heal all wounds." "When you are ready, support interventions can make a difference." "It's okay to exclude anyone who is not safe for you, and to advocate for safe spaces, safe places and safe persons."

P.A.U.S.E

(A Self-Care Tool For Clinicians)

The acronym **P.A.U.S.E.** is a helpful tool for any provider that is about to deliver bad news. Before entering the interaction, P.A.U.S.E. can be utilized to help through what can be a painful and difficult conversation between both bearer, and recipient, of bad news.

· · · · ·

P: Pause. Still yourself before meeting with your patient. Take a few deep breathing exercises to ground yourself.

A: Acknowledge. Name how difficult this news can be for your patient to hear and name how you feel delivering it. It's okay to feel however you are feeling.

U: Understand. Understand your patient's culture, intersectionality, and vulnerability.

S: Silence. Silence your cell phone during the consult to give yourself fully to your patient and the conversation.

E: Empathy. Prepare yourself to step into your patient's shoes as a respectful, compassionate provider/nurse.

CHAPTER 27: SUPPORTING PARTNERS IN TRAUMATIC DELIVERIES

Caring For Partners: **A.T.T.E.N.D.** Protocol

Supporting our patients in a family-centered manner of care, includes supporting their partners as well - especially during moments of increased trauma. This means special attention must be made to A.T.T.E.N.D. to fathers and partners at these times. While doing so, it is important to keep in mind some key values for providing support:

> Acknowledgement: Acknowledge them, and their fears, right away.
>
> Truth: Tell them the truth about the scenario.
>
> Treatment: Treat them with dignity, and as a vital part of their partner's health.
>
> Educate: Inform them of current happenings and educate them with any appropriate projections.
>
> Normalize: Normalize their feelings, frustration, fears, and anger.
>
> Dignify: Help them feel dignified in their experience.

CHAPTER 31: TEAM BUILDING FOR BIRTH EQUITY GROUPS

5 Steps to Receiving Feedback

Wakeman further offers five steps to gleaning the maximum benefit from negative feedback. Bad feedback does not have the power to stall your career, but an unwillingness or inability

to absorb it and act on it does. She warns her readers, "don't avoid the teachers in your workplace. Treat them as valued coaches who show you what you need to work on. Your coach will not necessarily come to you with the attitude of a cheerleader."

In our collaborative work in birth equity it is essential that we strive to give and receive feedback in the most beneficial ways possible. To do this, here are five5 steps we can take, adapted from Wakeman's work:

Welcome the news with respect and gratitude, rather than defense.

Beware of your ego-centric side, and letting ego control your reaction. Maximize your learning and respond with openness and willingness.

If hearing feedback feels challenging, consider Cy Wakeman's suggestions for effective ways to receive feedback. Rather than personalizing, it can be helpful to react with one of these five responses instead:

"Thank you for caring enough about me to give me that feedback."

"I've noticed that about myself too, and it's something I'm working on."

"Will you help me to improve?"

"I am willing to see if I can find some truth in that."

"I used to think that about myself, too, and here is what I did to change it."

For birth equity groups, you can adapt these per- sonal approaches to your whole team's needs by pluralizing these five5 considerations. I.e. for response "a" consider: " Thank you for caring enough about us to offer that feedback."

If feedback is given in a perceived disrespectful or harsh manner, you may want to consider address- ing it head on, so you can focus on the true intent behind the message, rather than the tone. For example: "I really respect you as an expert in this work, and admittedly, I am having a hard time receiving this feedback due to your delivery. Would you mind re-stating what you would like me/us to do in a more encouraging tone?"

Feedback is often given when we need to grow, or learn a lesson. When we try to ignore these lessons, we are only inviting them to return again, and again, until we are finally open to receiving the message we are being given. It is better

to face these lessons head on, and learn to be accountable for the thoughts and actions that led to these results, rather than become a victim of circumstance.

Once you have become open and willing to learn and grow from negative feedback, be sure to stay focused on yourself, rather than resorting to pointing fingers or placing blame on others. When we remember that the only things we can affect are our own thoughts and actions, we take back our own agency and are more likely to view these experiences as positive ones where we are in control of our choices, growth, and progress.

CHAPTER 32: RACISM AMID NURSING STAFF

Ten Tips for Solutions

1. Recognize and acknowledge your own biases and prejudices.

2. Avoid making assumptions and respect others' privacy rather than jumping to negative conclusions.

3. Remember that all people are different individuals, and no one person of any group should be considered the "expert" based solely on their personal experiences.

4. Listen well - both to what is said, and what might be unspoken, but seen.

5. Be respectful, and remember that respect is a two-way street.

6. Embrace differences and diversity as beneficial.

7. Care well for others, and allow others to care for you.

8. Adhere to the nursing Code of Ethics.

9. Communicate thoughtfully by asking questions with respect, listening to and reflecting on different lived experiences, and seeking to understand.

10. Learn about and embrace other cultures, but be careful not to appropriate them.

CHAPTER 33: ETHNIC DIVERSITY IN THE NURSING WORKFORCE

5 Strategies for Increasing Diversity in Nursing

1. Working to improve equity in healthcare is of

the utmost importance. In order to accomplish this, healthcare executives and management teams must make the hiring of a culturally diverse workforce a priority.

This means creating specific plans for recruiting, and maintaining, diverse nursing staff.

2. Plans for recruiting diverse staff should be varied, adaptable, multi-layered, and include supports for maintaining new hires. Added efforts should be made for increasing diversity in leadership roles, as the goal should be increased inclusivity throughout every level of the organization's infrastructure.

3. Supports for maintaining diverse hires include encouraging professional development, advocating for mentorship, and providing employee resources that incorporate affinity- based support groups.

4. These dedications to increasing diversity in the overall workplace, and especially to encouraging advancement to leadership roles, will ensure continued diversity in staff through both future, and maintained, diverse hires. This will ultimately benefit everything in the organization from patient outcomes, to clinical care, to workplace culture.

5. All aspects of the healthcare profession can, and should, use these strategies to diversify their workforce in order to improve health equity, enhance family-centered care, and provide the best experience possible for both patients and staff.

REFERENCES:

Articles (Online)

3M. "Soothe the Burn Infographic." *3M In the United States*, M*Modal - Health Information Systems, 2022, https://www.3m.com/3M/en_US/health-information-systems-us/resources/library/soothe-the-burn-infographic.

Benz, Larry. "Compassionate Care Is Being Replaced by Institutional Care." *Medium*, Renee Kemper, 17 Sept. 2020, https://medium.com/book-bites/compassionate-care-is-being-replaced-by-institutional-care-ab5328472cd.

Bloom, Stephen G. "Lesson of a Lifetime." *Smithsonian Magazine*, 1 Sept. 2005, www.smithsonianmag.com/science-nature/lesson-of-a-lifetime-72754306.

Brassel, Sheila, et al. "Allyship and Curiosity Drive Inclusion for People of Color at Work (Report)." *Catalyst*, 22 Nov. 2022, www.catalyst.org/reports/allyship-curiosity-employees-of-color/.

Brenan, Megan. "Nurses Retain Top Ethics Rating in U.S., but Below 2020 High." *Gallup.com*, Gallup, 24 Jan. 2023, news.gallup.com/poll/467804/nurses-retain-top-ethics-rating-below-2020-high.aspx.

Britannica, The Editors of Encyclopaedia. "Hippocratic oath". *Encyclopedia Britannica*, 29 Apr. 2023, https://www.britannica.com/topic/Hippocratic-oath.

Buckman, Robert and Yvonne Kason. *How To Break Bad News: A Guide for Health Care Professionals*. University of Toronto Press, 1992. *JSTOR*, http://www.jstor.org/stable/10.3138/j.ctt1h1hrxp.

Cambridge University. "Culture." *Definition in the Cambridge English Dictionary*, Cambridge Dictionary, 2023, https://dictionary.cambridge.org/us/dictionary/english/culture.

Cherry, Kendra. "How the Myers-Briggs Type Indicator Works." Edited by David Susman, *Verywell Mind*, Personality Psychology, 28 July 2022, https://www.verywellmind.com/the-myers-briggs-type-indicator-2795583.

Daley, George Q. "Heart of Justice." *Harvard Medical School*, The President and Fellows of Harvard College, 24 May 2018, hms.harvard.edu/news/heart-justice.

Dannhausser, Danny, and Belinda van Rensburg. "Conflict Resolution Styles." *Knowledge2Motion*, 21 May 2019, k2mskills.com/conflict-resolution-styles/.

"Decision-Making for Patients with Multiple Chronic Conditions: Patient Priorities Care." *ACP Online*, American College of Physicians, 10 Nov. 2023, www.acponline.org/clinical-information/clinical-resources-products/decision-making-for-patients-with-multiple-chronic-conditions-patient-priorities-care.

Demby, Gene. "Making the Case That Discrimination Is Bad for Your Health." *NPR*, KCRW, 14 Jan. 2018, https://www.npr.org/sections/codeswitch/2018/01/14/577664626/making-the-case-that-discrimination-is-bad-for-your-health.

"Disparities in NICU Care." *California Perinatal Quality Care Collaborative*, Center for Academic Medicine Neonatology - Stanford University, 2023. www.cpqcc.org/analysis/our-research-priorities/disparities-nicu-care.

Drenth, A. J. "Myers-Briggs / MBTI & Enneagram Correlations." *Personality Junkie*, 2009, https://personalityjunkie.com/07/myers-briggs-enneagram-mbti-types-correlations-relationship/.

"Equity Lens: Moving From Commitment to Action." *AMAPCEO*, 16 June 2021, https://amapceo.on.ca/equitylens#whatistheequitylens.

Erskine, Samantha E., et al. "Exposé of Women's Workplace Experiences Challenges Antiracist Leaders to Step up (Report)" *Catalyst*, 1 Mar. 2023, www.catalyst.org/reports/antiracism-workplace-leadership.

Eurich, Tasha. "What Self-Awareness Really Is (and How to Cultivate It)." *Harvard Business Review*, 18 Jan. 2023, https://hbr.org/2018/01/what-self-awareness-really-is-and-how-to-cultivate-it.

Feloni, Richard, and Skye Gould. "The Best Jobs for Every Personality Type." *Business Insider*, Insider Inc., 28 Aug. 2015, https://www.businessinsider.com/the-best-jobs-for-every-personality-type-2015-8.

"Four in 5 Pregnancy-Related Deaths in the U.S. Are Preventable." *CDC Newsroom*, Centers for Disease Control and Prevention, 19 Sept. 2022, https://www.cdc.gov/media/releases/2022/p0919-pregnancy-related-deaths.html.

Hampson, Sue. "The Johari Window Model: How To Improve Communication, Self-Awareness And Productivity At Work." *TSW Training*, 7 Oct. 2021, https://www.tsw.co.uk/blog/leadership-and-management/the-johari-window/.

HealthTimes. "Resilience in Nursing." *Health Times*, 2 Sept. 2022, https://healthtimes.com.au/hub/nursing-careers/6/practice/healthinsights/resilience-in-nursing/2353/.

Hess, Joni. "Why Do Black Women in the US Have More C-Sections than White Women?" *OpenDemocracy*, 13 July 2021, https://www.opendemocracy.net/en/why-do-Black-women-us-have-more-c-sections-White-women/.

Hitchcock, Layne. "Wellness Check." *Be Well Health,* West Virginia University, 1 June 2022, https://health.wvu.edu/bewell/blog/wellness-check/.

Holland, Brynn. "The 'Father of Modern Gynecology' Performed Shocking Experiments on Enslaved Women." *History.com*, A&E Television Networks, 29 Aug. 2017 https://www.history.com/news/the-father-of-modern-gynecology-performed-shocking-experiments-on-slaves.

Horta, Rachel Pitek. "Cultural Awareness." *Boston University*, Boston University Medical Campus, 2023, https://sphweb.bumc.bu.edu/otlt/mph-modules/PH/CulturalAwareness/CulturalAwareness_print.html

ICM. "The Origins of Midwifery." *International Confederation of Midwives*, LDSC, 1 Feb. 2022, https://www.internationalmidwives.org/icm-news/the-origins-of-midwifery.html.

Kirti, Kamna. "The Tragic Plight of Enslaved Wet Nurses." *Medium*, Lessons from History, 8 Sept. 2021, https://medium.com/lessons-from-history/the-tragic-plight-of-enslaved-wet-nurses-b1c80b73f290.

Kugler, Sara. "Day 17: Mississippi Appendectomies and Reproductive Justice." *MSNBC*, NBC Universal News Group, 27 Mar. 2014, https://www.msnbc.com/msnbc/day-17-mississippi-appendectomies-msna293361.

"Lack of Optimal Breastfeeding May Cause Alarming Disparities in Infant Deaths, Study Finds." *UNC Gillings School of Global Public Health*, University of North Carolina, 23 Nov. 2016, https://sph.unc.edu/sph-news/study-lack-of-optimal-breastfeeding-may-cause-alarming-disparities-in-infant-deaths/.

Martin, Nina, et. al. "Black Mothers Keep Dying After Giving Birth. Shalon Irving's Story Explains Why." *NPR*, KCRW 7 Dec. 2017, www.npr.org/2017/12/07/568948782/Black-mothers-keep-dying-after-giving-birth-shalon-irvings-story-explains-why

McCarthy, Claire. "Breastfeeding Benefits Your Baby's Immune System." *HealthyChildren*, American Academy of Pediatrics, 19 July 2022, https://healthychildren.org/English/ages-stages/baby/breastfeeding/Pages/Breastfeeding-Benefits-Your-Babys-Immune-System.aspx

McClendon, Shannon. "New Survey Data: Racism Within the Nursing Profession Is a Substantial Problem." *American Nurses Association*, ANA, ANCC, American Nurses Foundation, 25 Jan. 2022, www.nursingworld.org/news/news-releases/2021/new-survey-data-racism-in-nursing/.

Mcleod, Saul. "Maslow's Hierarchy of Needs Theory." *Simply Psychology,* 21 Mar. 2023, https://simplypsychology.org/maslow.html#:~:text=Fromthebottomoftheattendtoneedshigherup.

Merriam-Webster. "Culture." *Merriam-Webster.com Dictionary,* Merriam-Webster, 2023 https://www.merriam-webster.com/dictionary/culture.

Mitson, Leslie. "What's in Breast Milk?" *American Pregnancy Association*, 9 Dec. 2021, https://americanpregnancy.org/healthy-pregnancy/first-year-of-life/whats-in-breastmilk/

Müller, Sanan. "Cultural Integration: Definition, Examples, and Benefits." *Germany Daily*, 14 Dec. 2021, https://germanydaily.de/culture/cultural-integration/.

Neff, Kristin. "Why Self-Compassion Trumps Self-Esteem." *Greater Good Magazine*, UC Berkeley, 27 May 2011, https://greatergood.berkeley.edu/article/item/try_selfcompassion.

Nevils-Karakeci, Raycene. "Collective Memory: Are We the Sum of Our Ancestors' Experiences?" *Interesting Engineering*, 18 May 2020, interestingengineering.com/health/collective-memory-are-we-the-sum-of-our-ancestors-experiences.

Newkirk, Vann R., II. "The Tuskegee Study and Black Culture." *The Atlantic*, 20 June 2016,www.theatlantic.com/politics/archive/2016/06/tuskegee-study-research-Black-experiences/487646.

OMH. " Infant Mortality and African Americans." *The Office of Minority Health*, U.S. Department of Health and Human Services, 17 Feb. 2023, https://minorityhealth.hhs.gov/omh/browse.aspx?lvl=4&lvlid=23.

Sandoiu, Ana. "'Weathering': The Health Effects of Stress and Discrimination." *Medical News Today*, MediLexicon International, 26 Feb. 2021, https://www.medicalnewstoday.com/articles/weathering-what-are-the-health-effects-of-stress-and-discrimination.

Scott, Maiken. "How Did Birth Move from the Home to the Hospital, and Back Again?" *WHYY,* PBS, 13 Dec. 2013, https://whyy.org/segments/how-did-birth-move-from-the-home-to-the-hospital-and-back-again/

Serwer, Adam. "Why a Statue of the 'Father of Gynecology' Had to Come Down." *The Atlantic*, Atlantic Media Company, 19 Apr. 2018, https://www.theatlantic.com/politics/archive/2018/04/why-a-statue-of-the-father-of-gynecology-had-to-come-down/558311/

Shapiro, Fred R. "Who Wrote the Serenity Prayer." *Yale Alumni Magazine*, Yale Alumni Publications, July 2008, http://archives.yalealumnimagazine.com/issues/2008_07/serenity.html.

Southwick, Ron. "Nursing Profession Is 'Steeped in Racism.'" *Chief Healthcare Executive,* OncLive, 21 Feb. 2022, www.chiefhealthcareexecutive.com/view/nursing-profession-is-steeped-in-racism-

Staats, Sarah Jane. "Overcoming Racial Disparities in California Neonatal Intensive Care Units." *Stanford Impact Labs*, Stanford University, 5 May 2021, impact.stanford.edu/article/overcoming-racial-disparities-california-neonatal-intensive-care-units.

Steel, Flora Annie. "The Three Little Pigs." *Short Stories & Classic Literature for Readers & Teachers*, American Literature, 2014, https://americanliterature.com/childrens-stories/the-three-little-pigs.

Sze, David. "Maslow: The 12 Characteristics of a Self-Actualized Person." *HuffPost*, Huffington Post, 6 Dec. 2017, https://www.huffpost.com/entry/maslow-the-12-characteris_b_7836836.

Tafesse, Kidi. "What the 'Mississippi Appendectomy' Says about the Regard of the State towards the Agency of Black Women's Bodies." *The Movement for Black Women's Lives*, Black Freedom Struggles, 1 May 2019, https://BlackwomenintheBlackfreedomstruggle.voices.wooster.edu/2019/05/01/what-the-mississippi-appendectomy-says-about-the-regard-of-the-state-towards-the-agency-of-Black-womens-bodies/.

Taylor, Jamila, et al. "Eliminating Racial Disparities in Maternal and Infant Mortality." *American Progress*, Center for American Progress, 2 May 2019, https://www.americanprogress.org/article/eliminating-racial-disparities-maternal-infant-mortality/.

Terreri, Cara. "Black History Month: The Importance of Black Midwives, Then, Now and Tomorrow." *Lamaze International*, 14 Feb. 2020, https://www.lamaze.org/Connecting-the-Dots/Black-history-month-the-importance-of-Black-midwives-then-now-and-tomorrow-1.

Trost, Susanna, et al. "Pregnancy-Related Deaths: Data from Maternal Mortality Review Committees in 36 US States, 2017–2019." *Centers for Disease Control and Prevention*, U.S. Department of Health & Human Services, 19 Sept. 2022, www.cdc.gov/reproductivehealth/maternal-mortality/erase-mm/data-mmrc.html.

Zdrojeski, Heidi. "Building Trust in High Performing Distributed Teams." *Coaching Right Now*, TopLine Communication, 12 Aug. 2020, www.coachingrightnow.com/blog/building-trust-in-high-performing-distributed-teams/.

Zhang, Sarah. "The Surgeon Who Experimented on Slaves." *The Atlantic*, Atlantic Media Company, 16 Aug. 2021, https://www.theatlantic.com/health/archive/2018/04/j-marion-sims/558248/.

Books

Benz, Laurence N. *Called to Care: A Medical Provider's Guide for Humanizing Healthcare.* Lioncrest Publishing, 2020.

Buckman, Robert, and Yvonne Kason. *How To Break Bad News: A Guide for Health Care Professionals*. University of Toronto Press, 1992, p4. *JSTOR*, http://www.jstor.org/stable/10.3138/j.ctt1h1hrxp.

Richo, David. *How to Be an Adult: A Handbook on Psychological and Spiritual Integration*, Paulist, Mahwah, NJ, 2018, pp. 57–63.

Roberts, Dorothy E. *Fatal Invention: How Science, Politics, and Big Business Re-Create Race in the Twenty-First Century*. The New Press, NY, 2012.

Simpson, John A. "Culture." *The Oxford English Dictionary*, Clarendon Press, 1991.

Thieman, LeAnn. *Selfcare for Healthcare: Your Guide to Physical, Spiritual, and Mental Health*. Priority Pub., 2012.

Wakeman, Cy. *Reality-Based Leadership: Ditch the Drama, Restore Sanity to the Workplace, and Turn Excuses into Results*. Jossey-Bass, 2010.

Washington, Harriet A. "Introduction: The American Janus of Medicine and Race." *Medical Apartheid: The Dark History of Medical Experimentation on Black Americans from Colonial Times to the Present*, Anchor Books (Random House), New York, NY, 2008, pp. 1–25.

Journals (Online)

Alhusen, Jeanne L., et al. "Racial Discrimination and Adverse Birth Outcomes: An Integrative Review." *Journal of Midwifery & Women's Health*, vol. 61, no. 6, Wiley, Oct. 2016, pp. 707–720. https://doi.org/10.1111/jmwh.12490.

Bartick, Melissa, et al. "Disparities in Breastfeeding: Impact on Maternal and Child Health Outcomes and Costs." *The Journal of Pediatrics,* Nov. 10, 2016; Vol. 181, P49-55.E6. DOI: 10.1016/j.jpeds.2016.10.028 https://www.jpeds.com/article/S0022-3476(16)31096-4/fulltext

Bright, Rachel A., et al. "Maternal Heart Failure ." *Journal of the American Heart Association*, American Heart Association, Vol 10, 14 (14 July 2021), https://www.ahajournals.org/doi/10.1161/JAHA.121.021019.

Broome, Barbara. "Racism, Nursing, and Strategies for Change." *Journal of obstetric, gynecologic, and neonatal nursing.* National Library of Medicine. *JOGNN* vol. 50,5 (2021): 507-511. doi:10.1016/j.jogn.2021.07.008. https://pubmed.ncbi.nlm.nih.gov/34389286/.

Geronimus, A T. "The weathering hypothesis and the health of African-American women and infants: evidence and speculations." *Ethnicity & disease,* National Library of Medicine, Vol. 2,3 (1992): 207-21. https://pubmed.ncbi.nlm.nih.gov/1467758/.

Greenwood, Brad N., et al. "Physician–Patient Racial Concordance and Disparities in Birthing Mortality for Newborns." Edited by Christopher W. Kuzawa, *Proceedings of the National Academy of Sciences of the United States of America*, vol. 117, no. 35, National Academy of Science, 17 Aug. 2020, pp. 21194–21200. https://doi.org/10.1073/pnas.1913405117.

"Henrietta Lacks: Science Must Right a Historical Wrong." *Nature - The International Journal of Science*, Springer Nature Limited, Vol. 585, No. 7823, Nature Portfolio, Sept. 2020, p. 7. https://doi.org/10.1038/d41586-020-02494-z.

Henriksen, Danah, et al. "Mindfulness and Creativity: Implications for Thinking and Learning." *Thinking Skills and Creativity*, vol. 37, Science Direct - Elsevier, Aug. 1 2020, 100689. https://doi.org/10.1016/j.tsc.2020.100689.

Holmes, Laurens Jr et al. "Implication of Vaginal and Cesarean Section Delivery Method in Black-White Differentials in Infant Mortality in the United States: Linked Birth/Infant Death Records, 2007-2016." *International Journal of Environmental Research and Public Health*, National Library of Medicine, Vol. 17,9 3146 (30 Apr. 2020), doi:10.3390/ijerph17093146, https://www.ncbi.nlm.nih.gov/pmc/articles/PMC7246527/.

Hook, Joshua N et al. "Cultural humility: measuring openness to culturally diverse clients." *Journal of counseling psychology,* National Library of Medicine, Vol. 60,3 (2013): 353-366. doi:10.1037/a0032595, https://pubmed.ncbi.nlm.nih.gov/23647387/.

Hurst, Danielle J., et al. "Prenatal care experiences among pregnant women with obesity in Wisconsin, United States: a qualitative quality improvement assessment." *BMC Pregnancy and Childbirth*, Vol. 21, No. 139, BioMed Central, Feb. 2021, https://doi.org/10.1186/s12884-021-03629-4.

MacDorman, Marian F et al. "Recent Increases in the U.S. Maternal Mortality Rate: Disentangling Trends From Measurement Issues." *Obstetrics and gynecology* Vol. 128, 3 (2016): 447-455. doi:10.1097/AOG.0000000000001556. https://www.ncbi.nlm.nih.gov/pmc/articles/PMC5001799/.

Main, Elliott K et al. "Reduction of severe maternal morbidity from hemorrhage using a state perinatal quality collaborative." *American journal of obstetrics and gynecology*, National Library of Medicine, Vol. 216,3 (2017): 298.e1-298.e11. doi:10.1016/j.ajog.2017.01.017, https://pubmed.ncbi.nlm.nih.gov/28153661/.

Mammaro, Alessia et al. "Hypertensive disorders of pregnancy." *Journal of prenatal medicine*, National Library of Medicine, Vol. 3,1 (2009): 1-5, https://www.ncbi.nlm.nih.gov/pmc/articles/PMC3279097/.

Maslow, A. H. "A theory of human motivation." *Psychological Review*, Jul 1943;50(4), 370–396. https://doi.org/10.1037/h0054346.

Ojewole, Foluso Oladayo, and Afolarin Olutunde Ojewole. "Nurse, Heal Yourself: Wholeness for Nurses." *Journal of Natural Sciences Research*, IISTE - International Knowledge Sharing Platform, 2017; ISSN 2224-3186 (Paper) ISSN 2225-0921 (Online) Vol.7, No.18, 2017 https://www.iiste.org/Journals/index.php/JNSR/article/view/38723/39824

Pearson SD, Raeke LH. "Patients' trust in physicians: many theories, few measures, and little data." *J Gen Intern Med.* 2000 Jul;15(7):509-13. doi: 10.1046/j.1525-1497.2000.11002.x. PMID: 10940139; PMCID: PMC1495476. https://www.ncbi.nlm.nih.gov/pmc/articles/PMC1495476.

Rakesh, Gopalkumar, et al. "A Call for Action: Cultivating Resilience in Healthcare Providers." *Psychiatry Online*, The American Journal of Psychiatry, 3 Apr. 2017; Vol. 12, Issue #4 ` https://ajp.psychiatryonline.org/doi/10.1176/appi.ajp-rj.2017.120402.

Smith, Kendra M., et al. "'Ignored and Invisible': Perspectives From Black Women, Clinicians, and Community-Based Organizations for Reducing Preterm Birth." *Maternal and Child Health Journal*, Vol. 26, No. 4, Springer Science+Business Media, Jan. 2022, pp. 726–35. https://doi.org/10.1007/s10995-021-03367-1.

Thomas, Erin V. "Why Even Bother; They Are Not Going to Do It?" The Structural Roots of Racism and Discrimination in Lactation Care." *Qualitative health research,* National Library of Medicine, Vol. 28,7 (2018): 1050-1064. doi:10.1177/1049732318759491. https://pubmed.ncbi.nlm.nih.gov/29557297/.

Vinekar, Kavita. "Pathology of Racism - a Call to Desegregate Teaching Hospitals." *The New England Journal of Medicine*, Massachusetts Medical Society, Sept. 2021, Electronic ISSN 1533-4406, DOI: 10.1056/NEJMpv2113508, https://doi.org/10.1056/nejmpv2113508.

Yeager, Katherine A, and Susan Bauer-Wu. "Cultural humility: essential foundation for clinical researchers." *Applied nursing research,* National Library of Medicine, Vol. 26,4 (2013): 251-6. doi:10.1016/j.apnr.2013.06.008, https://www.ncbi.nlm.nih.gov/pmc/articles/PMC3834043/.

Videos

Daley, George Q.. "2018 Class Day Address: HMS Dean George Q Daley." *YouTube*, Harvard Medical School, 25 May 2018, www.youtube.com/watch?v=FVuv4lCWN4k.Eiselt, Paula and Tonya Lewis, directors. "Aftershock." *Hulu*, 19 July 2022, https://www.hulu.com/movie/aftershock-c1414fdf-0741-4bd2-b62c-554db3d8f643.

Frontline PBS, Official. "A Class Divided (Full Documentary) | FRONTLINE." *YouTube*, 18 Jan. 2019, www.youtube.com/watch?v=1mcCLm_LwpE.

"Harnessing the Power of Team-Based Care: Medicine and Midwifery as Partners in Care." Presented by Holly Smith, et al., *YouTube*, California Maternal Quality Care Collaborative, 7 Feb. 2023, https://www.youtube.com/watch?v=Nsf6MGXs4m0.

"Jane Elliott 'Blue Eyes - Brown Eyes' Experiment Anti-Racism." *YouTube*, uploaded by chel.by.the.seas, 18 June 2020, www.youtube.com/watch?v=dLAi78hluFc.

Websites

AWHONN. "Back to Basics - Be Present for Your Patient.". *AWHONN,* Association of Women's Health, Obstetric, and Neonatal Nurses, 2019. www.awhonn.org/wp-content/uploads/2020/07/Back-to-Basics-Be-Present-8.5x11.pdf.

Centers for Disease Control. "Preventing Maternal Deaths: Supporting Maternal Mortality Review Committees." GRANTS.GOV, Health and Human Services / USA.Gov, 5 Mar. 2019, www.grants.gov/web/grants/view-opportunity.html?oppId=311065.

"Commentaries." *Still Resilient*, Still Resilient Consulting, 2023, https://www.stillresilient.com.

"Free Personality Test." *16Personalities*, NERIS Analytics Limited, 2011, https://www.16personalities.com/free-personality-test.

"Hearts in Healthcare." *Charter for Compassion*, 2022, https://charterforcompassion.org/healthcare-partners/hearts-in-healthcare.

"Hypertensive Disorders of Pregnancy." *California Maternal Quality Care Collaborative*, Center for Academic Medicine, Neonatology, 2023, https://www.cmqcc.org/content/hypertensive-disorders-pregnancy.

"Hypertensive Disorders of Pregnancy Toolkit." California Maternal Quality Care Collaborative, Center for Academic Medicine, Neotalogy, 2023, https://www.cmqcc.org/resources-tool-kits/toolkits/HDP.

Mitchell, S, et al. "SB-464 California Dignity in Pregnancy and Childbirth Act." *California Legislative Information*, 7 Oct. 2019, leginfo.legislature.ca.gov/faces/billTextClient.xhtml?bill_id=201920200SB464.

"Obstetric Hemorrhage." *California Maternal Quality Care Collaborative*, Center for Academic Medicine, Neonatology, 2023, https://www.cmqcc.org/content/obstetric-hemorrhage.

"The Nine Enneagram Type Descriptions." *The Enneagram Institute*, 2021, https://www.enneagraminstitute.com/type-descriptions.

ADDITIONAL REFERENCES:

AWHONN.ORG Association of Women's Health, Obstetric and Neonatal Nurses

CMQCC.ORG California Maternal Quality Care Collaborative

ReimagineJustice.us Transforming healthcare leaders and organizations through equitable empathy.

StillResilient.org Evidence-based training addressing bias, microaggressions, and disparities.

OPTIONAL RESOURCE:

Eiselt, Paula and Tonya Lewis, directors. *Aftershock*, Hulu, 19 July 2022, https://www.hulu.com/movie/aftershock-c1414fdf-0741-4bd2-b62c-554db3d8f643.

ABOUT THE AUTHOR

Rev. Dr. Candace Cole-Kelly is an NAACP award winning writer and producer for her social justice conscious musical stage productions. She is an accomplished author, and has written over 25 books. Dr. Cole-Kelly received her Doctorate from United Theological Seminary, and her Masters of Divinity, MDIV., from Fuller Theological Seminary. She is a Certified Grief Counselor from The American Academy of Grief Counselors. She has also earned a Certificate in Diversity, Inclusion and Equity, HR from Cornell University, as well as many other professional certifications.

Dr. Cole-Kelly currently serves as Co-Chair for the City of Lakewood's Interfaith Council, an organization committed to advocating for diversity, inclusion, and equity. She is bi-vocational, serving as both a Senior Pastor in Lakewood, CA and as a staff Chaplain for maternal health in the BirthCare Center at a hospital in Long Beach, CA. Dr. Cole-Kelly serves as Lead on both the birth equity team at her hospital, and on the organization Cherished Futures for Black Moms and Babies. She is also Chair for the Respectful Maternal Care Initiative by AWHONN.

Dr. Cole-Kelly's qualitative and quantitative collaborative research project for new grads, and new to specialty nurses, was acknowledged as a poster presentation at AWHONN's 50th Anniversary. This was to recognize and honor her TEA (Therapeutic Engagement Activity) program, which was designed to build resilience and sustain retention. Dr. Cole-Kelly is a member of CMQCC's pilot program to build birth equity toolkits for hospitals around the nation, in efforts to close the disparity gaps in Black mothers and Black infant mortality and morbidity.

Dr. Candace Cole-Kelly is **Owner and Founder** of Still Resilient International Training Consultants, LLC. The team of Still Resilient provides evidence-based training designed to address bias, inclusion and healthcare disparities.

ADDITIONAL BOOKS BY CANDACE COLE-KELLY

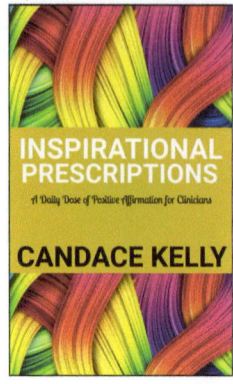

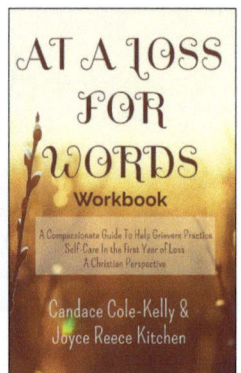

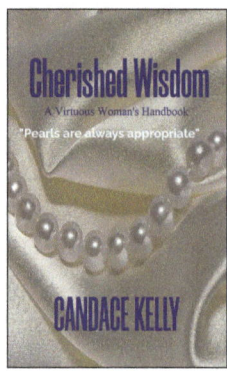

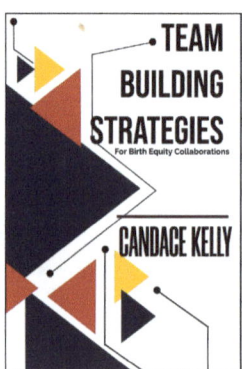

These books also by Candace Cole-Kelly are available for sale on the website:

STILLRESILIENT.ORG

Inspirational Prescriptions
(A Daily Dose of Positive Affirmations for Clinicians)

Relaxation and Mindful Moments
(Nurturing Self-Awareness, Mitigating Stress, and Managing Negative Emotions)

Nurse Word Search (Anxiety and Pressure Relief Exercises)

At a Loss For Words Adult Workbook
(A Compassionate Guide to Help Grievers Practice Self-Care In the First Year of Loss)

Cherished Wisdom
(A Virtuous Woman's Handbook)

The Art of Healing Workbook
(Navigating through the Pain of Pregnancy Loss in the First Year)

Chaplains Word Search
(Self Reducing Stress Exercises and Creative Writing)

Team Building Strategies for Birth Equity Collaborations

www.ingramcontent.com/pod-product-compliance
Lightning Source LLC
Chambersburg PA
CBHW041754050426
R18089200001B/R180892PG42337CBX00002B/1